ANALYTIC GEOMETRY

ANALYTIC GEOMETRY

by

GORDON FULLER

Department of Mathematics
Texas Technological College

SECOND EDITION

ADDISON-WESLEY PUBLISHING COMPANY, INC.

READING, MASSACHUSETTS · PALO ALTO · LONDON

PREFACE

Although analytic geometry is viewed largely as a preparation for the study of calculus, there are many valuable concepts of this discipline which are applicable in other areas of mathematics. Accordingly, this book contains substantially the topics usually covered in a first course of analytic geometry and emphasizes basic principles which are needed in calculus and later mathematics courses. Inasmuch as this particular course is taught almost exclusively in college, this publication is designed for college freshmen. The book also finds ready application in high schools which provide such a study for their mathematically inclined students.

There are numerous improvements in this new edition, made possible by experience with the first edition. Teachers who have used the first edition will observe particularly the following major changes:

1. The material on graphing, along with discussions of symmetry, extent of curves, and asymptotes, has been considerably enlarged and removed from the first chapter to later chapters.

2. A return has been made to a more standard treatment of conics.

3. The chapter on calculus is omitted.

4. There is an extension of the applications of vectors in the solid analytic geometry to include the vector product.

In addition, many minor changes and rearrangements have been made in response to suggestions from teachers who have used the previous edition.

The beginning of this text is devoted to an introduction of basic concepts and tools of analytic geometry. Exceptional care has been exercised in the choice and presentation of these new ideas in order to avoid confusion and bewilderment on the part of the student. Certain relatively abstruse concepts, often concentrated at the outset of such a book, are deferred to later chapters. Specifically, the ideas of symmetry, extent of curve, and asymptotes are treated more logically, as needed, in the further development of the subject.

Once the fundamental groundwork has been laid, an approach is made to the straight line and the circle. Since most students of elementary algebra are told (often without proof) that the graph of a linear equation in two variables is a straight line, it seems sensible to prove this fact directly from the equation $Ax + By + C = 0$. The equation can then be altered in a straightforward procedure to yield the various special forms. Although the discussion of the circle is adequate, it is not unnecessarily lengthy. By limiting the space devoted to the circle, added emphasis may be placed on the basic principles which point more directly toward the calculus. This section is an appropriate place for the introduction of translation of axes; so here, as in other instances, a new concept is brought forth when needed and is applied in a simple setting.

The conics are deservingly treated somewhat more fully than is essential for the study of calculus. However, the time for coverage of this part can be shortened, if desired, by assigning fewer problems from the exercises. As in the case of the circle, the translation of axes is applied early to obtain, from the simplified equations, the more general forms of equations of conics involving h and k.

Since proficiency in sketching graphs with a minimum of point-by-point plotting is a highly important objective of analytic geometry, considerable attention is given to aids and shortcuts which can be employed in graphing. Many students come to calculus with little understanding of polar coordinates; hence, the accentuation on drawing graphs extends to this system of coordinates.

The method of least squares is developed in the chapter on curve fitting.

The elements of solid analytic geometry are treated in two concluding chapters. The first of these takes up quadric surfaces and the second deals with planes and lines. This order is chosen because a class which takes only one of these two chapters should preferably study the space illustrations of second-degree equations. Vectors are introduced and applied in the chapter on planes and lines. This study is facilitated, of course, by the use of vectors and provides the student with a more than passing encounter with this valuable concept.

Five numerical tables in the Appendix meet the needs which arise in the problems. Exercises occur at short intervals and are carefully graded, with an abundance of problems appearing on each exercise. There are many problems of theoretical implication which will be of special appeal to the abler student. Answers to odd-numbered problems are included in the text.

This book is written for a course of three semester hours. Although an exceptionally well-prepared group of students will be able to cover the entire book in one semester, there will, of course, be excess material for many classes. It is suggested that omissions may be made from Chapters 6, 9, and 11.

January, 1962   G. F.

CONTENTS

CHAPTER 1

FUNDAMENTAL CONCEPTS

1–1 Introduction. Previous to the seventeenth century, algebra and geometry were largely distinct mathematical sciences, each having been developed independently of the other. In 1637, however, a French mathematician and philosopher, René Descartes, published his *La Géométrie*, which introduced a device for unifying these two branches of mathematics. The basic feature of this new process, now called *analytic geometry*, is the use of a coordinate system. By means of coordinate systems algebraic methods can be applied powerfully in the study of geometry, and perhaps of still greater importance is the advantage gained by algebra through the pictorial representation of algebraic equations. Since the time of Descartes analytic geometry has had a tremendous impact on the development of mathematical knowledge. And today analytic methods enter vitally into the diverse theoretical and practical applications of mathematics.

1–2 Directed lines and segments. A line on which one direction is defined as positive and the opposite direction as negative is called a *directed line*. The part of a line between two of its points is called a *segment*. In plane geometry, line segments are not assigned directions. In analytic geometry, however, line segments are often considered as having directions as well as lengths. Thus in Fig. 1–1, AB means the segment from A to B, and BA stands for the segment from B to A. The segment AB is positive, since the direction from A to B agrees with the assigned positive direction as indicated by the arrowhead. The segment BA, on the other hand, is negative. If there are 3 units of length between A and B, for example, then $AB = +3$ and $BA = -3$. Hence, with reference to directed line segments,

$$AB = -BA.$$

If A, B, and C are three points of a directed line, then the directed segments determined by these points satisfy the equations

$$AB + BC = AC, \qquad AC + CB = AB, \qquad BA + AC = BC.$$

If B is between A and C, the segments AB, BC, and AC have the same direction, and AC is obviously equal to the sum of the other two segments (Fig. 1–2). The second and third equations can be found readily

1

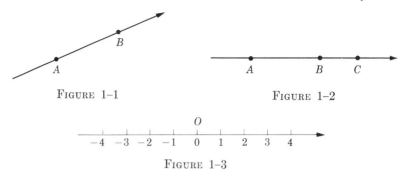

FIGURE 1-1   FIGURE 1-2

FIGURE 1-3

from the first. To find the second, we transpose BC and use the fact that $BC = -CB$. Thus

$$AB = AC - BC = AC + CB.$$

A fundamental concept of analytic geometry is the representation of all real numbers by the points of a directed line. The *real numbers*, we note, are the positive numbers, the negative numbers, and zero. We first choose a direction on a line as positive (to the right in Fig. 1–3). We select a point O of the line, which we shall call the *origin*, to correspond to the number zero. Then we take a unit of length and, proceeding to the right of the origin, we mark points one unit apart. We let these points represent, in order, the numbers $+1$, $+2$, $+3$, and so on. We mark points, in the same way, to the left of the origin and label them successively -1, -2, -3, and so on. Any positive number p is represented by the point p units to the right of the origin. A negative number $-n$ has its point n units to the left of the origin. Thus any point of the line has a corresponding real number and, conversely, any real number has a corresponding point. The line of Fig. 1–3, with its points representing numbers, is said to have a *number scale* established on it.

1–3 Rectangular coordinates. As we have mentioned, the basic feature of analytic geometry is the use of a coordinate system. We shall describe the rectangular coordinate system which the student has previously met in elementary algebra and trigonometry.

We draw two perpendicular lines meeting at O (Fig. 1–4). The point O is called the *origin*; the line OX, the *x-axis*; and the line OY, the *y-axis*. The x-axis, usually drawn horizontally, is called the *horizontal* axis and the y-axis the *vertical* axis. Using a convenient unit of length, we make a number scale on each axis, letting the origin be the zero point. The positive numbers are to the right of the origin on the x-axis and above the origin on the y-axis. Arrows are sometimes placed on the positive sides of the axes to distinguish these sides from the negative sides.

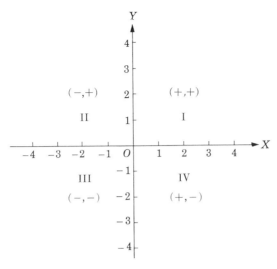

FIGURE 1–4

Each point of the plane determined by the axes has associated with it a pair of numbers called *coordinates*. The x-coordinate, or *abscissa*, is the distance from the y-axis to the point and is preceded by a minus sign if the point is to the left of the y-axis, or by a plus sign (understood) if the point is to the right of the y-axis. The y-coordinate, or *ordinate*, is the distance from the x-axis to the point and is preceded by a minus sign if the point is below the x-axis or by a plus sign if the point is above the x-axis. A point whose abscissa is x and whose ordinate is y is designated by the notation (x, y) with the abscissa always designated first.

The coordinate axes divide their plane into four parts, called *quadrants*, which are numbered I to IV in Fig. 1–4. Both coordinates of a point in the first quadrant are positive. This is indicated in the figure by (+, +). The signs in each of the other quadrants are similarly indicated.

To *plot* a point of given coordinates means to measure the proper distances from the axes and to mark the point thus determined. We illustrate by showing how to locate the point whose coordinates are (−4, 3). The abscissa −4 means the point is 4 units to the left of the y-axis, and the ordinate 3 (plus sign understood) means the point is 3 units above the x-axis. Consequently, we locate the point (Fig. 1–5) by going from the origin 4 units to the left along the x-axis and then 3 units upward parallel to the y-axis.

Points can be more readily and accurately plotted by the use of coordinate paper, that is, paper ruled into small squares. It is easy to plot a point whose coordinates are distances from the axes to an intersection of two rulings. For other coordinate values the point is not at a corner

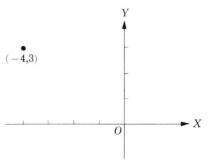

FIGURE 1-5

of one of the small squares, and its position within or on a side of the square must be estimated. If a coordinate is an irrational number, a decimal approximation is used in plotting the point.

We assume that to any pair of real numbers (coordinates) there corresponds one definite point of the coordinate plane. Conversely, we assume that to each point of the plane there corresponds one definite pair of coordinates. This relation of points in a plane and pairs of real numbers is called a *one-to-one correspondence*.

EXERCISE 1–1

1. Plot the points whose coordinates are (4, 3), (4, −3), (−4, 3), (−4, −3), (5, 0), (0, −2), (0, 0).

2. Plot the points whose coordinates are $(\frac{1}{2}, \frac{3}{4})$, $(\frac{3}{5}, \frac{5}{2})$, $(\frac{11}{3}, -4)$, $(\frac{21}{4}, \frac{7}{5})$, $(\sqrt{2}, 1)$, $(\sqrt{3}, \sqrt{3})$, $(\sqrt{5}, -\sqrt{10})$. (See Table I in the Appendix to obtain square roots.)

3. Draw the triangle whose vertices are (a) (2, −1), (0, 4), (5, 1); (b) (2, −3), (4, 4), (−2, 3).

4. In which quadrant is a point if (a) both coordinates are negative, (b) the abscissa is positive and the ordinate is negative?

5. Where may a point lie if (a) its ordinate is zero; (b) its abscissa is zero?

6. What points have their abscissas equal to 3? For what points are the ordinates equal to −4?

7. Where may a point lie if (a) the abscissa is equal to the ordinate, (b) the abscissa is equal to the negative of the ordinate?

8. Draw the right triangle whose vertices are (a) (−1, 1), (3, 1), (3, −2); (b) (−5, 3), (7, 3), (7, −2). From the figure determine the lengths of the perpendicular sides of each triangle. Apply the Pythagorean theorem to find the length of the hypotenuse.*

---

* The Pythagorean theorem states that *the sum of the squares on the perpendicular sides of a right triangle is equal to the square on the hypotenuse.* Thus, if a and b are the lengths of the sides and c is the length of the hypotenuse, then $a^2 + b^2 = c^2$.

9. Two vertices of an equilateral triangle are $(-3, 0)$ and $(3, 0)$. What are the coordinates of the two possible positions of the third vertex? Compute the area of the triangle.

10. Three vertices of a rectangle are at $(2, 3)$, $(6, 0)$, and $(8, 11)$. Draw a figure and determine the position of the fourth vertex.

11. If three of the vertices of a rectangle are at $(1, 1)$, $(4, -2)$, and $(8, 2)$, find the coordinates of the fourth vertex.

12. The points $A(0, 0)$, $B(5, 1)$, and $C(1, 3)$ are vertices of a parallelogram. Find the coordinates of the fourth vertex (a) if BC is a diagonal, (b) if AB is a diagonal, (c) if AC is a diagonal.

13. The points $(-2, -1)$, $(4, 0)$, and $(3, 3)$ are vertices of a parallelogram. Find the coordinates of the three possible positions of the fourth vertex.

14. Use Fig. 1–2 and prove that $BA + AC = BC$.

1–4 Distance between two points. In many problems the distance between two points of the coordinate plane is required. The distance between any two points, or the length of the line segment connecting them, can be determined from the coordinates of the points. We shall classify a line segment as *horizontal, vertical,* or *slant,* and derive appropriate formulas for the lengths of these kinds of segments. In making the derivations, we shall use the idea of directed segments.

Let $P_1(x_1, y)$ and $P_2(x_2, y)$ be two points on a horizontal line, and let A be the point where the line cuts the y-axis (Fig. 1–6). We have

$$AP_1 + P_1P_2 = AP_2,$$

$$P_1P_2 = AP_2 - AP_1$$

$$= x_2 - x_1.$$

Similarly, for the vertical segment Q_1Q_2,

$$Q_1Q_2 = Q_1B + BQ_2 = BQ_2 - BQ_1 = y_2 - y_1.$$

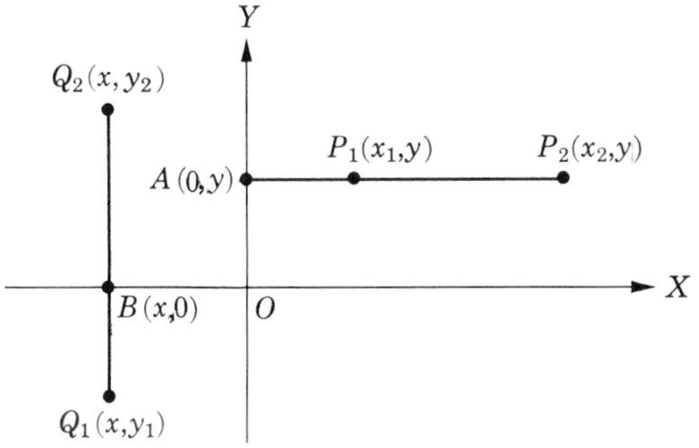

FIGURE 1–6

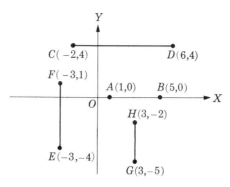

FIGURE 1–7

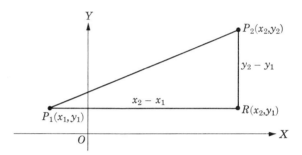

FIGURE 1–8

Hence the directed distance from a first point to a second point on a horizontal line is equal to the abscissa of the second point minus the abscissa of the first point. The distance is positive or negative according as the second point is to the right or left of the first point. A corresponding statement can be made relative to a vertical segment.

Since the lengths of line segments, without regard to direction, are often desired, we state a rule which gives results as positive quantities.

RULE. *The length of a horizontal line segment joining two points is the abscissa of the point on the right minus the abscissa of the point on the left. The length of a vertical line segment joining two points is the ordinate of the upper point minus the ordinate of the lower point.*

We apply this rule to find the lengths of the line segments in Fig. 1–7:

$$AB = 5 - 1 = 4, \qquad CD = 6 - (-2) = 6 + 2 = 8,$$

$$EF = 1 - (-4) = 1 + 4 = 5, \qquad GH = -2 - (-5) = -2 + 5 = 3.$$

We next consider the points $P_1(x_1, y_1)$ and $P_2(x_2, y_2)$ which determine a slant line. Draw a line through P_1 parallel to the x-axis and a line through P_2 parallel to the y-axis (Fig. 1–8). These two lines intersect at the point R, whose abscissa is x_2 and whose ordinate is y_1. Hence

$$P_1R = x_2 - x_1 \quad \text{and} \quad RP_2 = y_2 - y_1.$$

By the Pythagorean theorem,

$$(P_1P_2)^2 = (x_2 - x_1)^2 + (y_2 - y_1)^2.$$

Denoting the length of P_1P_2 by d, we have

$$d = \sqrt{(x_2 - x_1)^2 + (y_2 - y_1)^2}.$$

The positive square root is chosen because we shall usually be interested only in the magnitude of the segment. We state this distance formula in words.

RULE. *To find the distance between two points, add the square of the difference of the abscissas to the square of the difference of the ordinates and take the positive square root of the sum.*

In employing the distance formula either point may be designated by (x_1, y_1) and the other by (x_2, y_2). This results from the fact that the two differences involved are squared. The square of the difference of two numbers is unchanged when the order of the subtraction is reversed.

EXAMPLE. Find the lengths of the sides of the triangle with the vertices $A(-2, -3)$, $B(5, 1)$, and $C(-2, 5)$.

Solution. The abscissas of A and C are the same, and therefore side AC is vertical (Fig. 1–9). The length of the vertical side is the difference of the ordinates. The other sides are slant segments, and the general distance formula yields their lengths. Hence we get

$$AC = 5 - (-3) = 5 + 3 = 8,$$

$$AB = \sqrt{(5 + 2)^2 + (1 + 3)^2} = \sqrt{65},$$

$$BC = \sqrt{(5 + 2)^2 + (1 - 5)^2} = \sqrt{65}.$$

The lengths show that the triangle is isosceles.

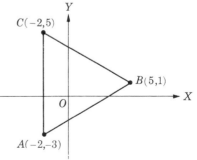

FIGURE 1–9

Exercise 1–2

1. Plot the points $A(-2, 0)$, $B(1, 0)$, and $C(5, 0)$. Then find the directed distances AB, AC, BC, BA, CA, and CB.

2. Given the points $A(2, -3)$, $B(2, 0)$, and $C(2, 4)$, find the directed distances AB, BA, AC, CA, BC, and CB.

3. Plot the points $A(-2, 0)$, $B(2, 0)$, and $C(5, 0)$, and verify the following equations by numerical substitutions:

$$AB + BC = AC; \qquad AC + CB = AB; \qquad BA + AC = BC.$$

Find the distances between the pairs of points in problems 4 through 9.

4. $(1, 3)$, $(4, 7)$ 5. $(-3, 4)$, $(2, -8)$ 6. $(-2, -3)$, $(1, 0)$
7. $(5, -12)$, $(0, 0)$ 8. $(0, -4)$, $(3, 0)$ 9. $(2, 7)$, $(-1, 4)$

In each problem 10 through 13 draw the triangle with the given vertices and find the lengths of the sides.

10. $A(1, -1)$, $B(4, -1)$, $C(4, 3)$ 11. $A(-1, 2)$, $B(2, 4)$, $C(0, 5)$
12. $A(0, 0)$, $B(-2, 5)$, $C(2, -3)$ 13. $A(-3, 0)$, $B(0, 3)$, $C(-4, 0)$

Draw the triangles in problems 14 through 17 and show that each is isosceles.

14. $A(6, 1)$, $B(2, -4)$, $C(-2, 1)$ 15. $A(6, 4)$, $B(3, 0)$, $C(-1, 3)$
16. $A(1, -1)$, $B(1, 7)$, $C(8, 3)$ 17. $A(-3, -3)$, $B(3, 3)$, $C(-4, 4)$

Show that the triangles in problems 18 through 21 are right triangles.

18. $A(1, 4)$, $B(10, 6)$, $C(2, 2)$ 19. $A(-2, 1)$, $B(5, -2)$, $C(3, 3)$
20. $A(0, 4)$, $B(-3, -3)$, $C(2, -1)$ 21. $A(4, -3)$, $B(0, 0)$, $C(3, 4)$

22. Show that $A(-1, 0)$, $B(3, 0)$ and $C(1, 2\sqrt{3})$ are vertices of an equilateral triangle.

23. Show that $A(-\sqrt{3}, 2)$, $B(2\sqrt{3}, -1)$, and $C(2\sqrt{3}, 5)$ are vertices of an equilateral triangle.

24. Given the points $A(1, 0)$, $B(5, 3)$, $C(2, 7)$, and $D(-2, 4)$, show that the sides of the quadrilateral $ABCD$ are equal.

25. Determine whether the points $(-5, 7)$, $(2, 6)$, and $(1, -1)$ are all the same distance from $(-2, 3)$.

26. Prove that the points $(-2, 6)$, $(5, 3)$, $(-1, -11)$, and $(-8, -8)$ are vertices of a rectangle.

Determine, by the distance formula, whether the points in each problem 27 through 30 lie on a straight line.

27. $(3, 2)$, $(0, 0)$, $(9, 6)$ 28. $(2, 1)$, $(-1, 2)$, $(5, 0)$
29. $(-4, 0)$, $(0, 2)$, $(9, 7)$ 30. $(-1, -1)$, $(6, -4)$, $(-10, 3)$

31. If the point $(x, 3)$ is equidistant from $(3, -2)$ and $(7, 4)$, find x.

32. Find the point on the y-axis which is equidistant from $(-5, -2)$ and $(3, 2)$.

33. Plot a point $P_1(x_1, y_1)$ in the first quadrant and a point $P_2(x_2, y_2)$ in the fourth quadrant. Draw a suitable right triangle with P_1P_2 as the hypotenuse. From the diagram *derive* the distance formula.

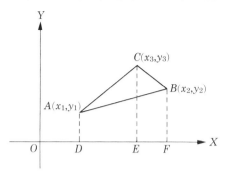

FIGURE 1–10

34. Let the vertices of a triangle, reading counterclockwise, be $A(x_1, y_1)$, $B(x_2, y_2)$, and $C(x_3, y_3)$, as in Fig. 1–10. Observe that $DECA$, $EFBC$, and $DFBA$ are trapezoids. The sum of the areas of the first two trapezoids minus the area of the third trapezoid is equal to the area of triangle ABC. Recalling that the area of a trapezoid is equal to half the sum of the parallel sides times the altitude, we have area $DECA = \frac{1}{2}(y_1 + y_3)(x_3 - x_1)$. With this start, show that the area S of the triangle is

$$S = \tfrac{1}{2}[x_1(y_2 - y_3) - y_1(x_2 - x_3) + (x_2 y_3 - x_3 y_2)].$$

By expanding the determinant, show that the area of the triangle can be expressed as

$$S = \tfrac{1}{2} \begin{vmatrix} x_1 & y_1 & 1 \\ x_2 & y_2 & 1 \\ x_3 & y_3 & 1 \end{vmatrix}.$$

Using the determinant of problem 34, find the area of each triangle ABC in problems 35 through 40.

35. $A(0, 0)$, $B(6, 0)$, $C(4, 3)$ 36. $A(-2, 4)$, $B(2, -6)$, $C(5, 4)$
37. $A(-2, -7)$, $B(-1, -1)$,   38. $A(5, -1)$, $B(-1, 4)$, $C(3, 6)$
     $C(-10, -8)$
39. $A(1, 5)$, $B(6, 1)$, $C(8, 7)$ 40. $A(-2, -3)$, $B(3, 2)$, $C(-1, -8)$

1–5 Inclination and slope of a line. If a line intersects the x-axis, the *inclination* of the line is defined as the positive angle less than 180° whose initial side extends to the right along the x-axis and whose terminal side is upward along the line.* In Fig. 1–11 the angle θ is the inclination

---

* When an angle is measured from the first side to the second side, the first side is called the initial side and the second side the terminal side. Further, the angle is positive or negative according as it is measured in a counterclockwise or a clockwise direction.

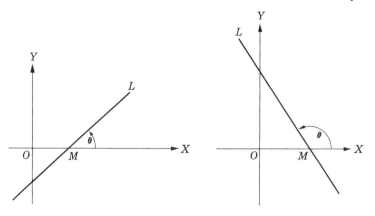

FIGURE 1–11

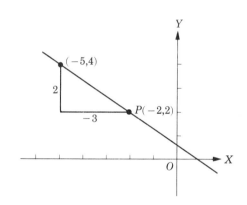

FIGURE 1–12

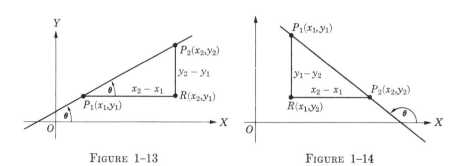

FIGURE 1–13   FIGURE 1–14

of the line, MX is the initial side and ML the terminal side. The inclination of a line parallel to the x-axis is $0°$.

The *slope* of a line is defined as the tangent of its angle of inclination. A line which leans to the right has a positive slope because the inclination is an acute angle. The slopes of lines which lean to the left are negative. The slope of a horizontal line is zero. Vertical lines do not have a slope, however, since $90°$ has no tangent.

If the inclination of a nonvertical line is known, the slope can be determined by the use of a table of trigonometric functions. Conversely, if the slope of a line is known, its inclination can be found. In most problems, however, it is more convenient to deal with the slope of a line rather than with its inclination.

EXAMPLE 1. Draw a line through the point $P(-2, 2)$ with slope $-\frac{2}{3}$.

Solution. We move 3 units to the left of P and then 2 units upward. The line through the point thus located and the given point P clearly has the required slope (Fig. 1–12).

The definitions of inclination and slope lead immediately to a theorem concerning parallel lines. If two lines have the same slope, their inclinations are equal. Hence the lines are parallel. Conversely, if two nonvertical lines are parallel, they have equal angles of inclination, and consequently have equal slopes.

THEOREM. *Two nonvertical lines are parallel if, and only if, their slopes are equal.*

If the coordinates of two points on a line are known, we may find the slope of the line from the given coordinates. We now derive a formula for this purpose.

Let $P_1(x_1, y_1)$ and $P_2(x_2, y_2)$ be the two given points, and indicate the slope by m. Then, referring to Fig. 1–13, we have

$$m = \tan \theta = \frac{RP_2}{P_1R} = \frac{y_2 - y_1}{x_2 - x_1}.$$

If the line slants to the left, as in Fig. 1–14,

$$m = \tan \theta = -\frac{y_1 - y_2}{x_2 - x_1} = \frac{y_2 - y_1}{x_2 - x_1}.$$

Hence the slope is determined in the same way for lines slanting either to the left or to the right.

THEOREM. *The slope m of a line passing through two given points $P_1(x_1, y_1)$ and $P_2(x_2, y_2)$ is equal to the difference of the ordinates divided by the difference of the abscissas taken in the same order; that is,*

$$m = \frac{y_2 - y_1}{x_2 - x_1}.$$

This formula yields the slope if the two points are on a slant or a horizontal line. If the line is vertical, the denominator of the formula becomes zero, a result in keeping with the fact that slope is not defined for a vertical line. We observe further that either of the points may be designated as $P_1(x_1, y_1)$ and the other as $P_2(x_2, y_2)$, since

$$\frac{y_2 - y_1}{x_2 - x_1} = \frac{y_1 - y_2}{x_1 - x_2}.$$

EXAMPLE 2. Given the points $A(-2, -1)$, $B(4, 0)$, $C(3, 3)$, and $D(-3, 2)$, show that $ABCD$ is a parallelogram.

Solution. We determine from the slopes of the sides whether the figure is a parallelogram.

Slope of $AB = \dfrac{0 - (-1)}{4 - (-2)} = \dfrac{1}{6}$,   slope of $BC = \dfrac{3 - 0}{3 - 4} = -3$,

slope of $CD = \dfrac{2 - 3}{-3 - 3} = \dfrac{1}{6}$,   slope of $DA = \dfrac{2 - (-1)}{-3 - (-2)} = -3$.

The opposite sides have equal slopes, and therefore $ABCD$ is a parallelogram.

1–6 Angle between two lines. Two intersecting lines form two pairs of equal angles, and an angle of one pair is the supplement of an angle of the other pair. We shall show how to find a measure of each angle in terms of the slopes of the lines. Noticing Fig. 1–15 and recalling that an exterior angle of a triangle is equal to the sum of the remote interior angles, we see that

$$\phi + \theta_1 = \theta_2 \quad \text{or} \quad \phi = \theta_2 - \theta_1.$$

Using the formula for the tangent of the difference of two angles, we find

$$\tan \phi = \tan (\theta_2 - \theta_1) = \frac{\tan \theta_2 - \tan \theta_1}{1 + \tan \theta_1 \tan \theta_2}.$$

If we let $m_2 = \tan \theta_2$ and $m_1 = \tan \theta_1$, then we have

$$\tan \phi = \frac{m_2 - m_1}{1 + m_1 m_2},$$

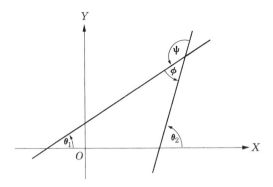

FIGURE 1–15

where m_2 is the slope of the terminal side, m_1 is the slope of the initial side, and ϕ is measured in a counterclockwise direction.

The angle ψ is the supplement of ϕ, and therefore

$$\tan \psi = -\tan \phi = \frac{m_1 - m_2}{1 + m_1 m_2}.$$

This formula for $\tan \psi$ is the same as the one for $\tan \phi$ except that the terms in the numerator are reversed. We observe from the diagram, however, that the terminal side of ψ is the initial side of ϕ and that the initial side of ψ is the terminal side of ϕ, as indicated by the counterclockwise arrows. Hence, in terms of the slopes of initial and terminal sides, the tangent of either angle may be found by the same rule. We state this conclusion as a theorem.

THEOREM. *If ϕ is an angle, measured counterclockwise, between two lines, then*

$$\tan \phi = \frac{m_2 - m_1}{1 + m_1 m_2}, \tag{1}$$

where m_2 is the slope of the terminal side and m_1 is the slope of the initial side.

This formula will not apply if either of the lines is vertical, since a vertical line does not possess slope. For this case the problem would be that of finding the angle, or function of the angle, which a line of known slope makes with the vertical. Hence no new formula is needed.

For any two slant lines which are not perpendicular, Eq. (1) will yield a definite number as the value of $\tan \phi$. Conversely, if the formula yields a definite number, the lines are not perpendicular. Hence we conclude that the lines are perpendicular when, and only when, the denominator

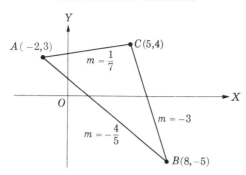

FIGURE 1–16

of the formula is equal to zero. The relation $1 + m_1 m_2 = 0$ may be written in the form $m_2 = -1/m_1$, which expresses one slope as the negative reciprocal of the other slope.

THEOREM. *Two slant lines are perpendicular if, and only if, the slope of one is the negative reciprocal of the slope of the other.*

Perpendicularity of two lines occurs, of course, if one line is parallel to the x-axis and the other is parallel to the y-axis. The slope of the line parallel to the x-axis is zero, but the line parallel to the y-axis does not possess slope.

EXAMPLE. Find the tangents of the angles of the triangle whose vertices are $A(-2, 3)$, $B(8, -5)$, and $C(5, 4)$. Find each angle to the nearest degree. (See Table II of the Appendix.)

Solution. We first find the slope of each side. Thus from Fig. 1–16,

$$m_{AB} = \frac{3 - (-5)}{-2 - 8} = -\frac{4}{5},$$

$$m_{BC} = \frac{4 - (-5)}{5 - 8} = -3, \qquad m_{AC} = \frac{3 - 4}{-2 - 5} = \frac{1}{7}.$$

Now we substitute in Eq. (1) and get

$$\tan A = \frac{\frac{1}{7} - (-\frac{4}{5})}{1 + (-\frac{4}{5})(\frac{1}{7})} = \frac{33}{31} = 1.06, \qquad A = 47°,$$

$$\tan B = \frac{-\frac{4}{5} - (-3)}{1 + (-3)(-\frac{4}{5})} = \frac{11}{17} = 0.647, \qquad B = 33°,$$

$$\tan C = \frac{-3 - \frac{1}{7}}{1 + (\frac{1}{7})(-3)} = \frac{-22}{4} = -5.5, \qquad C = 100°.$$

Exercise 1–3

Draw a line segment through the given point with the slope indicated in problems 1 through 4.

1. $(2, -3)$, $m = \frac{3}{4}$ 2. $(4, 0)$, $m = -3$
3. $(-1, -4)$, $m = -\frac{5}{3}$ 4. $(3, 5)$, $m = -5$

5. Give the slopes for the inclinations (a) $45°$, (b) $0°$, (c) $60°$, (d) $120°$, (e) $135°$.

Find the slope of the line passing through the two points in each problem 6 through 11. Find also the angle of inclination to the nearest degree. (See Table II in the Appendix.)

6. $(3, 2)$, $(7, 3)$ 7. $(6, -13)$, $(0, 3)$ 8. $(4, -8)$, $(-7, 3)$
9. $(4, 5)$, $(-2, -3)$ 10. $(0, -9)$, $(20, 3)$ 11. $(4, 11)$, $(-8, -3)$

12. Show that each of the following sets of four points are vertices of the parallelogram $ABCD$.

(a) $A(2, 0)$, $B(6, 0)$, $C(4, 3)$, $D(0, 3)$
(b) $A(-2, 2)$, $B(6, 0)$, $C(5, -3)$, $D(-3, -1)$
(c) $A(0, -2)$, $B(4, -6)$, $C(12, -1)$, $D(8, 3)$
(d) $A(-1, 0)$, $B(5, 2)$, $C(8, 7)$, $D(2, 5)$

13. Verify that each triangle with the given points as vertices is a right triangle by showing that the slope of one of the sides is the negative reciprocal of the slope of another side.

(a) $(3, -4)$, $(3, 4)$, $(-1, 0)$ (b) $(-1, 1)$, $(3, -7)$, $(3, 3)$
(c) $(8, 1)$, $(1, -2)$, $(6, -4)$ (d) $(1, 5)$, $(-6, 7)$, $(-3, -9)$
(e) $(0, 0)$, $(3, -2)$, $(2, 3)$ (f) $(0, 0)$, $(17, 0)$, $(1, 4)$

14. Show that the four points in each of the following sets are vertices of a rectangle.

(a) $(-5, 3)$, $(-1, -2)$, $(4, 2)$, $(0, 7)$
(b) $(1, 2)$, $(6, -3)$, $(9, 0)$, $(4, 5)$
(c) $(0, 0)$, $(2, 6)$, $(-1, 7)$, $(-3, 1)$
(d) $(5, -2)$, $(7, 5)$, $(0, 7)$, $(-2, 0)$
(e) $(4, 2)$, $(3, 9)$, $(-4, 8)$, $(-3, 1)$
(f) $(4, 6)$, $(0, 0)$, $(3, -2)$, $(7, 4)$

Using slopes, determine which of the sets of three points, in problems 15 through 18, lie on a straight line.

15. $(3, 0)$, $(0, -2)$, $(9, 4)$ 16. $(2, 1)$, $(-1, 2)$, $(5, 0)$
17. $(-4, -1)$, $(0, 1)$, $(9, 6)$ 18. $(-1, -2)$, $(6, -5)$, $(-10, 2)$

Find the tangents of the angles of the triangle ABC in each problem 19 through 22. Find the angles to the nearest degrees.

19. $A(-3, 1)$, $B(3, 5)$, $C(-1, 6)$ 20. $A(-2, 1)$, $B(1, 3)$, $C(6, -7)$
21. $A(-3, 1)$, $B(4, 2)$, $C(2, 3)$ 22. $A(1, 3)$, $B(-2, -4)$, $C(3, -2)$

23. The line through the points (4, 3) and (−6, 0) intersects the line through (0, 0) and (−1, 5). Find the angles of intersection.

24. Two lines passing through (2, 3) make an angle of 45°. If the slope of one of the lines is 2, find the slope of the other (two solutions).

25. What acute angle does a line of slope $-\frac{2}{3}$ make with a vertical line?

26. Find y if the slope of the line segment joining (3, −2) to (4, y) is −3.

27. The line segment drawn from $P(x, 3)$ to (4, 1) is perpendicular to the segment drawn from (−5, −6) to (4, 1). Find the value of x.

Find the relation between x and y if the point $P(x, y)$ is to satisfy the conditions in problems 28 through 31.

28. The line segment joining $P(x, y)$ and (1, 5) has slope 3.

29. The line segment joining $P(x, y)$ to (2, 4) is parallel to the segment joining (−2, −1) and (6, 8).

30. The line segment joining $P(x, y)$ to (2, 4) is perpendicular to the segment joining (−2, −1) and (6, 8).

31. The point $P(x, y)$ is on the line passing through (2, −5) and (7, 1).

1–7 Division of a line segment. In this section we shall show how to find the coordinates of a point which divides a line segment into two parts which have a specified relation. We first find formulas for the coordinates of the point midway between two points of given coordinates.

Let $P_1(x_1, y_1)$ and $P_2(x_2, y_2)$ be the extremities of a line segment, and let $P(x, y)$ be the mid-point of P_1P_2. From similar triangles (Fig. 1–17), we have

$$\frac{P_1P}{P_1P_2} = \frac{P_1M}{P_1N} = \frac{MP}{NP_2} = \frac{1}{2}.$$

Hence

$$\frac{P_1M}{P_1N} = \frac{x - x_1}{x_2 - x_1} = \frac{1}{2} \quad \text{and} \quad \frac{MP}{NP_2} = \frac{y - y_1}{y_2 - y_1} = \frac{1}{2}.$$

Solving for x and y gives

$$x = \frac{x_1 + x_2}{2}, \qquad y = \frac{y_1 + y_2}{2}.$$

THEOREM. *The abscissa of the mid-point of a line segment is half the sum of the abscissas of the end points; the ordinate is half the sum of the ordinates.*

This theorem may be generalized by letting $P(x, y)$ be any division point of the segment P_1P_2. If the ratio of P_1P to P_1P_2 is a number r instead of $\frac{1}{2}$, then

$$\frac{P_1P}{P_1P_2} = \frac{x - x_1}{x_2 - x_1} = r \quad \text{and} \quad \frac{P_1P}{P_1P_2} = \frac{y - y_1}{y_2 - y_1} = r.$$

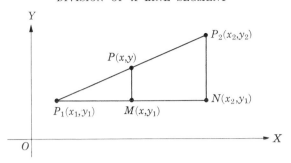

FIGURE 1–17

These equations, when solved for x and y, give

$$x = x_1 + r(x_2 - x_1), \qquad y = y_1 + r(y_2 - y_1).$$

If P is between P_1 and P_2, as in Fig. 1–17, the segments P_1P and P_1P_2 have the same direction, and the value of their ratio r is positive and less than 1. If, however, P is a point on the segment P_1P_2 extended through P_2, then the segment P_1P is greater than P_1P_2, and $r > 1$. Conversely, if $r > 1$, the formulas yield the coordinates of a point on the extension of the segment through P_2. In order to find a point on the segment extended in the other direction, and still use a positive value for r, we designate the two given points P_1 and P_2 so that P_1 is farther from P than P_2 is.

EXAMPLE 1. Find the mid-point and the trisection point nearer P_2 of the line segment determined by $P_1(-3, -5)$ and $P_2(-1, 7)$.

Solution. By applying the mid-point formulas, we have

$$x = \frac{x_1 + x_2}{2} = \frac{-3 - 1}{2} = -2, \qquad y = \frac{y_1 + y_2}{2} = \frac{-5 + 7}{2} = 1.$$

For the trisection point nearer P_2, we use $r = \frac{2}{3}$. Thus

$$x = x_1 + r(x_2 - x_1) = -3 + \tfrac{2}{3}(-1 + 3) = -\tfrac{5}{3},$$
$$y = y_1 + r(y_2 - y_1) = -5 + \tfrac{2}{3}(7 + 5) = 3.$$

Hence the coordinates of the mid-point are $(-2, 1)$ and of the desired trisection point $(-\tfrac{5}{3}, 3)$.

EXAMPLE 2. A point $P(x, y)$ is on an extension of the line segment joining $A(-1, 4)$ and $B(5, 1)$. Find (a) the coordinates of the point P if it is twice as far from A as from B, (b) the coordinates if P is three times as far from B as from A.

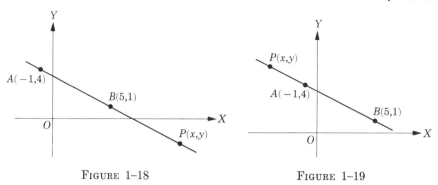

FIGURE 1-18   FIGURE 1-19

Solution. (a) Since $AP = 2(BP)$, it follows that $BP = AB$ (Fig. 1–18). Hence the ratio of AP to AB is 2. Accordingly we treat the point A as $P_1(x_1, y_1)$ of the formulas and the point B as $P_2(x_2, y_2)$. Thus we have

$$x = -1 + 2(5 + 1) = 11, \qquad y = 4 + 2(1 - 4) = -2.$$

(b) For this position of P we have $BP = 3(AP)$, and therefore $BA = 2(AP)$ (Fig. 1–19). Hence r, the ratio of BP to BA, is $\frac{3}{2}$. Since P is farther from B than from A, we use B as P_1 and A as P_2 and obtain

$$x = 5 + \tfrac{3}{2}(-1 - 5) = -4, \qquad y = 1 + \tfrac{3}{2}(4 - 1) = \tfrac{11}{2}.$$

1–8 Analytic proofs of geometric theorems. By the use of a coordinate system many of the theorems of elementary geometry can be proved with surprising simplicity and directness. We illustrate the procedure in the following example.

EXAMPLE. Prove that the diagonals of a parallelogram bisect each other.

Solution. We first draw a parallelogram and then introduce a coordinate system. A judicious location of the axes relative to the figure makes the writing of the coordinates of the vertices easier and also simplifies the algebraic operations involved in making the proof. Therefore we choose a vertex as the origin and a coordinate axis along a side of the parallelogram (Fig. 1–20). Then we write the coordinates of the vertices as $O(0, 0)$, $P_1(a, 0)$, $P_2(b, c)$, and $P_3(a + b, c)$. It is essential that the coordinates of P_2 and P_3 express the fact that P_2P_3 is equal and parallel to OP_1. This is achieved by making the ordinates of P_2 and P_3 the same and making the abscissa of P_3 exceed the abscissa of P_2 by a.

To show that OP_3 and P_1P_2 bisect each other, we find the coordinates of the mid-point of each diagonal.

$$\text{Mid-point of } OP_3: \quad x = \frac{a + b}{2}, \quad y = \frac{c}{2}.$$

$$\text{Mid-point of } P_1P_2: \quad x = \frac{a + b}{2}, \quad y = \frac{c}{2}.$$

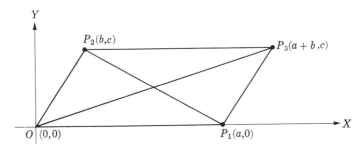

FIGURE 1–20

Since the mid-point of each diagonal is

$$\left(\frac{a+b}{2},\ \frac{c}{2}\right),$$

the theorem is proved.

Note. In making a proof by this method, it is essential that a general figure be used. For example, neither a rectangle nor a rhombus (a parallelogram with all sides equal) should be used for a parallelogram. A proof of a theorem based on a special case would not constitute a general proof.

EXERCISE 1–4

1. Find the mid-point of AB in each of the following.

(a) $A(-2, 6)$, $B(4, -6)$ (b) $A(7, -2)$, $B(-3, 10)$
(c) $A(-6, 12)$, $B(12, 0)$ (d) $A(0, -7)$, $B(3, 10)$

2. The vertices of a triangle are $A(1, 7)$, $B(6, -1)$, and $C(0, 3)$. Find the coordinates of the mid-points of the sides.

3. The points $A(-4, -1)$, $B(2, 7)$, $C(6, 5)$, and $D(8, -5)$ are vertices of the quadrilateral $ABCD$. Find the coordinates of the mid-point of each line segment connecting the mid-points of opposite sides.

Find the coordinates of the trisection points of the line segment AB in problems 4 through 7.

4. $A(-6, -9)$, $B(6, 9)$ 5. $A(6, -5)$, $B(0, 7)$
6. $A(3, -4)$, $B(-3, 8)$ 7. $A(0, -1)$, $B(6, 4)$

8. The points $A(2, 2)$, $B(0, 6)$, and $C(8, 10)$ are vertices of a triangle. Determine whether the medians are concurrent by finding the point on each median which is $\frac{2}{3}$ of the way from the vertex to the other extremity. (A median of a triangle is the line segment joining a vertex and the mid-point of the opposite side.)

9. The points $A(1, 2)$, $B(-3, 6)$, and $C(5, 4)$ are vertices of a triangle. Find the trisection point on each median which is nearer the opposite side.

10. The line segment joining $A(2, -3)$ and $B(-3, 5)$ is extended through each end by a length equal to its original length. Find the coordinates of the new ends.

11. The line segment joining $A(-1, -4)$ to $B(6, 3)$ is doubled in length by having half its length added at each end. Find the coordinates of the new ends.

The points P_1, P_2, and P are on a straight line in each problem 12 through 15. Find r, the ratio of P_1P to P_1P_2.

12. $P_1(-3, -1)$, $P_2(1, 5)$, $P(-1, 2)$ 13. $P_1(1, 3)$, $P_2(3, 6)$, $P(5, 9)$
14. $P_1(1, 2)$, $P_2(-1, 5)$, $P(-5, 11)$
15. $P_1(2, -4)$, $P_2(-2, 1)$, $P(-10, 11)$

16. The mid-points of the sides of a triangle are at $(2, 0)$, $(4, 1)$, and $(3, 4)$. Find the coordinates of the vertices. [*Hint:* The line joining the mid-points of two sides of a triangle bisects the median to the third side.]

17. Draw the triangle whose vertices are $P_1(x_1, y_1)$, $P_2(x_2, y_2)$, and $P_3(x_3, y_3)$. Find the coordinates of the trisection point of each median which is nearer the opposite side.

18. If r is negative in the point of division formulas, where will the point $P(x, y)$ be relative to P_1 and P_2? Describe the behavior of P as r decreases from a numerically small negative number to a numerically large negative number.

19. Plot the points $P_1(4, 5)$ and $P_2(7, 8)$. Then find $P(x, y)$ using (a) $r = -\frac{1}{3}$, (b) $r = -1$, (c) $r = -2$, (d) $r = -3$. Plot these various positions of P.

Give analytic proofs of the theorems in problems 20 through 38.

20. The diagonals of the rectangle are equal. [*Hint:* Choose the axes so that the vertices of the rectangle are $(0, 0)$, $(a, 0)$, $(0, b)$, and (a, b).]

21. The mid-point of the hypotenuse of a right triangle is equidistant from the three vertices.

22. The line segment joining the mid-points of two sides of a triangle is parallel to the third side and equal to half of it.

23. The diagonals of an isosceles trapezoid are equal. [*Hint:* Note that the axes may be placed so that the coordinates of the vertices are $(0, 0)$, $(a, 0)$, (b, c), and $(a - b, c)$.]

24. The line segment joining the mid-points of the nonparallel sides of a trapezoid is parallel to and equal to half the sum of the parallel sides.

25. The line segments which join the mid-points of the sides of any quadrilateral, if taken in order, form a parallelogram.

26. The line segments which join the mid-points of the opposite sides of a quadrilateral bisect each other.

27. The diagonals of a rhombus are perpendicular and bisect each other.

28. The sum of the squares of the sides of a parallelogram is equal to the sum of the squares of the diagonals.

29. The lines drawn from a vertex of a parallelogram to the mid-points of the opposite sides trisect a diagonal.

30. The medians of a triangle meet in a point which lies two-thirds of the way from each vertex to the mid-point of the opposite side.

31. If vertices of a triangle are $P_1(x_1, y_1)$, $P_2(x_2, y_2)$, and $P_3(x_3, y_3)$, the medians intersect at the point $[\frac{1}{3}(x_1 + x_2 + x_3), \frac{1}{3}(y_1 + y_2 + y_3)]$.

32. If one of the parallel sides of a trapezoid is twice the other, the diagonals meet at a trisection point.

33. The line segment joining the mid-points of two sides of a triangle bisects the median to the third side.

34. The line segment joining the mid-points of the diagonals of a trapezoid is equal to half the difference of the bases.

35. If the diagonals of a quadrilateral bisect each other, the figure is a parallelogram.

36. If the diagonals of a quadrilateral bisect each other at right angles, the figure is a rhombus.

37. If the diagonals of a quadrilateral are equal and bisect each other, the figure is a rectangle.

38. The line segment joining the mid-points of the nonparallel sides of a trapezoid bisects the diagonals.

1–9 Two aspects of analytic geometry. We close this chapter by introducing the two fundamental problems of analytic geometry. As previously hinted, the sciences of algebra and geometry are correlated by means of coordinate systems. In plane analytic geometry, the underlying feature is the correspondence between an equation in x and y and a geometric figure. Accordingly, one problem is that of starting with an equation and finding the associated figure and, conversely, the other problem is that of passing from a given geometric figure to the corresponding equation.

In these problems, we shall deal with constants and variables. A symbol which stands for a fixed number is called a *constant*. A symbol which may assume different numerical values is called a *variable*. A quadratic expression in the variable x, for example, may be represented by

$$ax^2 + bx + c,$$

where a, b, and c are unspecified constants which assume fixed values in a particular problem or situation.

Restrictions are usually placed on the values which a variable may take. In the formula $c = 2\pi r$, giving the circumference of a circle in terms of the radius, the variables r and c take only positive values. In this book, we shall consider variables which have only real values.* The variable x in the equation $y^2 = x - 2$, for example, can be assigned only values equal to or greater than 2; otherwise y^2 would be negative, and y would be imaginary.

---

* A number of the form $a + b\sqrt{-1}$, where a and b are real and $b \neq 0$, is called an *imaginary number*.

1–10 The graph of an equation. Consider the equation

$$y = x^2 - 3x - 3.$$

Any pair of numbers for x and y which satisfy the equation is called a *solution* of the equation. If a value is assigned to x, the corresponding value of y may be computed. Thus setting $x = -2$, we find $y = 7$. Several values of x and the corresponding values of y are shown in the table. These pairs of values, each constituting a solution, furnish a picture of the relation of x and y. A better representation is had, however, by plotting each value of x and the corresponding value of y as the abscissa and ordinate of a point and then drawing a smooth curve through the points thus obtained. This process is called *graphing the equation*, and the curve is called the *graph* or *locus* of the equation.

x	-2	-1	0	1	1.5	2	3	4	5
y	7	1	-3	-5	-5.25	-5	-3	1	7

The plotted points (Fig. 1–21) extend from $x = -2$ to $x = 5$. Points corresponding to smaller and larger values of x could be plotted, and also any number of intermediate points could be located. But the plotted points show approximately where the intermediate points would be. Hence we can use a few points to draw a curve which is reasonably accurate. The exact graph satisfies the following definition.

DEFINITION. *The graph (or locus) of an equation consists of all points (x, y) whose coordinates satisfy the given equation.*

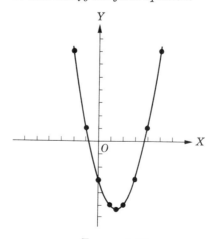

FIGURE 1–21

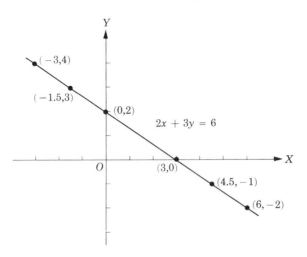

FIGURE 1–22

In the next chapter, we shall prove that the graph of a first-degree equation in x and y is a straight line. For this reason, the equation is said to be *linear*. Figure 1–22 shows points whose coordinates satisfy the equation $2x + 3y = 6$. Observe that the points appear to be on a line.

As a final example, we construct the graph of the equation

$$4x^2 + 9y^2 = 36.$$

Solving for y, we get the equation

$$y = \pm\tfrac{2}{3}\sqrt{9 - x^2},$$

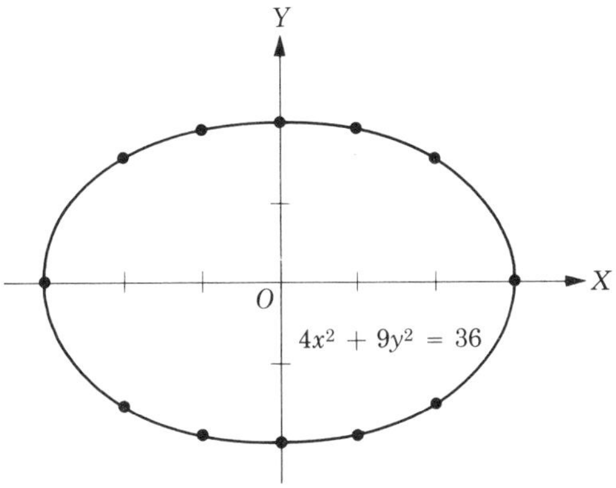

FIGURE 1–23

which is suitable for making a table of values. We see that x can take values from -3 to 3; other values for x would yield imaginary values for y.

x	-3	-2	-1	0	1	2	3
y	0	± 1.5	± 1.9	± 2	± 1.9	± 1.5	0

The plotted points and the curve drawn through them appear in Fig. 1–23.

This curve is called an *ellipse*. The curve of Fig. 1–21 is a *parabola*. Later we shall study curves of this kind in considerable detail.

EXERCISE 1–5

Draw the graph of each of the following equations. (To obtain square roots see Table I of the Appendix.)

1. $y = 2x$
2. $y = 3x - 5$
3. $y = -4x$
4. $y = -x + 4$
5. $2x - 4y = 5$
6. $5x + 3y = 15$
7. $x + 3 = 0$
8. $2x - 7 = 0$
9. $y - 4 = 0$
10. $3y + 5 = 0$
11. $y = x^2$
12. $x^2 = y$
13. $y = x^2 - 2x - 1$
14. $y = x^2 + 4x$
15. $x = y^2 - 4$
16. $x = 9 - y^2$
17. $x^2 + y^2 = 16$
18. $x^2 + y^2 - 25 = 0$
19. $x^2 + 4y^2 = 4$
20. $4x^2 + 9y^2 = 36$
21. $xy = 4$
22. $xy = -4$
23. $4x^2 - 9y^2 = 36$
24. $x^2 - y^2 = 1$

1–11 The equation of a locus. Having obtained loci of equations, we naturally surmise that a locus or curve in a plane has a corresponding equation. We shall consider the problem of writing the equation of a locus all of whose points are definitely fixed by given geometric conditions. It will be convenient to describe a locus as the path of a point which moves in accordance with specified restrictions.

DEFINITION. *An equation of a locus is a relation between x and y which is satisfied by the coordinates of all points of the locus and by no others.*

The procedure for finding the equation of a locus is straightforward. Each point $P(x, y)$ of the locus must satisfy the specified conditions. The desired equation can be written by requiring the point P to obey the conditions. The examples illustrate the method.

EXAMPLE 1. Find the equation of the locus of a point $P(x, y)$ moving along the line with slope 2 which passes through $(-3, 4)$.

Solution. We apply the formula for the slope of a line through two points (Section 1–5). Thus the slope of the line through $P(x, y)$ and $(-3, 4)$ is

$$m = \frac{y - 4}{x - (-3)} = \frac{y - 4}{x + 3}.$$

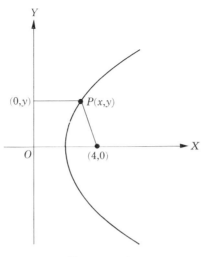

FIGURE 1–24

We equate this expression for the slope to the given slope. Hence

$$\frac{y - 4}{x + 3} = 2,$$

or

$$2x - y + 10 = 0.$$

EXAMPLE 2. A point moves so that its distance from the y-axis is always equal to its distance from the point (4, 0). Find the equation of the locus of the moving point.

Solution. We take a point $P(x, y)$ of the locus (Fig. 1–24). Then, referring to the distance formulas of Section 1–4, we find the distance of P from the y-axis to be simply the abscissa x, and the distance from the point (4, 0) to be

$$\sqrt{(x - 4)^2 + (y - 0)^2} = \sqrt{x^2 - 8x + 16 + y^2}.$$

Equating the two distances, we obtain

$$\sqrt{x^2 - 8x + 16 + y^2} = x.$$

By squaring both sides, we get

$$y^2 - 8x + 16 = 0.$$

EXAMPLE 3. Find the equation of the locus of a point which is twice as far from (4, 4) as from (1, 1).

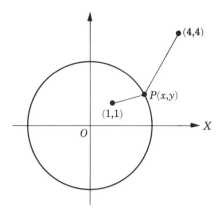

FIGURE 1–25

Solution. We apply the distance formula to find the distance of a point of the locus $P(x, y)$ from each of the given points. Thus we obtain the expressions

$$\sqrt{(x-1)^2 + (y-1)^2} \quad \text{and} \quad \sqrt{(x-4)^2 + (y-4)^2}.$$

Since the second distance is twice the first, we have the equation

$$2\sqrt{(x-1)^2 + (y-1)^2} = \sqrt{(x-4)^2 + (y-4)^2}.$$

Simplifying, we get

$$4(x^2 - 2x + 1 + y^2 - 2y + 1) = x^2 - 8x + 16 + y^2 - 8y + 16,$$

or

$$x^2 + y^2 = 8.$$

The graph of the equation appears in Fig. 1–25.

EXERCISE 1–6

In the following problems, find the equation of the locus of $P(x, y)$ which satisfies the given conditions.

1. P is on the line passing through the origin with slope 2.
2. P is on the line passing through $(2, 4)$ with slope -3.
3. P is on the line passing through $(-2, 3)$ with slope $\frac{1}{2}$.
4. P is on the line passing through $(-4, 3)$ with slope $-\frac{2}{3}$.
5. P is on the vertical line passing through $(6, 0)$.
6. P is on the line parallel to the y-axis and 4 units to the left of the axis.
7. P moves along the horizontal line passing through $(-3, 3)$.
8. Every point of the path of P is 2 units below the x-axis.

9. P moves along the line passing through $(-4, 2)$ and $(1, -1)$.

10. P moves along the line passing through the origin and $(-6, -5)$.

11. Each point of the path of P is 5 units from the origin.

12. Each point on P's path is 3 units from $(2, 3)$.

13. The distance of P from $(5, 0)$ is equal to the abscissa of P.

14. The distance of P from $(0, 3)$ is equal to the ordinate of P.

15. P is equidistant from the points $(2, -4)$ and $(-1, 5)$.

16. P is equidistant from the origin and $(5, -3)$.

17. The sum of the squares of the distances between P and the points $(4, 2)$ and $(-3, 1)$ is 50 units.

18. P is twice as far from $(0, 3)$ as from $(3, 0)$.

19. P is three times as far from $(1, 1)$ as from $(-3, 4)$.

20. P is twice as far from the x-axis as from $(0, 3)$.

21. P is twice as far from $(5, 0)$ as from the y-axis.

22. The distance of P from $(4, 0)$ is equal to its distance from the line $x = -4$.

23. The distance of P from $(1, 4)$ is equal to its distance from the line $y = 2$.

24. The distance of P from $(4, -3)$ is equal to $\frac{2}{3}$ its distance from the line $x = 1$.

25. The distance of P from $(3, 3)$ is equal to $\frac{4}{3}$ its distance from the line $x = -2$.

26. P is the vertex of a right triangle whose hypotenuse is the line segment joining $(-5, 0)$ and $(5, 0)$.

27. P is the vertex of a right triangle whose hypotenuse is the line segment joining $(-2, -1)$ and $(3, 5)$.

28. The sum of the distances from P to $(0, -3)$ and $(0, 3)$ is 10.

29. The sum of the distances from P to $(0, -2)$ and $(0, 2)$ is 5.

30. The difference of the distances from P to $(-5, 0)$ and $(5, 0)$ is numerically equal to 8.

CHAPTER 2

THE STRAIGHT LINE AND CIRCLE

2-1 Introduction. The straight line is the simplest geometric curve. Despite its simplicity, the line is a vital concept of mathematics and enters into our daily experiences in numerous interesting and useful ways. In Section 1–10 we stated that the graph of a first-degree equation in x and y is a straight line; we shall now establish that statement. Furthermore, we shall write linear equations in different forms such that each reveals useful information concerning the location of the line which it represents.

2-2 The locus of a first-degree equation. The equation

$$Ax + By + C = 0, \qquad (1)$$

where A, B, and C are constants with A and B not both zero, is a general equation of the first degree. We shall prove that the locus, or graph, of this equation is a straight line by showing that all points of the locus lie on a line and that the coordinates of all points of the line satisfy the equation.

Let $P_1(x_1, y_1)$ and $P_2(x_2, y_2)$ be any two points of the graph (Fig. 2–1). Then the coordinates of these points satisfy Eq. (1), and therefore we have

$$Ax_1 + By_1 + C = 0, \qquad (a)$$

$$Ax_2 + By_2 + C = 0. \qquad (b)$$

By subtraction, these equations yield

$$A(x_1 - x_2) + B(y_1 - y_2) = 0,$$

$$B(y_1 - y_2) = -A(x_1 - x_2),$$

and if $B \neq 0$,

$$\frac{y_1 - y_2}{x_1 - x_2} = -\frac{A}{B}.$$

The last equation shows that the slope of a line passing through two points of the graph is $-(A/B)$. Therefore if $P_3(x_3, y_3)$ is any other point of the locus, the slope of the segment P_1P_3 is also $-(A/B)$. From the equality of these slopes, we conclude that P_1, P_2, and P_3, and hence all

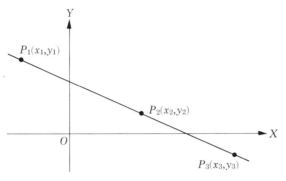

FIGURE 2–1

points of the locus, lie on a line. To determine whether the graph consists of all points of this line, we need to show that the coordinates of any other point of the line satisfy the given equation (1). Denoting a point of the line by $P_4(x_4, y_4)$, we have

$$\frac{y_4 - y_1}{x_4 - x_1} = -\frac{A}{B}.$$

By clearing fractions and transposing terms, we reduce this equation to the form

$$Ax_4 + By_4 - Ax_1 - By_1 = 0.$$

From equation (a), $-Ax_1 - By_1 = C$, and hence

$$Ax_4 + By_4 + C = 0.$$

The point (x_4, y_4) satisfies the given equation. This completes the proof except for the case in which $B = 0$. For this value of B Eq. (1) reduces to

$$x = -\frac{C}{A}.$$

The coordinates of all points, and only those points, having the abscissa $-(C/A)$ satisfy this equation. Hence the locus is a line parallel to the y-axis and located $-(C/A)$ units from the axis.

THEOREM. *The locus of the equation $Ax + By + C = 0$, where A, B, and C are constants with A and B not both zero, is a straight line. If $B = 0$, the line is vertical; otherwise the slope is $-(A/B)$.*

Special cases of Eq. (1) arise when one of the three constants A, B, and C is zero. The three cases are illustrated by the equations

$$2x = 5, \qquad y = -4, \qquad 3x - 4y = 0.$$

The graph of $2x = 5$ is the line parallel to the y-axis and 2.5 units to the right. The second equation represents the line 4 units below the x-axis. The graph of $3x - 4y = 0$ is the line with slope $\frac{3}{4}$ which passes through the origin.

If A, B, and C are all different from zero, the line cuts both axes and does not pass through the origin. The abscissa of the point where the line cuts the x-axis is called the x-*intercept*, and the ordinate of the point where the line cuts the y-axis is called the y-*intercept*. To find the x-intercept, we set $y = 0$ and solve for x. Similarly, we set $x = 0$ and solve for y to obtain the y-intercept. Thus by setting $y = 0$ in the equation $2x - 3y = 6$, we get $x = 3$. The point $(3, 0)$ is on the graph and the x-intercept is 3. A similar procedure yields -2 as the y-intercept.

2–3 Special forms of the first-degree equation. We shall now convert Eq. (1) of Section 2–2 to other forms and interpret the coefficients geometrically. Solving for y, when $B \neq 0$, gives

$$y = -\frac{A}{B}x - \frac{C}{B}.$$

The coefficient of x, as we have seen, is the slope of the line. By setting $x = 0$, we notice that the constant term $-(C/B)$ is the y-intercept. If we write m for the slope and b for the y-intercept (Fig. 2–2), we obtain the simpler form

$$\boxed{y = mx + b.} \tag{1}$$

This is called the *slope-intercept form* of the equation of a line. An equation in this form makes evident the slope and the y-intercept of the line which it represents. Conversely, the equation of the line of given slope and y-intercept may be written at once by substituting the proper values for m and b.

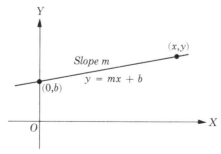

FIGURE 2–2

Illustration. The equation of the line of slope -2 which passes through $(0, 5)$ is $y = -2x + 5$.

Equation (1) represents a line which passes through $(0, b)$. The equation can be altered slightly to focus the attention on any other point of the line. If the line passes through (x_1, y_1), we have

$$y_1 = mx_1 + b \qquad \text{and} \qquad b = y_1 - mx_1.$$

Substituting this expression for b in Eq. (1) gives

$$y = mx + y_1 - mx_1,$$

and hence

$$y - y_1 = m(x - x_1). \tag{2}$$

This is called the *point-slope form* of the equation of a line.

Illustration. To write the equation of the line which passes through $(2, -3)$ and has a slope of 5, we substitute $x_1 = 2$, $y_1 = -3$, and $m = 5$. Thus we have

$$y + 3 = 5(x - 2), \qquad \text{or} \qquad 5x - y = 13.$$

Some mathematicians prefer an alternative form for the point-slope formula, Eq. (2). To obtain the other form, we substitute $m = -(A/B)$ and get

$$y - y_1 = -\frac{A}{B}(x - x_1).$$

Multiplying by B and transposing terms yields

$$Ax + By = Ax_1 + By_1. \tag{3}$$

Illustration. Suppose a line has slope $\frac{2}{5}$ and passes through $(-3, 4)$. Since the slope, $-(A/B)$, is equal to $\frac{2}{5}$, we let $A = 2$ and $B = -5$. Then these values for A and B and $x_1 = -3$, $y_1 = 4$ give

$$2x - 5y = 2(-3) - 5(4) = -26.$$

Equations (2) and (3) are directly applicable if the slope and one point of a line are known. They also serve if two points are known, since m can be found from the coordinates of the two points. Suppose the two

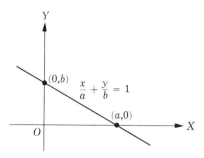

$$\frac{x}{a} + \frac{y}{b} = 1$$

FIGURE 2-3

points are (x_1, y_1) and (x_2, y_2). Then

$$m = \frac{y_2 - y_1}{x_2 - x_1},$$

and, consequently, Eq. (2) becomes

$$y - y_1 = \frac{y_2 - y_1}{x_2 - x_1}(x - x_1). \tag{4}$$

This form is called the *two-point form* of the equation of a line. It is evident that the coordinates (x_1, y_1) and (x_2, y_2) satisfy the equation.

If the two points of Eq. (4) are $(a, 0)$ and $(0, b)$, where $a \neq 0$ and $b \neq 0$ (Fig. 2-3), the equation may be reduced to

$$\frac{x}{a} + \frac{y}{b} = 1. \tag{5}$$

This is called the *intercept form* because the intercepts are exhibited in the denominators.

Illustration. To obtain the equation of the line through $(-3, 5)$ and $(4, 1)$, we substitute in Eq. (4) and obtain

$$y - 5 = \frac{1 - 5}{4 + 3}(x + 3).$$

On simplifying the above equation, we get

$$7y - 35 = -4x - 12, \quad \text{or} \quad 4x + 7y = 23.$$

Alternatively, we can arrive at this equation by employing Eq. (3). Since the slope of the line is $-\frac{4}{7}$, we let $A = 4$ and $B = 7$. Then either of the points serve as (x_1, y_1). Choosing $(4, 1)$, we get

$$4x + 7y = 4(4) + 7(1) = 23.$$

If a line cuts the coordinate axes so that the x-intercept is 3 and the y-intercept is -5, its equation by formula (5) is

$$\frac{x}{3} + \frac{y}{-5} = 1, \quad \text{or} \quad 5x - 3y = 15.$$

Equations (1), (2), (4), and (5) do not apply when the line is vertical. In this case, m is not defined and we cannot substitute properly for the intercepts in Eqs. (1) and (5). The equation of a vertical line can be written immediately, however, if any point of the line is known. Thus a vertical line through (x_1, y_1) has the abscissa x_1 for all points of the line, and its equation is

$$\boxed{x = x_1.}$$

A horizontal line through (x_1, y_1) has $m = 0$, and Eq. (2) applies. Of course, all the ordinates are the same, and we can write the equation directly as

$$\boxed{y = y_1.}$$

Equations (1) through (5) can be employed to write, quickly and simply, equations of lines which pass through two given points or through one known point with a given slope. The inverse problem, that of drawing the graph of a linear equation in x and y, is likewise simple. Since the locus is a straight line, two points are sufficient for constructing the graph. For this purpose the intercepts on the axes are usually the most convenient. For example, we find the intercepts of the equation $3x - 4y = 12$ to be $a = 4$ and $b = -3$. Hence the graph is the line drawn through $(4, 0)$ and $(0, -3)$. The intercepts are not sufficient for drawing a line which passes through the origin. For this case the intercepts a and b are both zero. Hence a point other than the origin is necessary.

We have seen that the slope of the line corresponding to the equation $Ax + By + C = 0$ is $-(A/B)$. That is, the slope is obtained from the equation by dividing the coefficient of x by the coefficient of y and reversing the sign of the result. Hence we can readily determine whether the lines represented by two equations are parallel, perpendicular, or whether they intersect obliquely. Lines are parallel if their slopes are equal, and we recall that two lines are perpendicular if the slope of one is the negative of the reciprocal of the slope of the other.

EXAMPLE. The extremities of a line segment are $C(3, -2)$ and $D(5, 6)$. Find the equation of the perpendicular bisector of the segment CD.

Solution. The slope of CD is 4, and the coordinates of the mid-point are $(4, 2)$. The perpendicular bisector therefore has a slope of $-\frac{1}{4}$ and passes through $(4, 2)$. Employing Eq. (3) with $A = 1$, $B = 4$, $x_1 = 4$, and $y_1 = 2$, we have

$$x + 4y = 4 + 8 = 12.$$

EXERCISE 2-1

By inspection, give the slope and intercepts of each line represented by equations 1 through 12. Reduce each equation to the slope-intercept form by solving for y.

1. $4x - y = 12$	2. $x - y = 7$	3. $x + y + 4 = 0$
4. $4x + 9y = 36$	5. $3x - 4y = 12$	6. $6x - 3y - 10 = 0$
7. $x + 7y = 11$	8. $2x + 3y = 14$	9. $7x + 3y + 6 = 0$
10. $2x - 8y = 5$	11. $8x + 3y = 4$	12. $3x + 3y = 1$

In each problem 13 through 20, write the equation of the line determined by the slope m and y-intercept b.

13. $m = 3$, $b = -4$	14. $m = 2$, $b = 3$
15. $m = -4$, $b = 5$	16. $m = -5$, $b = 0$
17. $m = \frac{2}{3}$, $b = -2$	18. $m = \frac{3}{2}$, $b = -6$
19. $m = 0$, $b = 7$	20. $m = 5$, $b = 0$

In each problem 21 through 30, write the equation of the line which passes through the point A with the slope m. Draw the lines.

21. $A(3, 1)$, $m = 2$	22. $A(-3, -5)$, $m = 1$
23. $A(-2, 0)$, $m = \frac{2}{3}$	24. $A(0, -3)$, $m = \frac{3}{2}$
25. $A(-3, -6)$, $m = -\frac{1}{2}$	26. $A(5, -2)$, $m = -\frac{5}{2}$
27. $A(0, 3)$, $m = 0$	28. $A(3, 0)$, $m = 0$
29. $A(0, 0)$, $m = -\frac{8}{3}$	30. $A(0, 0)$, $m = \frac{2}{7}$

Find the equation of the line determined by the points A and B in each problem 31 through 40. Check the answers by substitutions.

31. $A(3, -1)$, $B(-4, 5)$	32. $A(1, 5)$, $B(4, 1)$
33. $A(0, 2)$, $B(4, -6)$	34. $A(-2, -4)$, $B(3, \frac{3}{2})$
35. $A(3, -2)$, $B(3, 7)$	36. $A(0, 0)$, $B(3, -4)$
37. $A(5, -\frac{2}{3})$, $B(\frac{1}{2}, -2)$	38. $A(\frac{1}{2}, 5)$, $B(\frac{3}{4}, -1)$
39. $A(-6, -1)$, $B(4, -1)$	40. $A(0, 1)$, $B(0, 0)$

Write the equation of the line which has the x-intercept a and the y-intercept b in each problem 41 through 48.

41. $a = 3$, $b = 2$	42. $a = 5$, $b = 1$
43. $a = 4$, $b = -3$	44. $a = 7$, $b = -5$
45. $a = -2$, $b = -2$	46. $a = -\frac{3}{2}$, $b = 1$
47. $a = \frac{2}{3}$, $b = \frac{1}{2}$	48. $a = \frac{3}{4}$, $b = -\frac{4}{3}$

49. Show that $Ax + By = D_1$ and $Bx - Ay = D_2$ are equations of perpendicular lines.

50. Show that the graphs of $Ax + By = D_1$ and $Ax + By = D_2$ are (a) the same if $D_1 = D_2$, (b) parallel lines if $D_1 \neq D_2$.

In each problem 51 through 60, find the equation of two lines through A, one parallel and the other perpendicular to the line corresponding to the given equation.

51. $A(4, 1)$, $2x - 3y + 5 = 0$ 52. $A(-1, 2)$, $2x - y = 0$
53. $A(3, 4)$, $7x + 5y + 4 = 0$ 54. $A(0, 0)$, $x - y = 3$
55. $A(2, -3)$, $8x - y = 0$ 56. $A(0, 6)$, $2x - 2y = 1$
57. $A(-1, 1)$, $y = 1$ 58. $A(3, 5)$, $x = 0$
59. $A(7, 0)$, $9x + y - 3 = 0$ 60. $A(-4, 0)$, $4x + 3y = 2$

The points A, B, and C in each problem 61 through 64 are vertices of a triangle. For each triangle, find the following:

(a) the equations of the sides;
(b) the equations of the medians and their intersection point;
(c) the equations of the altitudes and their intersection point;
(d) the equations of the perpendicular bisectors of the sides and their intersection point.

61. $A(0, 0)$, $B(6, 0)$, $C(4, 4)$ 62. $A(0, 0)$, $B(9, 2)$, $C(0, 7)$
63. $A(1, 0)$, $B(9, 2)$, $C(3, 6)$ 64. $A(-2, 3)$, $B(6, -6)$, $C(8, 0)$

65. Show that the three intersection points involved in problem 61 are on a straight line. Show the same is true in problems 62 through 64.

2-4 Distance from a line to a point. The distance from a line to a point can be found from the equation of the line and the coordinates of the point. We shall derive a formula for this purpose. We observe first that the distance from a vertical line to a point is immediately obtainable by taking the difference of the abscissa of the point and the x-intercept of the line. Hence no additional formula is needed for this case.

Let the equation of a slant line be written in the form

$$Ax + By + C = 0, \tag{1}$$

and let $P_1(x_1, y_1)$ be any point not on the line. Since the line is a slant line, $B \neq 0$. Consider now the line through P_1 parallel to the given line, and the line through the origin perpendicular to the given line, whose equations respectively are

$$Ax + By + C' = 0, \tag{2}$$

$$Bx - Ay = 0. \tag{3}$$

The required distance d (Fig. 2–4) is equal to the segment PQ, where P

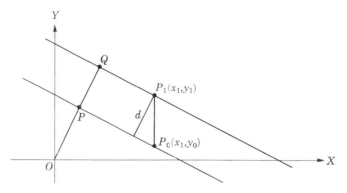

FIGURE 2–4

and Q are the intersection points of the perpendicular line and the parallel lines. The simultaneous solutions of Eqs. (1) and (3), and Eqs. (2) and (3) give the intersection points

$$P\left(\frac{-AC}{A^2 + B^2}, \frac{-BC}{A^2 + B^2}\right), \qquad Q\left(\frac{-AC'}{A^2 + B^2}, \frac{-BC'}{A^2 + B^2}\right).$$

We employ the formula for the distance between two points to find the length of PQ. Thus

$$d^2 = (PQ)^2 = \frac{(C - C')^2 A^2}{(A^2 + B^2)^2} + \frac{(C - C')^2 B^2}{(A^2 + B^2)^2}$$

$$= \frac{(C - C')^2 (A^2 + B^2)}{(A^2 + B^2)^2} = \frac{(C - C')^2}{A^2 + B^2},$$

and

$$d = \frac{C - C'}{\pm\sqrt{A^2 + B^2}}.$$

Since the line of Eq. (2) passes through $P_1(x_1, y_1)$, we have

$$Ax_1 + By_1 + C' = 0, \qquad \text{and} \qquad C' = -Ax_1 - By_1.$$

Hence, substituting for C', we get

$$d = \frac{Ax_1 + By_1 + C}{\pm\sqrt{A^2 + B^2}}.$$

To remove the ambiguity of sign, we agree to give the radical in the denominator the sign of B. In other words, the sign of the denominator is selected so that the coefficient of y_1 is positive. A consequence of this choice of signs may be found by referring to the figure again, where $P_0 P_1$

is parallel to the y-axis and $P_0(x_1, y_0)$ is a point of the given line. Since P_0 is a point on the line, we have

$$\frac{Ax_1 + By_0 + C}{\pm\sqrt{A^2 + B^2}} = 0.$$

Now if we replace y_0 by y_1 in the left side of this equation, we get an expression which is not equal to zero. The expression is positive if $y_1 > y_0$ and negative if $y_1 < y_0$. That is, the expression for d is positive if P_1 is above the line and negative if P_1 is below the line. We may therefore regard the distance from a line to a point as a directed distance.

The preceding discussion establishes the following theorem:

THEOREM. *The directed distance from the slant line $Ax + By + C = 0$ to the point $P_1(x_1, y_1)$ is given by the formula*

$$d = \frac{Ax_1 + By_1 + C}{\pm\sqrt{A^2 + B^2}}, \tag{4}$$

where the denominator is given the sign of B. The distance is positive if the point P_1 is above the line, and negative if P_1 is below the line.

If Eq. (1) is divided by $\pm\sqrt{A^2 + B^2}$, the form

$$\frac{Ax + By + C}{\pm\sqrt{A^2 + B^2}} = 0$$

is obtained. This is called the *normal form* of the equation of a line. When an equation is in the normal form, the distance from the line to a point is obtained by substituting the coordinates of the point in the left member of the equation. By substituting the coordinates of the origin, the constant term is seen to be the perpendicular, or normal, distance to the origin.

EXAMPLE 1. Find the distance from the line $12y = 5x - 26$ to each of the points $P_1(3, -5)$, $P_2(-4, 1)$, and $P_3(9, 0)$.

Solution. We write the equation in the form $-5x + 12y + 26 = 0$. The required distances are then found by making substitutions in Eq. (4). Hence

$$d_1 = \frac{-5(3) + 12(-5) + 26}{\sqrt{5^2 + 12^2}} = -\frac{49}{13},$$

$$d_2 = \frac{-5(-4) + 12(1) + 26}{13} = \frac{58}{13}, \qquad d_3 = \frac{-5(9) + 12(0) + 26}{13} = -\frac{19}{13}.$$

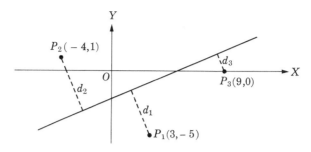

FIGURE 2–5

The positive sign is used in the denominators because the coefficient of y is positive. The signs of the results show that P_1 and P_3 are below the line and that P_2 is above the line (Fig. 2–5).

EXAMPLE 2. Find the distance between the parallel lines $15x - 8y - 51 = 0$ and $15x - 8y + 68 = 0$.

Solution. The distance can be found by computing the distance from each line to a particular point. To minimize the computations, we find the distance from each line to the origin. Thus

$$d_1 = \frac{15(0) - 8(0) - 51}{-\sqrt{15^2 + 8^2}} = \frac{-51}{-17} = 3,$$

$$d_2 = \frac{15(0) - 8(0) + 68}{-17} = \frac{68}{-17} = -4.$$

The origin is 3 units above the first line and 4 units below the second line. Hence the lines are 7 units apart.

An alternative method for this problem would be to find the distance from one of the lines to a particular point on the other. The point $(0, 8.5)$ is on the second line, and using this point and the first equation, we find

$$d = \frac{15(0) - 8(8.5) - 51}{-17} = \frac{-119}{-17} = 7.$$

2–5 Families of lines. We have expressed equations of lines in various forms. Among these are the equations

$$y = mx + b \quad \text{and} \quad \frac{x}{a} + \frac{y}{b} = 1.$$

Each of these equations has two constants which have geometrical significance. The constants of the first equation are m and b. When definite values are assigned to these letters, a line is completely determined. Other values for these, of course, determine other lines. Thus the quan-

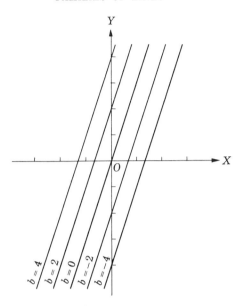

FIGURE 2–6

tities m and b are fixed for any particular line but change from line to line. These letters are called *parameters*. In the second equation a and b are the parameters.

A linear equation with only one parameter is obtained if the other parameter is replaced by a fixed value. The resulting equation represents all lines with a particular property if the remaining parameter is allowed to vary. Each value assumed by the parameter yields an equation which represents a definite line. The collection of lines defined by a linear equation with one parameter is called a *family*, or *system*, of lines. For example, if $m = 3$, the point-slope equation becomes

$$y = 3x + b.$$

This equation represents the family of lines of slope 3, one line for each value of b. There are, of course, infinitely many lines in the family. In fact, a line of the family passes through each point of the coordinate plane. Figure 2–6 shows a few lines of the family corresponding to the indicated values of the parameter b.

EXAMPLE 1. Write the equation of the system of lines defined by each of the following conditions:

(a) parallel to $3x - 2y = 5$,
(b) passing through $(5, -2)$,
(c) having the product of the intercepts equal to 4.

Solutions. The following equations are easily verified to be those required.

(a) $3x - 2y = D$ (b) $y + 2 = m(x - 5)$

(c) $\dfrac{x}{a} + \dfrac{y}{4/a} = 1$, or $4x + a^2 y = 4a$

EXAMPLE 2. Write the equation of the system of lines which are parallel to $5x + 12y + 7 = 0$. Find the members of the family which are 3 units distant from the point $(2, 1)$.

Solution. Each member of the family $5x + 12y + C = 0$ is parallel to the given line. We wish to find values of C which will yield lines 3 units from the point $(2, 1)$, one passing above and the other below the point. Using the formula for the distance from a line to a point, we obtain the equations

$$\frac{5(2) + 12(1) + C}{13} = 3, \qquad \frac{5(2) + 12(1) + C}{13} = -3.$$

The roots are $C = 17$ and $C = -61$. Hence the required equations are

$$5x + 12y + 17 = 0 \quad \text{and} \quad 5x + 12y - 61 = 0.$$

2–6 Families of lines through the intersection of two lines. The equation of the family of lines passing through the intersection of two given lines can be written readily. To illustrate, we consider the two intersecting lines

$$2x - 3y + 5 = 0, \qquad 4x + y - 11 = 0.$$

From the left members of these equations we form the equation

$$(2x - 3y + 5) + k(4x + y - 11) = 0, \tag{1}$$

where k is a parameter. This equation is of the first degree in x and y for any value of k. Hence it represents a system of lines. Furthermore, each line of the family goes through the intersection of the given lines. We verify this statement by actual substitution. The given lines intersect at $(2, 3)$. Then, using these values for x and y, we get

$$(4 - 9 + 5) + k(8 + 3 - 11) = 0,$$
$$0 + k(0) = 0,$$
$$0 = 0.$$

This result demonstrates that Eq. (1) is satisfied by the coordinates $(2, 3)$ regardless of the value of k. Hence the equation defines a family of lines passing through the intersection of the given lines.

More generally, let the equations

$$A_1x + B_1y + C_1 = 0,$$
$$A_2x + B_2y + C_2 = 0$$

define two intersecting lines. Then the equation

$$(A_1x + B_1y + C_1) + k(A_2x + B_2y + C_2) = 0$$

represents a system of lines through the intersection of the given lines. To verify this statement, we first observe that the equation is linear for any value of k. Next we notice that the coordinates of the intersection point reduce each of the parts in parentheses to zero, and hence satisfy the equation for any value of k.

EXAMPLE. Write the equation of the system of lines through the intersection of $x - 7y + 3 = 0$ and $4x + 2y - 5 = 0$. Find the member of the family which has the slope 3.

Solution. The equation of the system of lines passing through the intersection of the given lines is

$$(x - 7y + 3) + k(4x + 2y - 5) = 0,$$

or, collecting terms,

$$(1 + 4k)x + (-7 + 2k)y + 3 - 5k = 0.$$

The slope of each member of this system, except for the vertical line, is $-\dfrac{1 + 4k}{2k - 7}$.

Equating this fraction to the required slope gives

$$-\frac{1 + 4k}{2k - 7} = 3, \quad \text{and} \quad k = 2.$$

The member of the system for $k = 2$ is $9x - 3y - 7 = 0$.

EXERCISE 2–2

Find the distance from the line to the point in each problem 1 through 6.

1. $5x + 12y + 60 = 0$; $(3, 2)$ 2. $4x - 3y = 15$; $(4, 1)$
3. $x + y - 3 = 0$; $(4, 5)$ 4. $3x + y = 10$; $(-3, -1)$
5. $-2x + 5y + 7 = 0$; $(6, 0)$ 6. $y = 7$; $(3, -8)$

Determine the distance between the pair of parallel lines in each problem 7 through 10.

7. $4x - 3y - 9 = 0$, $4x - 3y - 24 = 0$
8. $12x + 5y = 13$, $12x + 5y = 104$
9. $15x - 8y - 34 = 0$, $15x - 8y + 51 = 0$
10. $x + y + 7 = 0$, $x + y - 11 = 0$

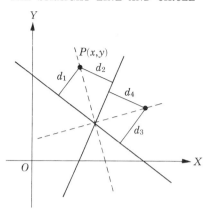

FIGURE 2-7

11. The vertices of a triangle are $A(2, 3)$, $B(-1, 1)$, and $C(7, -2)$. Find the length of the altitude from A and the length of side BC. Then compute the area of the triangle.

12. The vertices of a triangle are $A(-2, 1)$, $B(6, -2)$, and $C(4, 3)$. Find the length of one side of the triangle and the length of the altitude to that side, and then compute the area of the triangle.

13. Find the equation of the bisector of the acute angles formed by the lines $3x + 4y - 12 = 0$ and $12x - 5y - 20 = 0$. [*Hint:* Since any point $P(x, y)$ of the bisector is equally distant from the sides, $d_1 = d_2$ (Fig. 2-7). Hence

$$\frac{3x + 4y - 12}{5} = \frac{12x - 5y - 20}{-13}.\bigg]$$

14. Note that $d_3 = -d_4$ in Fig. 2-7, and find the equation of the bisector of the obtuse angles formed by the lines of problem 13.

15. Find the equations of the bisectors of the angles formed by the lines $x + 2y + 3 = 0$ and $2x + y - 2 = 0$.

16. Prove that the bisectors of the angles formed by any two intersecting lines, $A_1x + B_1y + C_1 = 0$ and $A_2x + B_2y + C_2 = 0$, are perpendicular.

17. Write the equation $Ax + By + C = 0$ in normal form. Show that in this form the coefficient of x is $\cos \omega$ and the coefficient of y is $\sin \omega$, where ω is the inclination of the perpendicular line segment drawn from the origin to the line.

Write the equation of the system of lines possessing the given property in problems 18 through 25. In each case assign three values to the parameter and draw the corresponding lines.

18. Parallel to $7x - 4y = 3$

19. Passing through $(-3, 4)$

20. With the x-intercept twice the y-intercept

21. Perpendicular to $2x - 5y + 3 = 0$

22. With the y-intercept equal to -4

23. With the sum of the intercepts equal to 10

24. Through the intersection of $x - 2y + 7 = 0$ and $5x - 7y - 3 = 0$

25. Forming with the coordinate axes a triangle of area 16

Tell what geometric property is possessed by all the lines of each system in problems 26 through 33.

26. $y = mx + 4$

27. $y = 2x + b$

28. $9x + 2y = k$

29. $y + 4 = m(x - 3)$

30. $\dfrac{x}{a} + \dfrac{y}{3} = 1$

31. $\dfrac{x}{a} + \dfrac{y}{4 + a} = 1$

32. $(4x - 7y - 7) + ky = 0$

33. $(4x + y + 1) + k(3x + 7y) = 0$

34. In the preceding problems 26 through 33, determine the line of the system which passes through $(3, 0)$.

35. Write the equation of the family of lines of slope -3, and find the two members passing 5 units from the origin.

36. Write an equation of the family of lines parallel to $12x - 5y + 6 = 0$. Find the members of the family which are 2 units from the point $(-2, 3)$.

37. The line $3x - 2y + 1 = 0$ is midway between two parallel lines which are 8 units apart. Find the equations of the two lines.

In each problem 38 through 43, find the equation of the line which passes through the intersection of the pair of lines and satisfies the other given condition.

38. $3x + y - 2 = 0$, $x + 5y - 4 = 0$; through $(5, 2)$

39. $5x + 3y + 2 = 0$, $x - y - 2 = 0$; $m = -3$

40. $x - 11y = 0$, $3x + y - 5 = 0$; a vertical line

41. $6x - 2y = 3$; $x - 5y = 4$; $m = 0$

42. $3x - 4y - 2 = 0$, $3x + 4y + 1 = 0$; intercepts are equal

43. $2x - y - 5 = 0$, $x + y - 4 = 0$; passing through $(0, 0)$

44. The sides of a triangle are on the lines defined by $2x - 3y + 4 = 0$, $x + y + 3 = 0$, and $5x - 4y - 20 = 0$. Without solving for the vertices, find the equations of the altitudes.

45. The sides of a triangle are on the lines defined by $3x + 5y + 2 = 0$, $x - y - 2 = 0$, and $4x + 2y - 3 = 0$. Without solving for the vertices, find the equations of the altitudes.

2–7 Equations of circles. We have seen how to write the equation of a line which is placed in any position of the coordinate plane. We shall discover that it is equally easy to write the equation of a circle if the location of its center and the length of the radius are known. We first give an explicit definition of a circle.

DEFINITION. *A circle is the locus of a point which moves on a plane in such a manner that its distance from a fixed point of the plane remains constant.*

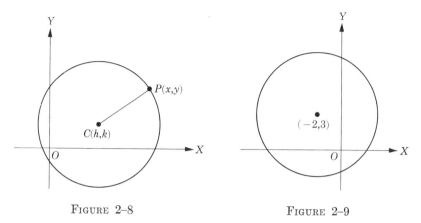

FIGURE 2–8   FIGURE 2–9

Let the center of the circle be at the fixed point $C(h, k)$ and the length of the radius equal to r. Then if $P(x, y)$ is any point of the circle (Fig. 2–8), the distance between C and P is equal to r. This condition requires that

$$\sqrt{(x - h)^2 + (y - k)^2} = r,$$

and, by squaring, we reduce the equation to

$$(x - h)^2 + (y - k)^2 = r^2. \tag{1}$$

This formula exhibits the coordinates of the center and the length of the radius and, consequently, is sometimes called the *center-radius form* of the equation of a circle.

Conversely, the graph of an equation of the form (1) is a circle with center at (h, k) and radius equal to r. This fact is evident since the equation is satisfied by, and only by, points whose distance from (h, k) is r. Hence it is an easy task to write the equation of a circle whose center and radius are known, or to draw the circle whose equation is expressed in the form (1).

If the center of a circle is at the origin ($h = 0$, $k = 0$) and the radius is r, its equation is

$$x^2 + y^2 = r^2. \tag{2}$$

Illustration. If the center of a circle is at $(3, -2)$ and the radius is 4, the equation is

$$(x - 3)^2 + (y + 2)^2 = 16.$$

Equation (1) can be presented in another form by squaring the binomials and collecting terms. Thus

$$x^2 - 2hx + h^2 + y^2 - 2ky + k^2 = r^2,$$
$$x^2 + y^2 - 2hx - 2ky + h^2 + k^2 - r^2 = 0.$$

The last equation is of the form

$$\boxed{x^2 + y^2 + Dx + Ey + F = 0.} \qquad (3)$$

This is called the *general form* of the equation of a circle.

An equation of the form (3) can be reduced to the form (1) by the simple expedient of completing the squares in the x-terms and the y-terms. We illustrate the procedure.

EXAMPLE 1. Determine the locus of the equation

$$x^2 + y^2 + 4x - 6y - 10 = 0.$$

Solution. We write

$$x^2 + 4x \qquad y^2 - 6y \qquad = 10,$$

leaving spaces for the terms to be added in order to complete the squares. When the necessary terms are inserted the equation becomes

$$x^2 + 4x + 4 + y^2 - 6y + 9 = 10 + 4 + 9,$$
$$(x + 2)^2 + (y - 3)^2 = 23.$$

Hence the locus of the given equation is a circle with center at $(-2, 3)$ and radius equal to $\sqrt{23}$ (Fig. 2–9).

Not all equations of the forms (1), (2), or (3) have circles as their loci. If $r = 0$, Eq. (1) becomes

$$(x - h)^2 + (y - k)^2 = 0.$$

The equation is satisfied only by the point (h, k). In this case the locus is sometimes called a *point circle*. The locus of Eq. (3) depends on the constants D, E, and F. By completing the squares the equation may be presented as

$$\left(x + \frac{D}{2}\right)^2 + \left(y + \frac{E}{2}\right)^2 = \frac{D^2}{4} + \frac{E^2}{4} - F.$$

The locus of this equation is a circle when the right member $D^2/4 + E^2/4 - F$ is positive. If the right member is equal to zero, the locus is a point circle, and there is no locus when the right member is negative.

EXAMPLE 2. What is the locus, if any, of the equation

$$x^2 + y^2 - 4x - 6y + 14 = 0?$$

Solution. Upon completing the squares, we find

$$(x - 2)^2 + (y - 3)^2 = -1.$$

Clearly the left member of this equation cannot be negative for any real values of x and y. Hence the equation has no locus.

2–8 Circles determined by geometric conditions. We have seen how to write the equation of a line from certain information which fixes the position of the line in the coordinate plane. We consider now a similar problem concerning the circle. Both the standard form and the general form of the equation of a circle will be useful in this connection. There are innumerable geometric conditions which determine a circle. It will be recalled, for example, that a circle can be passed through three points which are not on a straight line. We illustrate this case first.

EXAMPLE 1. Find the equation of the circle which passes through the points $P(1, -2)$, $Q(5, 4)$, and $R(10, 5)$.

Solution. The equation of the circle can be expressed in the form

$$x^2 + y^2 + Dx + Ey + F = 0.$$

Our problem is to find values for D, E, and F so that the equation is satisfied by the coordinates of each of the given points. Hence we substitute for x and y the coordinates of these points. This gives the system

$$1 + \ 4 + \ \ D - 2E + F = 0,$$
$$25 + 16 + \ \ 5D + 4E + F = 0,$$
$$100 + 25 + 10D + 5E + F = 0.$$

The solution of these equations is $D = -18$, $E = 6$, and $F = 25$. Therefore the required equation is

$$x^2 + y^2 - 18x + 6y + 25 = 0.$$

Alternatively, this problem can be solved by applying the fact that the perpendicular bisectors of two chords of a circle intersect at the center. Thus the equations of the perpendicular bisectors of PQ and QR (Fig. 2–10) are

$$2x + 3y = 9 \quad \text{and} \quad 5x + y = 42.$$

The solution of these equations is $x = 9$, $y = -3$. These are the coordinates of the center. The radius is the distance from the center to either of the given

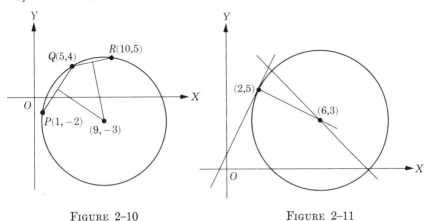

FIGURE 2-10   FIGURE 2-11

points. Hence the resulting equation, in standard form, is

$$(x - 9)^2 + (y + 3)^2 = 65.$$

EXAMPLE 2. A circle is tangent to the line $2x - y + 1 = 0$ at the point $(2, 5)$, and the center is on the line $x + y = 9$. Find the equation of the circle.

Solution. The line through $(2, 5)$ and perpendicular to the line $2x - y + 1 = 0$ passes through the center of the circle (Fig. 2-11). The equation of this line is $x + 2y = 12$. Hence the solution of the system

$$x + 2y = 12,$$
$$x + y = 9$$

yields the coordinates of the center. Accordingly, the center is at $(6, 3)$. The distance from this point to $(2, 5)$ is $\sqrt{20}$. The equation of the circle, therefore, is

$$(x - 6)^2 + (y - 3)^2 = 20.$$

EXERCISE 2-3

In each problem 1 through 16 write the equation of the circle which satisfies the given conditions.

1. Center $(2, -6)$, radius 5   2. Center $(10, 0)$, radius 3
3. Center $(0, 4)$, radius 4   4. Center $(-2, 0)$, radius 7
5. Center $(-12, 5)$, radius 13   6. Center $(4, 3)$, radius 5
7. Center $(\frac{1}{2}, -3)$, radius $\sqrt{11}$ 8. Center $(\frac{5}{3}, \frac{1}{3})$, radius $\sqrt{3}$

9. The line segment joining $A(0, 0)$ and $B(-8, 6)$ is a diameter.
10. The line segment joining $A(5, -1)$ and $B(-7, -5)$ is a diameter.
11. The center is at $(4, 2)$, and the circle passes through $(-1, -1)$.
12. The center is at $(-3, 1)$, and the circle passes through $(5, -3)$.

13. The circle is tangent to the x-axis, and the center is at $(-4, 1)$.

14. The circle is tangent to the y-axis, and the center is at $(3, 5)$.

15. The circle is tangent to the line $3x - 4y = 32$, and the center is at $(0, 7)$.

16. The circle is tangent to the line $5x + 12y = 26$, and the center is at the origin.

Reduce each equation 17 through 26 to the center-radius form and construct the circle.

17. $x^2 + y^2 - 6x + 4y - 12 = 0$ 18. $x^2 + y^2 - 4x - 12y + 36 = 0$

19. $x^2 + y^2 + 8x + 2y + 1 = 0$ 20. $x^2 + y^2 - 10x - 4y - 7 = 0$

21. $x^2 + y^2 - 8x - 6y = 0$ 22. $x^2 + y^2 + 10x + 24y = 0$

23. $x^2 + y^2 - 4x + 12y - 8 = 0$ 24. $x^2 + y^2 + 3x + 4y = 0$

25. $2x^2 + 2y^2 - 12x + 2y + 1 = 0$ 26. $3x^2 + 3y^2 + 6x - 5y = 0$

Determine whether the equation in each problem 27 through 35 represents a circle, a point, or has no locus.

27. $1 - x^2 - y^2 = 0$ 28. $x^2 + y^2 + 1 = 0$

29. $x^2 + y^2 + 2x + 1 = 0$ 30. $x^2 + y^2 - 6y = -9$

31. $x^2 + y^2 + x - y = 0$ 32. $x^2 + y^2 - 8x + 15 = 0$

33. $x^2 + y^2 + 2x + 10y + 26 = 0$ 34. $x^2 + y^2 - 7x - 5y + 40 = 0$

35. $x^2 + y^2 - 3x + 3y + 10 = 0$

Find the equation of the circle described in each problem 36 through 45.

36. The circle is tangent to the line $x + y = 2$ at the point $(4, -2)$, and the center is on the x-axis.

37. The circle is tangent to the line $2x - y = 3$ at the point $(2, 1)$, and the center is on the y-axis.

38. The circle is tangent to the line $3x - 4y = 4$ at the point $(-4, -4)$, and the center is on the line $x + y + 7 = 0$.

39. The circle is tangent to the line $5x - y = 3$ at the point $(2, 7)$, and the center is on the line $x + 2y = 19$.

40. The circle is tangent to the line $3x + 4y = 23$ at the point $(5, 2)$ and also tangent to the line $4x - 3y + 11 = 0$ at the point $(-2, 1)$.

41. The circle is tangent to the line $4x - 3y + 12 = 0$ at the point $(-3, 0)$ and also tangent to the line $3x + 4y - 16 = 0$ at the point $(4, 1)$.

42. The circle passes through the points $(3, 0)$, $(4, 2)$, and $(0, 1)$.

43. The circle passes through the points $(0, 0)$, $(5, 0)$, and $(3, 3)$.

44. The circle is circumscribed about the triangle whose vertices are $(-3, -1)$, $(4, -2)$, and $(1, 2)$.

45. The circle is circumscribed about the triangle whose vertices are $(-2, 3)$, $(5, 2)$, and $(6, -1)$.

46. Let the equations

$$x^2 + y^2 + D_1x + E_1y + F_1 = 0$$

and

$$x^2 + y^2 + D_2x + E_2y + F_2 = 0$$

represent circles which intersect in two points. Prove that the equation

$$(x^2 + y^2 + D_1x + E_1y + F_1) + k(x^2 + y^2 + D_2x + E_2y + F_2) = 0$$

represents a family of circles passing through the intersection points of the given circles if the parameter $k \neq -1$. What is the locus of the equation when $k = -1$?

47. Write an equation which represents the family of circles passing through the intersection points of $x^2 + y^2 - 16x - 10y + 24 = 0$ and $x^2 + y^2 - 4x + 8y - 6 = 0$. Find the member of the family which passes through the origin. Draw the three circles.

2-9 Translation of axes. The equation of a circle of radius r has the simple form $x^2 + y^2 = r^2$ if the origin of the coordinates is at the center of the circle. If the origin is not at the center, the corresponding equation may be expressed in either of the less simple forms (1) or (3), Section 2-7. This illustrates that the simplicity of the equation of a curve depends on the relative positions of the curve and the axes.

Suppose we have a curve in the coordinate plane and the equation of the curve. Let us consider the problem of writing the equation of the same curve with respect to another pair of axes. The process of changing from one pair of axes to another is called a *transformation of coordinates*. The most general transformation is one in which the new axes are not parallel to the old axes, and the origins are different. Just now, however, we shall consider transformations in which the new axes are parallel to the original axes and similarly directed. A transformation of this kind is called a *translation of axes*.

The coordinates of each point of the plane are changed under a translation of axes. To see how the coordinates are changed, observe Fig. 2-12. The new axes $O'X'$ and $O'Y'$ are parallel, respectively, to the old axes OX and OY. The coordinates of the origin O', referred to the original

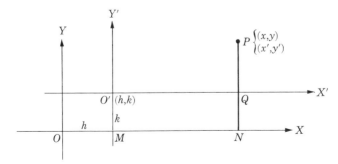

FIGURE 2-12

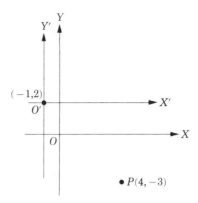

FIGURE 2–13

axes, are denoted by (h, k). Hence the new axes can be obtained by shifting the old axes h units horizontally and k units vertically while keeping their directions unchanged. Let x and y stand for the coordinates of any point P when referred to the old axes and let x' and y' be the coordinates of P with respect to the new axes. It is evident from the figure that

$$x = ON = OM + O'Q = h + x',$$
$$y = NP = MO' + QP = k + y'.$$

Hence

$$\boxed{x = x' + h, \qquad y = y' + k.}$$

These formulas give the relations of the old and new coordinates. They hold for all points of the plane, when the new origin O' is any point of the plane. Consequently, the substitutions $x' + h$ for x and $y' + k$ for y in the equation of a curve referred to the original axes yield the equation of the same curve referred to the translated axes.

EXAMPLE 1. Find the new coordinates of the point $P(4, -3)$ if the origin is moved to $(-1, 2)$ by a translation.

Solution. The original coordinates are $x = 4$, $y = -3$, and the coordinates of the new origin are $h = -1$, $k = 2$. Hence we write the translation formulas as $x' = x - h$ and $y' = y - k$, and then make the proper substitutions. This gives $x' = 4 - (-1) = 5$ and $y' = -3 - 2 = -5$. The new coordinates of P are $(5, -5)$. This result can be obtained directly from Fig. 2–13.

EXAMPLE 2. Find the new equation of the circle $x^2 + y^2 - 4x + 8y = 0$ after a translation which moves the origin to the point $(2, -4)$.

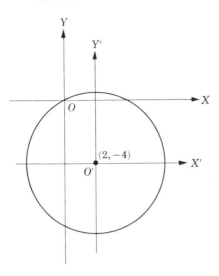

FIGURE 2–14

Solution. The translation formulas become $x = x' + 2$ and $y = y' - 4$. We make these substitutions in the given equation and have

$$(x' + 2)^2 + (y' - 4)^2 - 4(x' + 2) + 8(y' - 4) = 0,$$

or, by simplification,

$$x'^2 + y'^2 = 20.$$

Both sets of axes and the graph are drawn in Fig. 2–14.

EXAMPLE 3. Translate the axes so that the new equation of the circle

$$x^2 + y^2 - 6x + 10y + 11 = 0$$

will have no first-degree terms.

Solution. The given equation, when expressed in the center-radius form, becomes

$$(x - 3)^2 + (y + 5)^2 = 23.$$

We place the new origin at the center of the circle $(3, -5)$. The corresponding translation formulas are $x = x' + 3$ and $y = y' - 5$. These substitutions give

$$x'^2 + y'^2 = 23,$$

which is the equation of the circle referred to the translated axes.

EXERCISE 2–4

Find the new coordinates of the points in each problem 1 through 8 if the origin is moved to $(4, -3)$ by a translation of axes. Verify your answer by making a sketch.

1. $(4, -3)$	2. $(6, 5)$	3. $(-5, 2)$	4. $(-7, -4)$
5. $(1, 0)$	6. $(8, 9)$	7. $(3, -5)$	8. $(-1, -2)$

Find the new equation of the circle in each problem 9 through 12 after a translation which moves the origin to the point indicated. Draw both sets of axes and the circle.

9. $x^2 + y^2 - 6x - 2y + 6 = 0; O'(3, 1)$
10. $x^2 + y^2 + 4x + 2y - 3 = 0; O'(-2, -1)$
11. $x^2 + y^2 - 10x + 6y + 18 = 0; O'(5, -3)$
12. $x^2 + y^2 + 14x - 10y + 26 = 0; O'(-7, 5)$

Translate the axes in problems 13 through 16 so that the new equations of the circles will have no first-degree terms. Give the location of each new origin and the new equation.

13. $x^2 + y^2 - 4x - 8y + 3 = 0$ 14. $x^2 + y^2 + 10x + 6y - 2 = 0$
15. $x^2 + y^2 - 5x + 2y - 5 = 0$ 16. $x^2 + y^2 + 3x - 12y + 4 = 0$

17. Derive the translation formulas of Section 2–9 from a figure in which the new origin is in the fourth quadrant.

CHAPTER 3

CONICS

3–1 Introduction. In the preceding chapter, we defined a circle as a locus. In this chapter we shall give names to still other loci or curves and derive the corresponding equations. As in the case of the circle, the equations will be of the second degree, or quadratic, in two variables. The general quadratic equation in x and y may be expressed in the form

$$Ax^2 + Bxy + Cy^2 + Dx + Ey + F = 0. \tag{1}$$

The locus of a second-degree equation in the coordinates x and y is called a *conic section* or, more simply, a *conic*. This designation comes from the fact that the locus or curve can be obtained as the intersection of a right circular cone and a plane.*

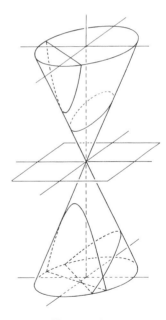

Conic sections were investigated, particularly by Greek mathematicians, long before analytic methods were introduced. Various properties of conics were discovered, and this phase of geometry received much emphasis. Today the interest in conic sections is enhanced by numerous important theoretical and practical applications.

Obviously, different kinds of conic sections are possible. A plane not passing the vertex of a cone may cut all the elements of one nappe and make a closed curve (Fig. 3–1). If the plane is parallel to an element, the intersection extends indefinitely far along one nappe but does not cut the other nappe. The plane may cut both nappes and make a section of two parts, each extending indefinitely far along a nappe. In addition to those sec-

FIGURE 3–1

---

* A right circular cone is the surface generated by a line which passes through a fixed point on a fixed line and moves so that it makes a constant angle with the fixed line. The fixed point is the *vertex* and the generating line in any position is called an *element*. The vertex separates the cone into two parts called *nappes*.

tions, the plane may pass through the vertex of the cone and determine a point, a line, or two intersecting lines. An intersection of this kind is sometimes called a *degenerate conic*.

3–2 The parabola. We now describe and name a curve which is one of the three important kinds of conics.

DEFINITION. *A parabola is the locus of a point which remains on a plane and is equally distant from a fixed point and a fixed line of the plane.*

The fixed point is called the *focus* and the fixed line the *directrix*. In Fig. 3–2 the point F is the focus and the line D the directrix. The point V midway between the focus and directrix is on the parabola. This point is called the *vertex*. Other points of the parabola can be located in the following way. Draw a line L parallel to the directrix. With F as a center and radius equal to the distance between D and L, describe arcs cutting the line L at P' and P. Each of these points being equidistant from the focus and directrix is on the parabola. The curve can be sketched by determining a few points in this manner. The line VF through the vertex and focus is the perpendicular bisector of PP' and of all other chords similarly drawn. For this reason the line is called the *axis* of the parabola.

Although points of a parabola can be located by a direct application of the definition of a parabola, it is easier to obtain them from an equation of the curve. The simplest equation of a parabola can be written by placing the coordinate axes in a special position. Let the x-axis be on the line through the focus and perpendicular to the directrix, and let the origin be at the vertex (Fig. 3–3). Denote the distance from the directrix to the focus by $2a$. The coordinates of the focus are then $(a, 0)$. Since any point $P(x, y)$ of the parabola is the same distance from the focus as from the directrix, we have

$$\sqrt{(x - a)^2 + y^2} = x + a.$$

On squaring and collecting terms, we obtain the equation

$$y^2 = 4ax.$$

This is the equation of a parabola whose vertex is at the origin and whose focus is at $(a, 0)$. If $a > 0$, as represented in Fig. 3–4, x may have any positive value or zero but no negative value. In this case the curve extends indefinitely far into the first and fourth quadrants, and the axis of the parabola is the positive x-axis.

The chord drawn through the focus and perpendicular to the axis of the parabola is given the Latin name *latus rectum*. The length of the

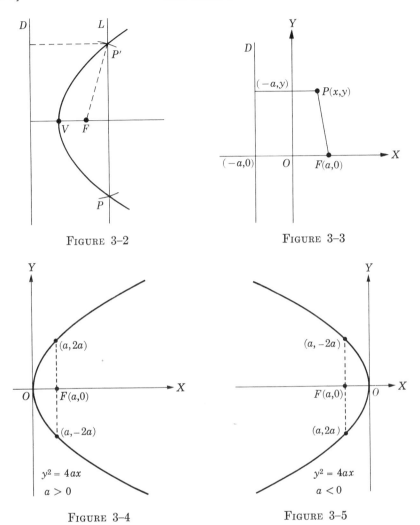

FIGURE 3–2

FIGURE 3–3

FIGURE 3–4

FIGURE 3–5

latus rectum can be determined from the coordinates of its end points. By substituting a for x in the equation $y^2 = 4ax$, we find

$$y^2 = 4a^2 \qquad \text{and} \qquad y = \pm 2a.$$

Hence the end points are $(a, -2a)$ and $(a, 2a)$. This makes the length of the latus rectum equal to the numerical value of $4a$. The vertex and the extremities of the latus rectum are sufficient for drawing a rough sketch of the parabola.

If $a < 0$ in $y^2 = 4ax$, the values of x could not be positive. The parabola in this case opens to the left, as shown in Fig. 3–5.

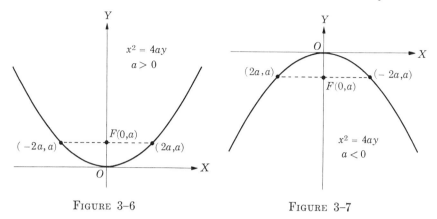

FIGURE 3–6   FIGURE 3–7

In the preceding discussion, we placed the x-axis on the line through the focus and perpendicular to the directrix. By choosing this position for the y-axis, the roles of x and y would be interchanged. Hence the equation of the parabola would then be

$$x^2 = 4ay.$$

The graph of this equation when $a > 0$ is in Fig. 3–6 and when $a < 0$ in Fig. 3–7.

Summarizing, we make the following statements.

THEOREM. *The equation of a parabola with vertex at the origin and focus at $(a, 0)$ is*

$$y^2 = 4ax. \tag{1}$$

The parabola opens to the right if $a > 0$ and opens to the left if $a < 0$.
The equation of a parabola with vertex at the origin and focus at $(0, a)$ is

$$x^2 = 4ay. \tag{2}$$

The parabola opens upward if $a > 0$ and opens downward if $a < 0$.

Equations (1) and (2) can be applied to find the equations of parabolas which satisfy specified conditions. We illustrate their use in some examples.

EXAMPLE 1. Write the equation of the parabola with vertex at the origin and the focus at $(0, 4)$.

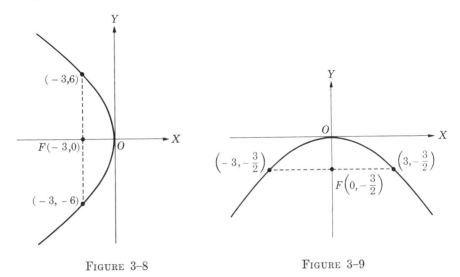

FIGURE 3–8   FIGURE 3–9

Solution. Equation (2) applies here. The distance from the vertex to the focus is 4, and hence $a = 4$. Substituting this value for a, we get

$$x^2 = 16y.$$

EXAMPLE 2. A parabola has its vertex at the origin, its axis along the x-axis, and passes through the point $(-3, 6)$. Find its equation.

Solution. The equation of the parabola is of the form $y^2 = 4ax$. To determine the value of a, we substitute the coordinates of the given point in this equation. Thus we obtain

$$36 = 4a(-3), \quad \text{and} \quad 4a = -12.$$

The required equation is $y^2 = -12x$. The focus is at $(-3, 0)$, and the given point is the upper end of the latus rectum. The graph is constructed in Fig. 3–8.

EXAMPLE 3. The equation of a parabola is $x^2 = -6y$. Find the coordinates of the focus, the equation of the directrix, and the length of the latus rectum.

Solution. The equation is of the form (2), where a is negative. Hence the focus is on the negative y-axis and the parabola opens downward. From the equation $4a = -6$, we find $a = -\frac{3}{2}$. Therefore the coordinates of the focus are $(0, -\frac{3}{2})$ and the directrix is $y = \frac{3}{2}$. The length of the latus rectum is numerically equal to $4a$, and in this case is 6. The latus rectum extends 3 units to the left and 3 units to the right of the focus. The graph may be sketched by drawing through the vertex and the ends of the latus rectum. For more accurate graphing a few additional points could be plotted. (See Fig. 3–9.)

Exercise 3-1

Find the coordinates of the focus, the coordinates of the ends of the latus rectum, and the equation of the directrix of each parabola in problems 1 through 6. Sketch each curve.

1. $y^2 = 4x$ 2. $y^2 = -16x$ 3. $x^2 = -10y$
4. $x^2 = 12y$ 5. $y^2 + 3x = 0$ 6. $x^2 - 8y = 0$

Write the equation of the parabola with vertex at the origin and which satisfies the given conditions in each problem 7 through 16.

7. Focus at $(3, 0)$ 8. Focus at $(-4, 0)$
9. Directrix is $x + 6 = 0$ 10. Directrix is $y - 4 = 0$

11. Latus rectum 12 and opens downward
12. Focus on the y-axis and passes through $(2, 8)$
13. Axis along the y-axis and passes through $(4, -3)$
14. Ends of latus rectum are $(-3, -6)$ and $(-3, 6)$
15. Opens to the left and passes through $(-1, -1)$
16. Opens to the right, and the length of the latus rectum is 16

17. A cable suspended from supports which are at the same height and 400 ft apart has a sag of 100 ft. If the cable hangs in the form of a parabola, find its equation, taking the origin at the lowest point.

18. Find the width of the cable of problem 17 at a height 50 ft above the lowest point.

19. Find the equation of the locus of a point whose distance from $(0, a)$ is equal to its distance from the line $y = -a$, and thus derive Eq. (2), Section 3-2.

3-3 Parabola with vertex at (h, k). We next consider a parabola whose axis is parallel to, but not on, a coordinate axis. In Fig. 3-10, the vertex is at (h, k) and the focus at $(h + a, k)$. We introduce another pair of axes by a translation to the point (h, k). Since the distance from the vertex to the focus is a, we have at once the equation

$$y'^2 = 4ax'.$$

To write the equation of the parabola with respect to the original axes, we apply the translation formulas of Section 2-9 and thus obtain

$$(y - k)^2 = 4a(x - h).$$

We observe from this equation, and also from the figure, that when $a > 0$, the factor $x - h$ of the right number must be greater than or equal to zero. Hence the parabola opens to the right. For $a < 0$, the factor $x - h$ must be less than or equal to zero, and therefore the parabola would open to the left. The axis of the parabola is on the line $y - k = 0$.

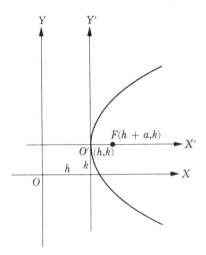

FIGURE 3–10

The length of the latus rectum is numerically equal to $4a$, and hence the extremities can be easily located.

A similar discussion can be made if the axis of a parabola is parallel to the y-axis. Consequently, we make the following statements.

THEOREM. *The equation of a parabola with vertex at $(h,\ k)$ and focus at $(h\ +\ a,\ k)$ is*

$$(y\ -\ k)^2\ =\ 4a(x\ -\ h). \tag{1}$$

The parabola opens to the right if $a\ >\ 0$ and opens to the left if $a\ <\ 0$.
   The equation of a parabola with vertex at $(h,\ k)$ and focus at $(h,\ k\ +\ a)$ is

$$(x\ -\ h)^2\ =\ 4a(y\ -\ k). \tag{2}$$

The parabola opens upward if $a\ >\ 0$ and opens downward if $a\ <\ 0$.

Each of Eqs. (1) and (2) is said to be in *standard form*. When $h\ =\ 0$ and $k\ =\ 0$ they reduce to the simpler equations of the preceding section. If the equation of a parabola is in standard form, its graph can be quickly sketched. The vertex and the ends of the latus rectum are sufficient for a rough sketch. The plotting of a few additional points would, of course, improve the accuracy.

We note that each of Eqs. (1) and (2) is quadratic in one variable and linear in the other variable. This fact can be expressed more vividly if we perform the indicated squares and transpose terms to obtain the general forms

$$x^2 + Dx + Ey + F = 0, \tag{3}$$

$$y^2 + Dx + Ey + F = 0. \tag{4}$$

Conversely, an equation in the form of Eq. (3) or (4) can be presented in a standard form, provided $E \neq 0$ in Eq. (3) and $D \neq 0$ in Eq. (4).

EXAMPLE 1. Draw the graph of the equation

$$y^2 + 8x - 6y + 25 = 0.$$

Solution. The equation represents a parabola because y appears quadratically and x linearly. The graph can be more readily drawn if we first reduce the equation to a standard form. Thus

$$y^2 - 6y + 9 = -8x - 25 + 9, \qquad (y - 3)^2 = -8(x + 2).$$

The vertex is at $(-2, 3)$. Since $4a = -8$ and $a = -2$, the focus is two units to the left of the vertex. The length of the latus rectum, numerically equal to $4a$, is 8. Hence the latus rectum extends 4 units above and below the focus. The graph is constructed in Fig. 3–11.

EXAMPLE 2. A parabola whose axis is parallel to the y-axis passes through the points $(1, 1)$, $(2, 2)$, and $(-1, 5)$. Find its equation.

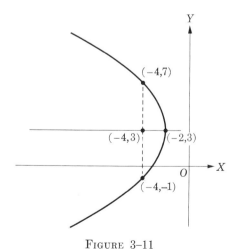

FIGURE 3–11

Solution. Since the axis of the parabola is parallel to the y-axis, the equation must be quadratic in x and linear in y. Hence we start with the general form

$$x^2 + Dx + Ey + F = 0.$$

This equation is to be satisfied by the coordinates of each of the given points. Substituting the coordinates of each point, in turn, we have the system

$$1 + D + E + F = 0,$$
$$4 + 2D + 2E + F = 0,$$
$$1 - D + 5E + F = 0.$$

The simultaneous solution of these equations is $D = -2$, $E = -1$, and $F = 2$. Hence the equation of the parabola is $x^2 - 2x - y + 2 = 0$.

3–4 Symmetry. We have observed that the axis of a parabola bisects all chords of the parabola which are perpendicular to the axis. For this reason a parabola is said to be *symmetric* with respect to its axis. Many other curves possess the property of symmetry. This leads us to the following discussion.

DEFINITIONS. *Two points A and B are said to be symmetric with respect to a line if the line is the perpendicular bisector of the segment AB. A curve is symmetric with respect to a line if each of its points is one of a pair of points symmetric with respect to the line.*

Two points A and B are symmetric with respect to a point O if O is the mid-point of the line segment AB. A curve is symmetric with respect to a point O if each of its points is one of a pair of points symmetric with respect to O.

Symmetry of a curve with respect to a coordinate axis or the origin is of especial interest. Hence we make the following observations. The points (x, y) and $(x, -y)$ are symmetric with respect to the x-axis. Accordingly, a curve is symmetric with respect to the x-axis if for each point (x, y) of the curve the point $(x, -y)$ also belongs to the curve. Similarly, a curve is symmetric with respect to the y-axis if for each point (x, y) of the curve the point $(-x, y)$ also belongs to the curve. The points (x, y) and $(-x, -y)$ are symmetric with respect to the origin. Hence a curve is symmetric with respect to the origin if for each point (x, y) of the curve the point $(-x, -y)$ also belongs to the curve. (See Fig. 3–12.)

An equation can be easily tested to determine whether its graph is symmetric with respect to either coordinate axis or the origin. Consider, for example, the equation $x^2 = 4y + 6$. If x is replaced by $-x$, the equation is not altered. This means that if x is given a value and then the negative of that value, the corresponding values of y are the same. Hence for each point (x, y) of the graph there is also the point $(-x, y)$

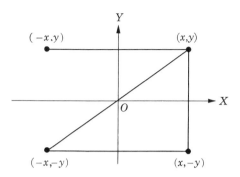

Figure 3–12

on the graph. Therefore the graph is symmetric with respect to the y-axis. On the other hand, the assigning of numerically equal values of opposite signs to y leads to different corresponding values for x. Hence the graph is not symmetric with respect to the x-axis. Similarly, the graph is not symmetric with respect to the origin.

From the definition of symmetry, we formulate the following tests:

1. *If an equation is unchanged when y is replaced by $-y$, then the graph of the equation is symmetric with respect to the x-axis.*

2. *If an equation is unchanged when x is replaced by $-x$, then the graph of the equation is symmetric with respect to the y-axis.*

3. *If an equation is unchanged when x is replaced by $-x$ and y by $-y$, then the graph of the equation is symmetric with respect to the origin.*

These types of symmetry are illustrated by the equations

$$y^4 - 2y^2 - x = 0, \qquad x^2 - 4y + 3 = 0, \qquad y = x^3.$$

The graphs of these equations are symmetric, respectively, with respect to the x-axis, the y-axis, and the origin. Replacing x by $-x$ and y by $-y$ in the third equation gives $-y = -x^3$, which may be reduced to $y = x^3$.

Exercise 3–2

Write the equation of the parabola, in standard form, which satisfies the given conditions in each problem 1 through 10.

1. Vertex $(0, 3)$, focus $(4, 3)$ 2. Vertex $(2, 0)$, focus $(2, 2)$
3. Vertex $(2, 3)$, focus $(6, 3)$ 4. Vertex $(-3, 1)$, focus $(1, 1)$
5. Vertex $(3, 3)$, focus $(-3, 3)$ 6. Vertex $(5, -2)$, focus $(-2, -2)$

7. Vertex $(-1, -2)$, latus rectum 12; opens downward
8. Vertex $(4, -1)$, latus rectum 8; opens to the right
9. Vertex $(2, 1)$, ends of latus rectum $(-1, -5)$ and $(-1, 7)$
10. Vertex $(3, -2)$, ends of latus rectum $(-2, 1)$ and $(8, 1)$

Express the equations in problems 11 through 24 in standard forms. In each case give the coordinates of the vertex, the focus, and the ends of the latus rectum. Sketch the graph.

11. $y^2 - 8x + 8 = 0$ 12. $x^2 - 4y + 8 = 0$
13. $y^2 + 12x - 48 = 0$ 14. $x^2 - 16y - 32 = 0$
15. $x^2 + 4x - 16y + 4 = 0$ 16. $y^2 + 6y - 4x + 9 = 0$
17. $y^2 - 8y + 6x + 16 = 0$ 18. $x^2 + 10x + 20y + 25 = 0$
19. $y^2 + 4y + 8x - 28 = 0$ 20. $x^2 + 2x - 12y + 37 = 0$
21. $x^2 - 8x + 6y - 8 = 0$ 22. $y^2 - 6y + 10x - 1 = 0$
23. $y^2 + 14y - 24x - 119 = 0$ 24. $x^2 - 12x + 16y - 60 = 0$

Find the equation of the parabola in each problem 25 through 32.

25. Vertex $(-1, -2)$, axis vertical; passes through $(3, 6)$
26. Vertex $(3, -4)$, axis horizontal; passes through $(2, -5)$
27. Axis horizontal; passes through $(1, 1)$, $(1, -3)$, and $(-2, 0)$
28. Axis vertical; passes through $(0, 0)$, $(3, 0)$, and $(-1, 4)$
29. Axis horizontal; passes through $(0, 4)$, $(0, -1)$, and $(6, 1)$
30. Axis vertical; passes through $(-1, 0)$, $(5, 0)$, and $(1, 8)$
31. Axis vertical; passes through $(-1, -3)$, $(1, -2)$, and $(2, 1)$
32. Axis horizontal; passes through $(-1, 1)$, $(3, 4)$, and $(2, -2)$

33. Derive Eq. (1), Section 3–3, by finding the equation of the locus of a point equally distant from the focus $(h + a, k)$ and the directrix $x = h - a$.

34. Derive Eq. (2), Section 3–3, by finding the equation of the locus of a point equally distant from the focus $(h, k + a)$ and the directrix $y = k - a$.

3–5 The ellipse. We now come to another kind of conic which, unlike the parabola, is a closed curve.

DEFINITION. *An ellipse is the locus of a point in a plane the sum of whose distance from two fixed points of the plane is constant.*

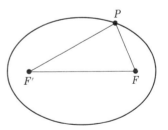

Each of the fixed points is called a *focus* (plural *foci*). Figure 3–13 shows how the foci can be used in drawing an ellipse. The ends of a string are fastened at the foci F' and F. As the pencil at P moves, with the string taut, the curve traced is an ellipse.

FIGURE 3–13

To find the equation of an ellipse, we take the origin of coordinates midway between the foci and one of the coordinate axes on the line through the foci (Fig. 3–14). We denote the distance between the foci by $2c$, and, accordingly, label the foci as $F'(-c, 0)$ and $F(c, 0)$. Now if we let the sum of the distances from a point $P(x, y)$ of the ellipse to

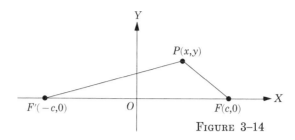

FIGURE 3–14

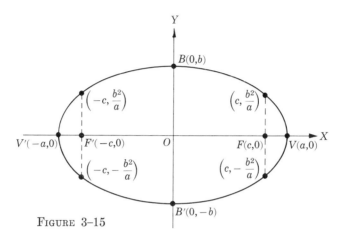

FIGURE 3–15

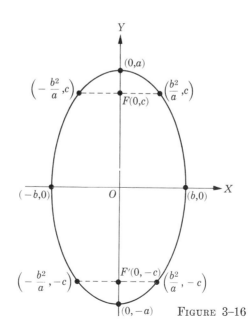

FIGURE 3–16

the foci be $2a$, we obtain

$$PF' + PF = 2a,$$

$$\sqrt{(x+c)^2 + y^2} + \sqrt{(x-c)^2 + y^2} = 2a.$$

By transposing the second radical, squaring, and simplifying, we get

$$cx - a^2 = -a\sqrt{(x-c)^2 + y^2}.$$

By squaring again and simplifying, we find

$$(a^2 - c^2)x^2 + a^2y^2 = a^2(a^2 - c^2).$$

We observe from the figure that the length of one side of triangle $F'PF$ is $2c$, and the sum of the lengths of the other sides is $2a$. Hence $2a > 2c$, and, consequently, $a^2 - c^2 > 0$. Letting $b^2 = a^2 - c^2$ and dividing by the nonzero quantity a^2b^2, we obtain the final form

$$\frac{x^2}{a^2} + \frac{y^2}{b^2} = 1. \qquad (1)$$

We first observe that the graph of Eq. (1) is symmetric with respect to both coordinate axes. When $y = 0$, then $x = \pm a$, and when $x = 0$, $y = \pm b$. Hence the ellipse cuts the x-axis at $V'(-a, 0)$ and $V(a, 0)$ and cuts the y-axis at $B'(0, -b)$ and $B(0, b)$. The segment $V'V(= 2a)$ is called the *major axis* of the ellipse and the segment $B'B(= 2b)$ the *minor axis*. The ends of the major axis are called *vertices*. The intersection of the axes of the ellipse is the *center*. The chord through a focus and perpendicular to the major axis is called a *latus rectum*. Substituting $x = c$ in Eq. (1) and using the relation $c^2 = a^2 - b^2$, we find the points $(c, -b^2/a)$ and $(c, b^2/a)$ to be the ends of one latus rectum. The ends of the other latus rectum are at $(-c, -b^2/a)$ and $(-c, b^2/a)$. These results show that the length of each latus rectum is $2b^2/a$. The major axis is longer than the minor axis. This is true because $b^2 = a^2 - c^2 < a^2$, and therefore $b < a$. We note also that the foci are on the major axis. The ellipse and several important points are shown in Fig. 3–15.

If we take the foci of an ellipse on the y-axis at $(0, -c)$ and $(0, c)$, we would obtain, by steps similar to those above, the equation

$$\frac{y^2}{a^2} + \frac{x^2}{b^2} = 1. \qquad (2)$$

In this case the major axis would be on the y-axis and the minor axis on the x-axis (Fig. 3–16).

3–6 Extent of a curve. From the definition of an ellipse, we know that its points do not extend indefinitely far from the foci. The fact that an ellipse is limited in extent can be deduced from its equation. Thus solving Eq. (1), Section 3–5, for x and y in turn, we get

$$x = \pm \frac{a}{b}\sqrt{b^2 - y^2} \quad \text{and} \quad y = \pm \frac{b}{a}\sqrt{a^2 - x^2}.$$

These equations reveal that y^2 must not exceed b^2, and x^2 must not exceed a^2. In other words, the permissible values are $-b \le y \le b$ and $-a \le x \le a$. Hence no point of the ellipse is outside the rectangle formed by the horizontal lines $y = -b$, $y = b$ and the vertical lines $x = -a$, $x = a$.

In many equations the extent of the graph can be readily determined by solving for each variable in terms of the other. The concept of extent, as well as that of symmetry, is often an aid in drawing a graph.

EXAMPLE 1. Find the equation of the ellipse with foci at $(0, \pm 4)$ and a vertex at $(0, 6)$.

Solution. The location of the foci shows that the center of the ellipse is at the origin, that the equation is in the form of Eq. (2), Section 3–5, and that $c = 4$. The given vertex, 6 units from the center, makes $a = 6$. Using the relation $b^2 = a^2 - c^2$, we find $b^2 = 20$. Hence the required equation is

$$\frac{y^2}{36} + \frac{x^2}{20} = 1.$$

EXAMPLE 2. Sketch the ellipse $9x^2 + 25y^2 = 225$.

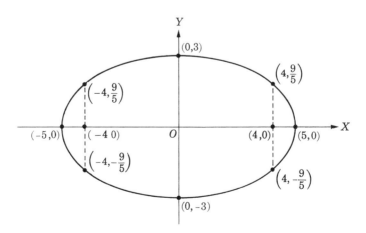

FIGURE 3–17

Solution. Dividing by 225 yields the form

$$\frac{x^2}{25} + \frac{y^2}{9} = 1.$$

Since the denominator of x^2 is greater than the denominator of y^2, the major axis is along the x-axis. We see also that $a^2 = 25$, $b^2 = 9$, and $c = \sqrt{a^2 - b^2} = 4$. Hence the vertices are at $(\pm 5, 0)$, the ends of the minor axis at $(0, \pm 3)$, and the foci at $(\pm 4, 0)$. The length of a latus rectum is $2b^2/a = \frac{18}{5}$. The locations of the ends of the axes and the ends of each latus rectum are sufficient for making a sketch of the ellipse. Figure 3–17 shows the curve with several important points indicated.

3–7 Focus-directrix property of an ellipse. We defined a parabola in terms of a focus and directrix, but we made no use of a directrix in defining an ellipse. It turns out, however, that an ellipse has a directrix. In deriving the equation of an ellipse (Section 3–5), we arrived at the equation

$$a\sqrt{(x - c)^2 + y^2} = a^2 - cx.$$

This equation implies the existence of a directrix which is evident after a slight modification. Thus, dividing by a and factoring the right member, we obtain

$$\sqrt{(x - c)^2 + y^2} = \frac{c}{a}\left(\frac{a^2}{c} - x\right).$$

The left member of this equation is the distance from a point (x, y) of the ellipse to the focus $(c, 0)$. The factor $a^2/c - x$ of the right member is the distance from the point of the ellipse to the line $x = a^2/c$ (Fig. 3–18), and the factor c/a is a constant between zero and unity. Hence we have a proof, based on our definition of an ellipse, of the following theorem.

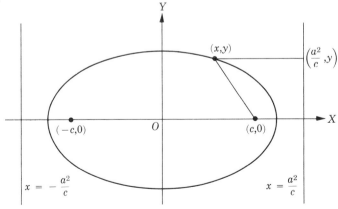

FIGURE 3–18

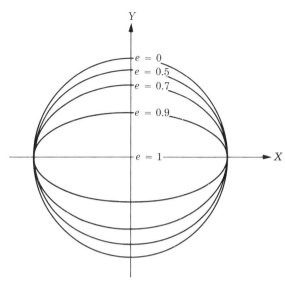

FIGURE 3–19

THEOREM. *An ellipse is the locus of a point whose distance from a fixed point is equal to a constant (between 0 and 1) times its distance to a fixed line.*

Sometimes an ellipse is defined in terms of a focus and directrix. When so defined, it is possible to prove the statement contained in our definition of an ellipse (Section 3–5).

The line $x = a^2/c$ is the directrix corresponding to the focus $(c, 0)$. It would be easy to show that the point $(-c, 0)$ and the line $x = -a^2/c$ constitute another focus and directrix. This fact is geometrically evident from considerations of symmetry.

We wish to discuss further the quantity c/a. This ratio is called the *eccentricity e* of the ellipse. The shape of an ellipse depends on the value of its eccentricity. Suppose, for example, we visualize an ellipse in which the major axis remains constant while e starts at zero and approaches unity. If $e = 0$, the equations $e = c/a$ and $b^2 = a^2 - c^2$ show that $c = 0$ and $a = b$. The two foci are then coincident at the center, and the ellipse is a circle. As e increases, the foci separate, each receding from the center, and b decreases. As e approaches 1, c approaches a, and b approaches 0. Hence the ellipse, starting as a circle, becomes narrow and narrower. If $e = 1$, or $c = a$, then $b = 0$. Equation (1), Section 3–5, would not then apply because b^2 is a denominator. But the definition of an ellipse requires the locus to be the line segment connecting the foci.

Summarizing, we have an actual ellipse if e is between 0 and 1. When e is close to 0, the ellipse is somewhat like a circle; when e is close to 1, the ellipse is relatively long and narrow.

Ellipses with the same major axis and different eccentricities are constructed in Fig. 3–19.

3–8 Ellipse with center at (h, k). If the axes of an ellipse are parallel to the coordinate axes and the center is at (h, k), we can obtain its equation by applying the translation formulas of Section 2–9. We draw a new pair of coordinate axes along the axes of the ellipse (Fig. 3–20). The equation of the ellipse referred to the new axes is

$$\frac{x'^2}{a^2} + \frac{y'^2}{b^2} = 1.$$

The substitutions $x' = x - h$ and $y' = y - k$ yield

$$\frac{(x - h)^2}{a^2} + \frac{(y - k)^2}{b^2} = 1. \tag{1}$$

Similarly, when the major axis is parallel to the y-axis, we have

$$\frac{(y - k)^2}{a^2} + \frac{(x - h)^2}{b^2} = 1. \tag{2}$$

These are the *standard forms* of equations of ellipses. They reduce to Eqs. (1) and (2), Section 3–5, when $h = k = 0$. The quantities a, b,

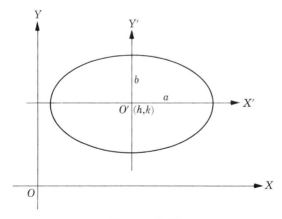

FIGURE 3–20

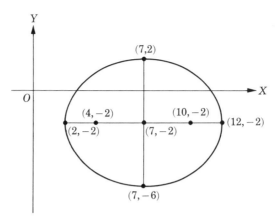

FIGURE 3-21

and c have the same meaning whether or not the center of the ellipse is at the origin. Therefore constructing the graph of an equation in either of the forms of Eqs. (1) or (2), Section 3-8, presents no greater difficulty than drawing the graph of one of the simpler Eqs. (1) or (2) of Section 3-5.

EXAMPLE 1. Find the equation of the ellipse with foci at $(4, -2)$ and $(10, -2)$, and a vertex at $(12, -2)$.

Solution. The center, midway between the foci, is at $(7, -2)$. The distance between the foci is 6 and the given vertex is 5 units from the center; hence $c = 3$ and $a = 5$. Then $b^2 = a^2 - c^2 = 16$. Since the major axis is parallel to the x-axis, we substitute in Eq. (1), Section 3-8, and get

$$\frac{(x-7)^2}{25} + \frac{(y+2)^2}{16} = 1.$$

The graph of this ellipse is constructed in Fig. 3-21.

EXAMPLE 2. Reduce, to standard form, the equation

$$4y^2 + 9x^2 - 24y - 72x + 144 = 0.$$

Solution. The essential steps in the process follow.

$$4(y^2 - 6y) + 9(x^2 - 8x) = -144,$$

$$4(y^2 - 6y + 9) + 9(x^2 - 8x + 16) = -144 + 36 + 144,$$

$$4(y - 3)^2 + 9(x - 4)^2 = 36,$$

$$\frac{(y-3)^2}{9} + \frac{(x-4)^2}{4} = 1.$$

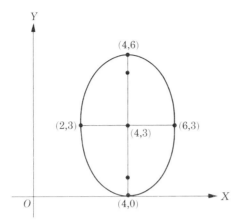

FIGURE 3–22

The coordinates of the center are $(4, 3)$; $a = 3$, $b = 2$, and $c = \sqrt{a^2 - b^2} = \sqrt{9 - 4} = \sqrt{5}$. The vertices are at $(4, 0)$ and $(4, 6)$, and the ends of the minor axis are at $(2, 3)$ and $(6, 3)$. The coordinates of the foci are $(4, 3 - \sqrt{5})$ and $(4, 3 + \sqrt{5})$. The graph is constructed in Fig. 3–22.

EXERCISE 3–3

Find the coordinates of the foci, the ends of the axes, and the ends of each latus rectum in problems 1 through 10. From this information sketch the curves.

1. $\dfrac{y^2}{25} + \dfrac{x^2}{9} = 1$

2. $\dfrac{x^2}{169} + \dfrac{y^2}{25} = 1$

3. $\dfrac{x^2}{169} + \dfrac{y^2}{144} = 1$

4. $\dfrac{y^2}{25} + \dfrac{x^2}{16} = 1$

5. $\dfrac{x^2}{49} + \dfrac{y^2}{25} = 1$

6. $\dfrac{x^2}{9} + \dfrac{y^2}{4} = 1$

7. $25x^2 + 4y^2 = 100$

8. $x^2 + 4y^2 = 9$

9. $4x^2 + y^2 = 4$

10. $2x^2 + 3y^2 = 12$

Write the equations of the ellipses whose axes coincide with the coordinate axes, and which satisfy the conditions given in problems 11 through 18.

11. Vertex $(4, 0)$, end of minor axis $(0, 3)$
12. Focus $(2, 0)$, vertex $(5, 0)$
13. Focus $(0, -4)$, minor axis 4
14. Minor axis 12, vertex $(9, 0)$
15. Focus $(3, 0)$, length of latus rectum 9
16. End of minor axis $(5, 0)$, length of latus rectum $\frac{50}{13}$
17. Passing through $(3, 5)$ and $(7, \frac{5}{3})$
18. Passing through $(3, \sqrt{2})$ and $(\sqrt{6}, 2)$

19. The perimeter of a triangle is 30, and the points $(0, -5)$ and $(0, 5)$ are two of the vertices. Find the locus of the third vertex.

20. A point moves so that the sum of its distances from $(-3, 0)$ and $(3, 0)$ is 8. Find the equation of its path.

21. Find the equation of the locus of the mid-points of the ordinates of the circle $x^2 + y^2 = 36$.

22. The ordinates of a curve are k times the ordinates of the circle $x^2 + y^2 = a^2$. Show that the curve is an ellipse if k is a positive number different from 1.

23. A line segment of length 12 moves with its ends always touching the coordinate axes. Find the equation of the locus of the point on the segment which is 4 units from the end in contact with the x-axis.

24. A rod of length $a + b$ moves with its ends in contact with the coordinate axes. Show that the point at a distance a from the end in contact with the x-axis describes an ellipse if $a \neq b$.

25. The earth's orbit is an ellipse with the sun at one focus. The length of the major axis is 186,000,000 mi, and the eccentricity is 0.0167. Find the distances from the ends of the major axis to the sun. These are the greatest and least distances from the earth to the sun.

26. The moon's orbit is an ellipse with the earth at one focus. The length of the major axis is 378,000 mi, and the eccentricity is 0.0549. Find the greatest and least distances from the earth to the moon.

27. The arch of an underpass is a semiellipse 60 ft wide and 20 ft high. Find the clearance at the right edge of a lane if the edge is 20 ft from the middle.

Reduce equations 28 through 35 to standard forms. In each, find the coordinates of the center, the vertices, the foci, and the ends of the minor axis. Sketch each curve.

28. $16x^2 + 25y^2 - 160x - 200y + 400 = 0$
29. $9x^2 + 25y^2 - 36x - 189 = 0$
30. $3x^2 + 2y^2 - 24x + 12y + 60 = 0$
31. $4x^2 + 8y^2 + 4x + 24y - 13 = 0$
32. $36(x + 2)^2 + 100(y - 2)^2 = 3600$
33. $25(x - 1)^2 + 169(y + 2)^2 = 4225$
34. $225(x + 2)^2 + 289(y + 3)^2 = 65{,}025$
35. $169(x - 1)^2 + 144(y - 3)^2 = 24{,}336$

Write the equation of the ellipse which satisfies the conditions in each problem 36 through 39. Sketch each curve.

36. Center $(5, 1)$, vertex $(5, 4)$, end of minor axis $(3, 1)$
37. Vertex $(6, 3)$, foci $(-4, 3)$ and $(4, 3)$
38. Ends of minor axis $(-1, 2)$ and $(-1, -4)$, focus $(1, -1)$
39. Vertices $(-1, 3)$ and $(5, 3)$, length of minor axis 4

40. A point moves so that the sum of its distances from $(-4, 3)$ and $(4, 3)$ is 12. Find the equation of its path.

41. The perimeter of a triangle is 20, and the points $(-2, -3)$ and $(-2, 3)$ are two of the vertices. Find the equation of the locus of the third vertex.

42. Find the equation of the locus of a point $P(x, y)$ which moves so that its distance from $(5, 0)$ is one-half its distance from the line $x = 20$.

43. Find the equation of the locus of a point $P(x, y)$ which moves so that its distance from $(-4, 0)$ is equal to two-thirds its distance from the line $x = -9$.

44. If p stands for any positive number, the equation

$$\frac{x^2}{a^2 + p} + \frac{y^2}{b^2 + p} = 1$$

is said to represent a *family* of ellipses. Show that all members of the family have the same foci. Let $a^2 = 15$, $b^2 = 1$, then write the equations when p is assigned, successively, the values 0, 15, 35, 48, 80. Find the ends of the axis corresponding to each value of p, and sketch the five ellipses.

45. Derive Eq. (2), Section 3–5.

3–9 The hyperbola. The third type of conic which we shall consider is the hyperbola. The equations of hyperbolas resemble those of ellipses, but the properties of these two kinds of conics differ considerably in some respects.

DEFINITION. *A hyperbola is the locus of a point in a plane the difference of whose distances from two fixed points (foci) in the plane is constant.*

To derive the equation of a hyperbola, we take the origin midway between the foci, and a coordinate axis on the line through the foci (Fig. 3–23). We denote the foci by $F'(-c, 0)$ and $F(c, 0)$ and the constant difference by $2a$. Then if $P(x, y)$ is a point of the locus, we have, from the above definition,

$$F'P - FP = 2a,$$

$$\sqrt{(x + c)^2 + y^2} - \sqrt{(x - c)^2 + y^2} = 2a.$$

By steps like those employed in Section 3–5 in the case of the ellipse, we reduce this equation to

$$(c^2 - a^2)x^2 - a^2y^2 = a^2(c^2 - a^2).$$

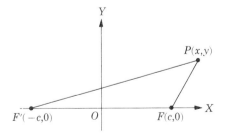

FIGURE 3–23

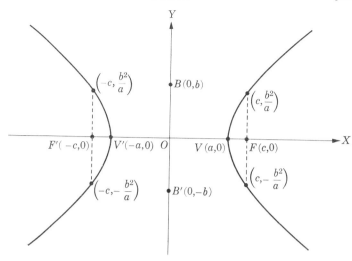

FIGURE 3–24

Then letting $b^2 = c^2 - a^2$ and dividing by a^2b^2, we have

$$\frac{x^2}{a^2} - \frac{y^2}{b^2} = 1. \tag{1}$$

The division is allowable if $c^2 - a^2 \neq 0$. In Fig. 3–23, the length of one side of triangle $F'PF$ is $2c$, and the difference of the other two sides is $2a$. Hence $c > a$ and $c^2 - a^2 > 0$.

The graph of Eq. (1) is symmetric with respect to the coordinate axes. The permissible values of x and y become evident where each is expressed in terms of the other. Thus we get

$$x = \pm \frac{a}{b} \sqrt{b^2 + y^2} \qquad \text{and} \qquad y = \pm \frac{b}{a} \sqrt{x^2 - a^2}.$$

We see from the first of these equations that y may have any real value and from the second that x may have any real value except those for which $x^2 < a$. Hence the hyperbola extends indefinitely far from the axes in each quadrant. But there is no part of the graph between the line $x = -a$ and the line $x = a$. Accordingly, the hyperbola consists of two separate parts, or *branches* (Fig. 3–24). The points $V'(-a, 0)$ and $V(a, 0)$ are called *vertices*, and the segment $V'V$ is called the *transverse axis*. The segment from $B'(0, -b)$ to $B(0, b)$ is called the *conjugate axis*. Although the conjugate axis has no point in common with the hyperbola, it has an important relation to the curve, as we shall discover. The intersection of the axes is the *center*. The chord through a focus and perpendicular to the transverse axis is called a *latus rectum*. By substituting $x = c$ in Eq. (1) and using the relation $c^2 = a^2 + b^2$, we find the extremities of a latus rectum to be $(c, -b^2/a)$ and $(c, b^2/a)$. Hence the length is $2b^2/a$.

It is important to note that the relation among the three positive quantities a, b, and c, as used in connection with the ellipse, is not the same as for the hyperbola. In the case of the ellipse, $a > c$ and $c^2 = a^2 - b^2$, where a is half the length of the major axis, b is half the length of the minor axis, and c is the distance from the center to a focus. It follows from these relations that $a > b$. For the hyperbola, $c > a$ and $c^2 = a^2 + b^2$, where a is half the transverse axis, b is half the conjugate axis, and c is the distance from the center to a focus. But no restriction is placed on the relative values of a and b.

The hyperbola

$$\frac{y^2}{a^2} - \frac{x^2}{b^2} = 1 \qquad (2)$$

has its vertices at $V'(0, -a)$ and $V(0, a)$, and its foci at $F'(0, -c)$ and $F(0, c)$, where still $c^2 = a^2 + b^2$.

The generalized equations of hyperbolas with axes parallel to the coordinate axes and the centers not at the origin are

$$\frac{(x - h)^2}{a^2} - \frac{(y - k)^2}{b^2} = 1, \qquad (3)$$

$$\frac{(y - k)^2}{a^2} - \frac{(x - h)^2}{b^2} = 1. \qquad (4)$$

3–10 Asymptotes of a hyperbola. Unlike the other conics, a hyperbola has associated with it two lines bearing an important relation to the curve. These lines are the extended diagonals of the rectangle in Fig. 3–25. One pair of sides of the rectangle pass through the vertices and are perpendicular to the transverse axis. The other pair pass through the ends of the conjugate axis. Suppose we consider the extended diagonal and the part of the hyperbola in the first quadrant. The equations of the diagonal and this part of the hyperbola are, respectively,

$$y = \frac{b}{a} x \qquad \text{and} \qquad y = \frac{b}{a} \sqrt{x^2 - a^2} .$$

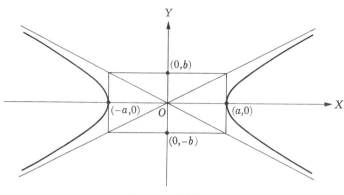

FIGURE 3–25

We see that for any $x > a$ the ordinate of the hyperbola is less than the ordinate of the line. If, however, x is many times as large as a, the corresponding ordinates are almost equal. This may be seen more convincingly by examining the difference of the two ordinates. Thus by subtracting and changing the form, we get

$$\frac{b(x - \sqrt{x^2 - a^2})}{a} = \frac{b(x - \sqrt{x^2 - a^2})(x + \sqrt{x^2 - a^2})}{a(x + \sqrt{x^2 - a^2})}$$

$$= \frac{ab}{x + \sqrt{x^2 - a^2}}.$$

The numerator of the last fraction is constant. The denominator, however, increases as x increases. In fact, we can make the denominator as large as we please by taking a sufficiently large value for x. This means that the fraction, which is the difference of the ordinates of the line and the hyperbola, gets closer and closer to zero as x gets larger and larger. The perpendicular distance from a point of the hyperbola to the line is less than the fraction. Consequently, we can make the perpendicular distance, though never zero, as near zero as we please by taking x sufficiently large. When a curve and a line are related in this manner, the line is said to be an *asymptote* of the curve. From considerations of symmetry, we conclude that the extended diagonals are asymptotes to the hyperbola in each of the four quadrants. The equation of the other asymptote is $y = -(b/a)x$.

Similarly, the equations of the asymptotes of the hyperbola of Eq. (2) are

$$y = \frac{a}{b}x \qquad \text{and} \qquad y = -\frac{a}{b}x.$$

We observe that for each of the hyperbolas in Eqs. (1) and (2), the equations of the asymptotes may be obtained by factoring the left member and equating each factor to zero.

The asymptotes of a hyperbola are helpful in sketching the hyperbola. A rough drawing can be made from the associated rectangle and its extended diagonals. The accuracy may be improved considerably, however, by plotting the end points of each latus rectum.

If $a = b$, the associated rectangle is a square and the asymptotes are perpendicular to each other. For this case, the hyperbola is said to be *equilateral* because its axes are equal or is said to be *rectangular* because its asymptotes intersect at right angles.

The ratio c/a is called the *eccentricity* e of the hyperbola. The angle of intersection of the asymptotes, and therefore the shape of the hyperbola, depends on the value of e. Since $c > a$, the value of e is greater than 1. If c is just slightly greater than a, so that e is near 1, the relation $c^2 = a^2 + b^2$ shows that b is small compared with a. Then the asymptotes make a pair of small angles. The branches of the hyperbola, enclosed by small angles, diverge slowly. If e increases, the branches are enclosed by larger angles; and the angles can be made near 180° by taking large values for e.

EXAMPLE 1. Sketch the curve $36x^2 - 64y^2 = 2304$.

Solution. We divide by 2304 and reduce the equation to

$$\frac{x^2}{64} - \frac{y^2}{36} = 1.$$

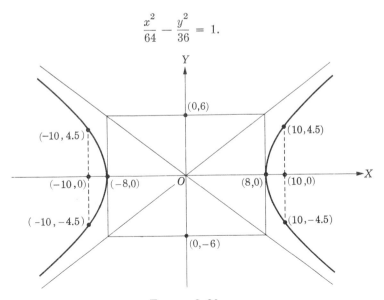

FIGURE 3–26

The graph is a hyperbola in which $a = 8$, $b = 6$, and $c = \sqrt{a^2 + b^2} = 10$. The vertices, therefore, are $(\pm 8, 0)$ and the foci $(\pm 10, 0)$. Each latus rectum has a length of $2b^2/a = 9$. The equations of the asymptotes are $3x - 4y = 0$ and $3x + 4y = 0$. From this information the hyperbola can be drawn (Fig. 3–26).

EXAMPLE 2. Draw the graph of $12y^2 - 4x^2 + 72y + 16x + 44 = 0$.

Solution. We first reduce the equation to a standard form. Thus

$$12(y^2 + 6y + 9) - 4(x^2 - 4x + 4) = -44 + 108 - 16,$$

$$12(y + 3)^2 - 4(x - 2)^2 = 48,$$

$$\frac{(y + 3)^2}{4} - \frac{(x - 2)^2}{12} = 1.$$

We see now that $a = 2$, $b = 2\sqrt{3}$, $c = \sqrt{4 + 12} = 4$, and the center of the hyperbola is at $(2, -3)$. Hence the ends of the transverse axis are at $(2, -5)$ and $(2, -1)$, and the ends of the conjugate axis at $(2 - 2\sqrt{3}, -3)$ and $(2 + 2\sqrt{3}, -3)$. The sides of the associated rectangle pass through these points (Fig. 3–27). The extended diagonals of the rectangle are the asymptotes. The coordinates of the foci, 4 units from the center, are $(2, -7)$ and $(2, 1)$. The length of each latus rectum is $2b^2/a = 12$, and therefore the ends of each latus rectum are 6 units from a focus. The vertices of the hyperbola, the ends of each latus rectum, and the asymptotes are sufficient for drawing a reasonably accurate graph. The equations of the asymptotes, though not needed for their drawing, are

$$\frac{y + 3}{2} + \frac{x - 2}{2\sqrt{3}} = 0 \quad \text{and} \quad \frac{y + 3}{2} - \frac{x - 2}{2\sqrt{3}} = 0.$$

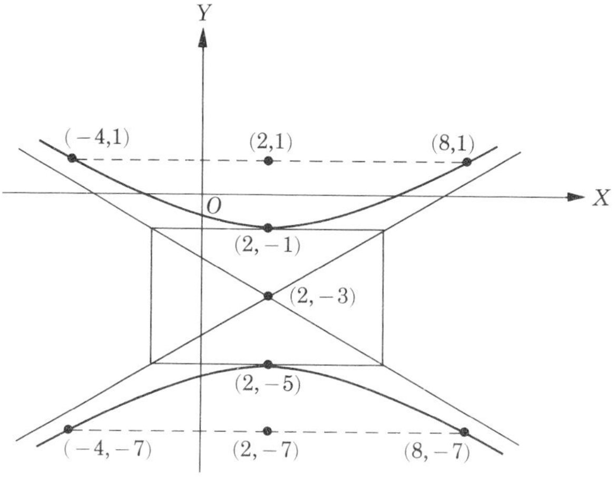

FIGURE 3–27

3–11 Applications of conics. Many examples of conics have been discovered in natural phenomena, and important applications of them abound in engineering and industry.

A projectile, for example, a ball or bullet, travels in a path which is approximately a parabola. The paths of some comets are nearly parabolic. Cables of some suspension bridges hang in the form of a parabola. The surface generated by revolving a parabola about its axis is called a paraboloid of revolution. A reflecting surface in this form has the property that light emanating at the focus is reflected in the direction of the axis. This kind of surface is used in headlights, in some telescopes, and in devices to reflect sound waves. A comparatively recent application of parabolic metal surfaces is found in radar and other microwave equipment. The surfaces reflect radio waves in the same way that light is reflected and are used in directing outgoing beams and also in receiving incoming beams.

The planets have elliptic paths with the sun at a focus. Much use is made of semi-elliptic springs and elliptic-shaped gears. A surface of the form generated by revolving an ellipse about its major axis is so shaped that sound waves emanating at one focus are reflected to arrive at the other focus. This principle is illustrated in whispering galleries and other buildings.

A very interesting and important application of the hyperbola is that of locating the place from which a sound, such as gunfire, emanates. From the difference in the times at which the sound reaches two listening posts, the difference between distances of the posts from the gun can be determined. Then the gun is known to be located on a branch of a hyperbola of which the posts are foci. The position of the gun on this curve can be found by the use of a third listening post. Either of the two posts and the third are foci of a branch of another hyperbola on which the gun is located. Hence the gun is at the intersection of the two branches.

The principle used in finding the location of a gun is also employed by a radar-equipped airplane to determine its location. In this case the plane receives signals from three stations of known locations.

Exercise 3–4

For each hyperbola 1 through 8 find the coordinates of the vertices and foci, the length of each latus rectum, and the equations of the asymptotes. Sketch each curve, using the asymptotes.

1. $\dfrac{x^2}{16} - \dfrac{y^2}{9} = 1$

2. $\dfrac{x^2}{36} - \dfrac{y^2}{64} = 1$

3. $\dfrac{y^2}{9} - \dfrac{x^2}{4} = 1$

4. $\dfrac{y^2}{9} - \dfrac{x^2}{25} = 1$

5. $\dfrac{x^2}{4} - \dfrac{y^2}{21} = 1$

6. $\dfrac{x^2}{20} - \dfrac{y^2}{16} = 1$

7. $y^2 - x^2 = 36$

8. $x^2 - y^2 = 49$

Write the equations of the hyperbolas whose axes are on the coordinate axes, and which also satisfy the conditions given in problems 9 through 16.

9. Vertex $(4, 0)$, end of conjugate axis $(0, 3)$
10. Focus $(6, 0)$, vertex $(4, 0)$
11. Focus $(0, 5)$, conjugate axis 4
12. Conjugate axis 6, vertex $(7, 0)$
13. Latus rectum 5, focus $(3, 0)$
14. End of conjugate axis $(3, 0)$, length of latus rectum 10
15. Passes through $(6, 5)$ and $(8, 2\sqrt{15})$
16. Passes through $(3, \sqrt{2})$ and $(2\sqrt{3}, 2)$

17. Derive Eq. (2), Section 3–9.
18. The hyperbolas

$$\frac{x^2}{a^2} - \frac{y^2}{b^2} = 1 \quad \text{and} \quad \frac{y^2}{b^2} - \frac{x^2}{a^2} = 1$$

are called *conjugate hyperbolas*. Show that conjugate hyperbolas have the same asymptotes. Are conjugate hyperbolas shaped alike when $a = b$? Sketch, on the same axes, the pair of conjugate hyperbolas corresponding to $a = 5$ and $b = 3$.

19. Derive Eq. (3), Section 3–9, using a translation of axes. Derive also Eq. (4).

20. Show that the hyperbola of Eq. (1), Section 3–9, has the point $(c, 0)$ as a focus and the line $x = a^2/c$ as a directrix. [*Hint:* Proceed as in the case of the ellipse, Section 3–7.]

21. Listening posts are at A, B, and C. Point A is 2000 ft north of point B, and point C is 2000 ft east of B. The sound of a gun reaches A and B simultaneously one second after it reaches C. Show that the coordinates of the gun's position are approximately $(860, 1000)$, where the x-axis passes through B and C and the origin is midway between B and C. Assume that sound travels 1100 ft/sec.

Reduce equations 22 through 25 to standard forms. In each, find the coordinates of the center, the vertices, and the foci. Sketch the locus of each equation.

22. $9x^2 - 16y^2 - 54x - 63 = 0$
23. $21x^2 - 4y^2 + 84x - 32y - 64 = 0$
24. $5y^2 - 4x^2 - 30y - 32x = 99$
25. $2y^2 - 3x^2 - 8y + 6x - 1 = 0$

Write the equations of the hyperbolas which satisfy the conditions given in problems 26 through 29.

26. Center $(1, 3)$, vertex $(4, 3)$, end of conjugate axis $(1, 1)$
27. Vertex $(-4, 0)$, foci $(-5, 0)$ and $(1, 0)$

28. Ends of conjugate axis $(3, -1)$ and $(3, 5)$, focus $(-1, 2)$

29. Vertices $(-1, 3)$ and $(5, 3)$, length of conjugate axis 6

30. A point moves so that the difference of its distances from $(-4, 3)$ and $(4, 3)$ is numerically equal to 6. Find the equation of its path.

31. The points $A(-10, 2)$ and $B(10, 2)$ are vertices of a triangle. The difference of the lengths of the sides drawn from the third vertex C is 12. Find the equation of the locus of C.

32. Find the equation of the locus of a point $P(x, y)$ which moves so that its distance from $(5, 0)$ is equal to $\frac{5}{4}$ its distance from the line $x = \frac{16}{5}$.

33. Find the equation of the locus of a point which moves so that its distance from $(4, 0)$ is twice its distance from the line $x = 1$.

34. Show that the equation

$$\frac{x^2}{a^2 + p} - \frac{y^2}{b^2 - p} = 1,$$

where $p > 0$ and $b^2 - p > 0$, represents a family of hyperbolas which have common foci on the x-axis.

CHAPTER 4

SIMPLIFICATION OF EQUATIONS

4–1 Simplification by translation. In Section 2–9, we discovered that the equation of a circle whose center is not at the origin can be expressed in a simpler form by an appropriate translation of axes. Also, in Chapter 3 we found that the equation of a parabola, an ellipse, or a hyperbola is simpler for a certain position of the coordinate axes relative to the curve. We might surmise, therefore, that the equations of conics are expressible in simplified forms. This is indeed true, and we shall consider transformations by which equations of the second degree can be reduced to simple forms.

The general equation of the second degree may be presented in the form

$$Ax^2 + Bxy + Cy^2 + Dx + Ey + F = 0. \tag{1}$$

Before taking up the general equation, however, we shall deal with special cases obtained by setting one or more of the coefficients equal to zero. We advise the student to review the derivation of the translation formulas (Section 2–9) and then to study carefully the following examples.

EXAMPLE 1. By a translation of axes, simplify the equation

$$x^2 - 6x - 6y - 15 = 0.$$

Solution. We do not know in advance what the translation should be. Hence we use the translation formulas $x = x' + h$, $y = y' + k$ (Section 2–9) with h and k unknown. Thus we have

$$(x' + h)^2 - 6(x' + h) - 6(y' + k) - 15 = 0,$$
$$x'^2 + 2hx' + h^2 - 6x' - 6h - 6y' - 6k - 15 = 0,$$
$$x'^2 + (2h - 6)x' - 6y' + (h^2 - 6h - 6k - 15) = 0.$$

We wish now to select values for h and k which will make the last equation as simple as possible. Clearly, then, this end is achieved by setting the coefficient of x equal to zero and the sum of the constant terms equal to zero. Thus solving

$$2h - 6 = 0 \qquad \text{and} \qquad h^2 - 6h - 6k - 15 = 0$$

simultaneously, gives $h = 3$, $k = -4$. The values for h and k lead to the equation

$$x'^2 - 6y' = 0.$$

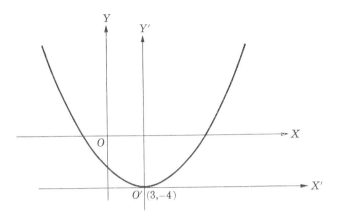

Figure 4–1

This result can also be obtained by completing the square in the x-terms and selecting the translation which will eliminate the x'-term and the constant terms. The given equation yields

$$x^2 - 6x + 9 = 6y + 15 + 9,$$
$$(x - 3)^2 = 6(y + 4).$$

When the origin is translated to $(3, -4)$, this equation becomes $x'^2 = 6y'$. Both sets of axes and the graph are drawn in Fig. 4–1. The equation of the parabola referred to the original axes is the given equation; the equation referred to the new axes is $x'^2 = 6y'$.

Example 2. Translate the axes so that the equation

$$2x^2 + 3y^2 + 10x - 18y + 26 = 0$$

is transformed to a simpler form.

Solution. We apply the translation formulas in order to determine suitable values for h and k. Thus we have

$$2(x' + h)^2 + 3(y' + k)^2 + 10(x' + h) - 18(y' + k) + 26 = 0,$$
$$2x'^2 + 3y'^2 + (4h + 10)x' + (6k - 18)y'$$
$$+ 2h^2 + 3k^2 + 10h - 18k + 26 = 0.$$

We set the coefficients of x' and y' equal to zero and get $4h + 10 = 0$ and $6k - 18 = 0$; hence $h = -\frac{5}{2}$ and $k = 3$. These values for h and k yield the transformed equation

$$2x'^2 + 3y'^2 - \tfrac{27}{2} = 0, \qquad \text{or} \qquad 4x'^2 + 6y'^2 = 27.$$

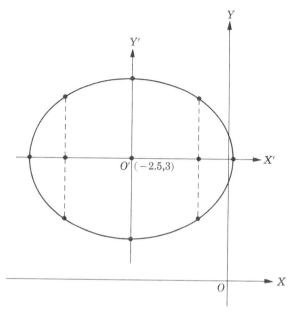

FIGURE 4–2

The simplification can also be made by completing the squares in the x- and y-terms. By this plan, we obtain from the original equation

$$2(x^2 + 5x) + 3(y^2 - 6y) = -26,$$
$$2(x^2 + 5x + \tfrac{25}{4}) + 3(y^2 - 6y + 9) = -26 + \tfrac{25}{2} + 27,$$
$$2(x + \tfrac{5}{2})^2 + 3(y - 3)^2 = \tfrac{27}{2}.$$

In the form above, we observe that the transformation equations $x = x' - \tfrac{5}{2}$ and $y = y' + 3$ will yield an equation free of first-degree terms. Thus we obtain, as before, $4x'^2 + 6y'^2 = 27$.

The graph is an ellipse with $a = \tfrac{3}{2}\sqrt{3}$, $b = \tfrac{3}{2}\sqrt{2}$, and $c = \tfrac{3}{2}$. Both sets of axes and the graph are in Fig. 4–2.

The preceding examples illustrate the procedure for simplifying equations of the form (1) with $B = 0$. If either A or C is zero, we can complete the square in the remaining second-degree term, as in Example 1. Then it is easy to pick the translation which will reduce the equation to one of the forms

$$C'y'^2 + D'x = 0 \qquad \text{or} \qquad A'x'^2 + E'y' = 0.$$

If both A and C are different from zero, we can complete the squares in the x- and y-terms, as in Example 2, and select the translation which will reduce the equation to the form $A'x'^2 + C'y'^2 + F' = 0$.

EXERCISE 4–1

Determine the new equation in each problem 1 through 12 if the origin is translated to the given point.

1. $3x + 2y = 6$, $(4, -3)$
2. $5x - 4y + 3 = 0$, $(1, 2)$
3. $y^2 - 6x - 4y + 22 = 0$, $(3, 2)$
4. $x^2 - 4x - 7y + 46 = 0$, $(2, 6)$
5. $3x^2 + 4y^2 + 12x + 8y + 8 = 0$, $(-2, -1)$
6. $9x^2 + y^2 + 36x - 8y + 43 = 0$, $(-2, 4)$
7. $4y^2 - 5x^2 - 8y - 10x - 21 = 0$, $(-1, 1)$
8. $16x^2 - 4y^2 - 160x - 24y + 300 = 0$, $(5, -3)$
9. $xy - x - y - 10 = 0$, $(1, 1)$
10. $3xy - 21x + 6y - 47 = 0$, $(-2, 7)$
11. $x^3 - 3x^2 + 3x - y - 3 = 0$, $(1, -2)$
12. $3x^3 - 18x^2 + 36x - 4y - 36 = 0$, $(2, -3)$

In each problem 13 through 22, find the point to which the origin must be translated in order that the transformed equation shall have no first-degree term. Find also the new equation.

13. $xy - 2x - 4y - 4 = 0$ 14. $xy + 3x - 3y - 3 = 0$
15. $2x^2 + 2y^2 - 8x + 5 = 0$ 16. $x^2 + 2y^2 + 6x + 4y + 2 = 0$

17. $3x^2 - 2y^2 + 24x - 8y + 34 = 0$
18. $2y^2 - 3x^2 - 12x + 16y + 14 = 0$
19. $x^2 - xy + y^2 - 9x + 6y - 27 = 0$
20. $2x^2 - 3xy - y^2 - x + 5y - 3 = 0$
21. $x^3 + 5x^2 + 2xy + 4x + 4y - 4 = 0$
22. $x^3 - 6x^2 + xy + 12x - 2y - 7 = 0$

In each problem 23 through 28, eliminate the constant term and one of the first-degree terms.

23. $y^2 - 6y + 4x + 5 = 0$ 24. $x^2 - 2x - 8y - 15 = 0$
25. $y^2 + 10x + 4y + 24 = 0$ 26. $y^2 - 4y - x + 1 = 0$
27. $2x^2 - 20x - 7y + 36 = 0$ 28. $3y^2 + 11x + 6y - 19 = 0$

4–2 Rotation of axes. We now wish to consider a transformation of coordinates where the new axes have the same origin but different directions from the original axes. Since the new axes may be obtained by rotating the original axes through an angle about the origin, the transformation is called a *rotation of axes*.

We shall derive transformation formulas, for a rotation through an angle θ, which express the old coordinates in terms of the new coordinates. In Fig. 4–3 the coordinates of the point P are (x, y) referred to the original axes OX and OY, and are (x', y') when referred to the new axes OX' and OY'. We notice that $x = OM$ and $y = MP$, $x' = OS$

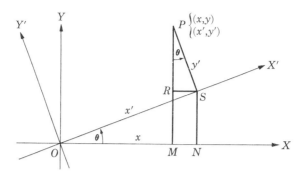

FIGURE 4–3

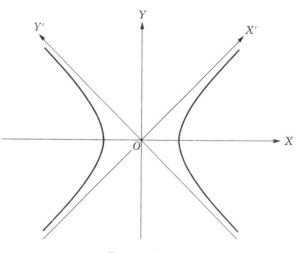

FIGURE 4–4

and $y' = SP$. The segment RS is drawn parallel to the x-axis and NS is parallel to the y-axis. Hence we have

$$x = OM = ON - MN = ON - RS = x' \cos \theta - y' \sin \theta,$$
$$y = MP = MR + RP = NS + RP = x' \sin \theta + y' \cos \theta.$$

The rotation formulas, therefore, are

$$\boxed{\begin{aligned} x &= x' \cos \theta - y' \sin \theta, \\ y &= x' \sin \theta + y' \cos \theta. \end{aligned}} \tag{1}$$

We have derived these formulas for the special case in which θ is an acute angle and the point P is in the first quadrant of both sets of axes. The formulas hold, however, for any θ and for all positions of P. A proof that the formulas hold generally could be made by observing the proper conventions as to the sign of θ and the signs of all distances involved.

EXAMPLE 1. Transform the equation $x^2 - y^2 - 9 = 0$ by rotating the axes through $45°$.

Solution. When $\theta = 45°$, the rotation formulas (1) are

$$x = \frac{x'}{\sqrt{2}} - \frac{y'}{\sqrt{2}}, \qquad y = \frac{x'}{\sqrt{2}} + \frac{y'}{\sqrt{2}}.$$

We make the substitutions in the given equation and have

$$\left(\frac{x'}{\sqrt{2}} - \frac{y'}{\sqrt{2}}\right)^2 - \left(\frac{x'}{\sqrt{2}} + \frac{y'}{\sqrt{2}}\right)^2 - 9 = 0,$$

$$\frac{x'^2}{2} - x'y' + \frac{y'^2}{2} - \frac{x'^2}{2} - x'y' - \frac{y'^2}{2} - 9 = 0,$$

$$2x'y' + 9 = 0.$$

The graph and both sets of axes are constructed in Fig. 4–4.

EXAMPLE 2. Find the acute angle of rotation such that the transformed equation of $2x^2 + \sqrt{3}\,xy + y^2 = 8$ will have no $x'y'$-term.

Solution. We employ the rotation formulas to find the required angle θ. Substituting for x and y, we get

$$2(x'\cos\theta - y'\sin\theta)^2 + \sqrt{3}\,(x'\cos\theta - y'\sin\theta)(x'\sin\theta + y'\cos\theta)$$
$$+ (x'\sin\theta + y'\cos\theta)^2 = 8.$$

We perform the indicated multiplications, collect like terms, and obtain

$$(2\cos^2\theta + \sqrt{3}\sin\theta\cos\theta + \sin^2\theta)x'^2 + (-2\sin\theta\cos\theta + \sqrt{3}\cos^2\theta$$
$$- \sqrt{3}\sin^2\theta)x'y' + (2\sin^2\theta - \sqrt{3}\sin\theta\cos\theta + \cos^2\theta)y'^2 = 8. \qquad (2)$$

Since the $x'y'$ term is to vanish, we set its coefficient equal to zero. Thus we have

$$-2\sin\theta\cos\theta + \sqrt{3}\,(\cos^2\theta - \sin^2\theta) = 0.$$

Using the identities $\sin 2\theta = 2\sin\theta\cos\theta$ and $\cos 2\theta = \cos^2\theta - \sin^2\theta$, we obtain the equation in the form

$$-\sin 2\theta + \sqrt{3}\cos 2\theta = 0,$$

whence

$$\tan 2\theta = \sqrt{3}, \qquad 2\theta = 60°, \qquad \theta = 30°.$$

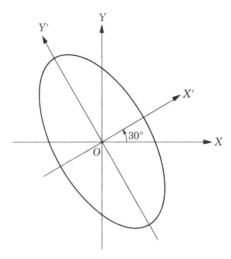

FIGURE 4–5

A rotation of 30° eliminates the $x'y'$-term. This value of θ reduces Eq. (2) to

$$5x'^2 + y'^2 = 16.$$

Figure 4–5 shows both sets of axes and the graph.

EXERCISE 4–2

Find the new equation in problems 1 through 8 when the axes are rotated through the given angle.

1. $\sqrt{3}\,x - y = 4,\ \theta = 60°$ 2. $x + y = 6,\ \theta = 45°$
3. $xy = 4,\ \theta = 45°$ 4. $x^2 + y^2 = a^2,\ \theta = 40°$
5. $x^2 + xy + y^2 = 1,\ \theta = 45°$ 6. $x^2 - \sqrt{3}\,xy + 2y^2 = 2,\ \theta = 30°$
7. $x^2 - 4xy + 4y^2 - 8\sqrt{5}\,x - 4\sqrt{5}\,y = 0,\ \theta = \arctan \tfrac{1}{2}$
8. $x^2 + \sqrt{3}\,xy + 2y^2 = 3,\ \theta = \arctan \sqrt{3}$

Find the angle of rotation in each problem 9 through 12 such that the transformed equation will have no $x'y'$-term.

9. $3xy + y - 2 = 0$ 10. $x^2 - xy + 5 = 0$
11. $x^2 - 3xy + 4y^2 + 7 = 0$ 12. $x^2 + 3xy - x + y = 0$

4–3 Simplifications involving rotations and translations. The general second-degree, or quadratic, equation in x and y is represented by

$$Ax^2 + Bxy + Cy^2 + Dx + Ey + F = 0. \tag{1}$$

At least one of the constants A, B, and C must be different from zero for the equation to be of the second degree. We assume, too, that not all the coefficients of terms involving one of the variables are zero; that is, both x and y appear in the equation.

In Section 4–1 we discussed the procedure for simplifying Eq. (1) when $B = 0$. If $B \neq 0$, an essential part of the simplification consists in obtaining a transformed equation lacking the product term $x'y'$. We shall show how to determine immediately an angle of rotation which will serve for this purpose. In Eq. (1) we substitute the right members of the rotation formulas for x and y. After collecting like terms, we obtain

$$A'x'^2 + B'x'y' + C'y'^2 + D'x' + E'y' + F' = 0,$$

where the new coefficients are

$$A' = A \cos^2 \theta + B \sin \theta \cos \theta + C \sin^2 \theta,$$
$$B' = B \cos 2\theta - (A - C) \sin 2\theta,$$
$$C' = A \sin^2 \theta - B \sin \theta \cos \theta + C \cos^2 \theta,$$
$$D' = D \cos \theta + E \sin \theta,$$
$$E' = E \cos \theta - D \sin \theta,$$
$$F' = F.$$

The $x'y'$-term will vanish only if its coefficient is zero. Hence θ must satisfy the equation $B' = B \cos 2\theta - (A - C) \sin 2\theta = 0$. If $A \neq C$, the solution is

$$\tan 2\theta = \frac{B}{A - C}.$$

This formula yields the angle of rotation except when $A = C$. If $A = C$, the coefficient of $x'y'$ is $B \cos 2\theta$. Then the term vanishes by giving θ the value 45°. Thus we see that an equation of the form (1) with an xy-term can be transformed into an equation free of the product term $x'y'$.

We summarize the preceding results in the following theorem.

THEOREM. *A second-degree equation*

$$Ax^2 + Bxy + Cy^2 + Dx + Ey + F = 0$$

in which $B = 0$ can be transformed by a translation into one of the forms

$$A'x'^2 + C'y'^2 + F = 0,$$
$$A'x'^2 + E'y' = 0, \tag{2}$$
$$C'y'^2 + D'x' = 0.$$

If $B \neq 0$, one of these forms can be obtained by a rotation and a translation (if necessary). The angle of rotation θ (chosen acute) is obtained from the equation

$$\tan 2\theta = \frac{B}{A - C}, \quad if \quad A \neq C,$$

or

$$\theta = 45°, \quad if \quad A = C.$$

By this theorem we see how to find the value of $\tan 2\theta$. The rotation formulas, however, contain $\sin \theta$ and $\cos \theta$. These functions can be obtained from the trigonometric identities

$$\sin \theta = \sqrt{\frac{1 - \cos 2\theta}{2}}, \quad \cos \theta = \sqrt{\frac{1 + \cos 2\theta}{2}}.$$

The positive sign is selected before each radical because we shall restrict θ to an acute angle.

We can interpret geometrically the transformations which reduce the equation of a conic to one of the simplified forms. The rotation orients the coordinate axes in the directions of the axes of an ellipse or hyperbola, and the translation brings the origin to the center of the conic. For a parabola, the rotation makes one coordinate axis parallel to the axis of the parabola, and the translation moves the origin to the vertex.

Although equations (2) above usually represent conics, there are exceptional cases, depending on the values of the coefficients. The exceptional cases are not our main interest, but we do observe them. The first of the equations has no locus if A', C', and F' all have the same sign, for then there are no real values of x' and y' for which the terms of the left member add to zero. If $F' = 0$ and A' and C' have the same sign, only the coordinates of the origin satisfy the equation. The values for the coefficients may be selected arbitrarily so that the equation represents two intersecting lines, two parallel lines, or one line. Each of the other equations always has a locus, but the locus is a line if the coefficient of the first-degree term is zero. The point and line loci of second-degree equations are called *degenerate* conics, as was previously noted.

EXAMPLE. Reduce the equation

$$73x^2 - 72xy + 52y^2 + 100x - 200y + 100 = 0$$

to one of the forms (2).

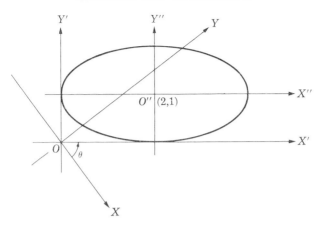

FIGURE 4–6

Solution. We first transform the equation so that the product term $x'y'$ will disappear. To find the angle of rotation, we use

$$\tan 2\theta = \frac{B}{A - C} = \frac{-72}{73 - 52} = \frac{-24}{7},$$

whence

$$\cos 2\theta = \frac{-7}{25}.$$

Hence

$$\sin \theta = \sqrt{\frac{1 - \cos 2\theta}{2}} = \frac{4}{5} \quad \text{and} \quad \cos \theta = \sqrt{\frac{1 + \cos 2\theta}{2}} = \frac{3}{5}.$$

The rotation formulas are then

$$x = \frac{3x' - 4y'}{5} \quad \text{and} \quad y = \frac{4x' + 3y'}{5}.$$

By substituting for x and y in the given equation and simplifying, we get

$$x'^2 + 4y'^2 - 4x' - 8y' + 4 = 0.$$

Completing the squares in the x'- and y'-terms, we obtain

$$(x' - 2)^2 + 4(y' - 1)^2 - 4 = 0.$$

Finally, a translation to the point $(2, 1)$ yields the desired form

$$x''^2 + 4y''^2 - 4 = 0.$$

It is much easier to draw the graph from this equation than by using the original equation. The graph and the three sets of axes are constructed in Fig. 4–6.

EXERCISE 4–3

Rotate the axes through an acute angle such that the x- or the y-term is eliminated in problems 1 and 2.

1. $3x - 4y = 6$ 2. $x + y = 0$

Reduce each of the equations in problems 3 through 6 to one of the simplified forms (2), Section 4–3.

3. $x^2 - 2xy + y^2 - 8\sqrt{2}\,y - 8 = 0$
4. $3x^2 + 2\sqrt{3}\,xy + y^2 - 2x - 2\sqrt{3}\,y - 16 = 0$
5. $73x^2 - 72xy + 52y^2 + 380x - 160y + 400 = 0$
6. $7x^2 + 48xy - 7y^2 - 150x - 50y + 100 = 0$

7. Prove that a translation of coordinates does not introduce any second-degree terms in the equation of a conic, and that a rotation does not introduce any first-degree terms. From these facts, explain why the equation of an ellipse or a hyperbola can be simplified by using first a translation and then a rotation.

Simplify the following equations using first a translation of axes and then a rotation of axes.

8. $30x^2 - 12xy + 35y^2 - 60x + 12y - 48 = 0$
9. $3x^2 - 10xy + 3y^2 + 22x - 26y + 43 = 0$
10. $35x^2 + 24xy - 35y^2 + 94x - 46y - 124 = 0$
11. $104x^2 + 60xy + 41y^2 - 60x - 82y - 75 = 0$

4–4 Identification of a conic. The kind of conic represented by an equation of the form

$$Ax^2 + Bxy + Cy^2 + Dx + Ey + F = 0$$

can be determined immediately from the coefficients of the second-degree terms. Let us assume in this discussion that the locus is a parabola, an ellipse, or a hyperbola, but not a degenerate conic. We considered this kind of equation with $B = 0$ in Chapter 3. From experience, we know that the values of A and C determine the kind of conic. The locus is an ellipse if A and C have the same sign, and a hyperbola if A and C have opposite signs. If either A or C is zero, the locus is a parabola. We remark that if A and C are equal, the locus is a circle, a special case of the ellipse.

We next establish a test for the case in which $B \neq 0$. We apply the rotation formulas of Section 4–2 and obtain

$$A'x'^2 + B'x'y' + C'y'^2 + D'x + F' = 0,$$

where

$$A' = A \cos^2 \theta + B \sin \theta \cos \theta + C \sin^2 \theta,$$
$$B' = B \cos 2\theta - (A - C) \sin 2\theta,$$
$$C' = A \sin^2 \theta - B \sin \theta \cos \theta + C \cos^2 \theta.$$

If these expressions are used for A', B', and C', and $B'^2 - 4A'C'$ is computed, the result, when simplified, is

$$B'^2 - 4A'C' = B^2 - 4AC.$$

This relation among the coefficients of the original equation and the transformed equation hold for any rotation. For this reason, $B^2 - 4AC$ is called an *invariant*. By selecting the particular rotation for which $B' = 0$, we have

$$-4A'C' = B^2 - 4AC.$$

With $B' = 0$ the kind of conic represented by the transformed equation, and therefore the original equation, can be determined from the signs of A' and C'. The conic is an ellipse if A' and C' have like signs, and a hyperbola if the signs are different. If either A' or C' is zero, the conic is a parabola. These relations of A' and C', in the order named, would make $-4A'C'$ negative, positive, or zero. Hence we have the following important theorem.

THEOREM. *The graph of*

$$Ax^2 + Bxy + Cy^2 + Dx + Ey + F = 0,$$

when it exists, is an ellipse, hyperbola, or a parabola according as $B^2 - 4AC$ is negative, positive, or zero.

It must be remembered that the degenerate conics are included in this theorem. The exceptional cases are indicated in the following résumé:

$B^2 - 4AC < 0$,   ellipse or an isolated point,

$B^2 - 4AC > 0$,   hyperbola or two intersecting lines,

$B^2 - 4AC = 0$,   parabola, two parallel lines, or one line.

Illustration. The equation $2x^2 - 2xy + y^2 + 8x - 12y + 36 = 0$ has $A = 2$, $B = -2$, and $C = 1$; hence $B^2 - 4AC = 4 - 4(2)(1) = -4 < 0$. The negative result means that the locus is either an ellipse or a degenerate conic. It turns out that the locus is an ellipse, as we shall see in the next section.

4–5 Addition of ordinates. The presence of an xy-term in the second-degree equation usually makes the construction of the graph much more difficult. A table of pairs of values of the variables can be prepared by assigning values to x or y and solving for the corresponding values of the other. This method, however, is very tedious. Another plan would be to rotate the axes and use the new equation and the new axes to draw the graph. But rotation transformations are not short, and usually the process is complicated by cumbersome radicals in the rotation formulas. A third way to handle the situation is to resort to a method known as the *addition of ordinates*. This method is applicable if y is the sum of two expressions in x, for example, $y = f(x) + g(x)$. First we draw separate graphs of $y_1 = f(x)$ and $y_2 = g(x)$. Then the ordinates of the curves, when added graphically, yield ordinates of the graph of the original equation. The utility of this method depends on the ease with which we obtain the two auxiliary graphs. The following example illustrates the process.

EXAMPLE 1. Draw the graph of the equation

$$2x^2 - 2xy + y^2 + 8x - 12y + 36 = 0.$$

Solution. To express y as the sum of two quantities, we treat the equation as a quadratic in y. Thus we have

$$y^2 + (-2x - 12)y + (2x^2 + 8x + 36) = 0,$$

and solving for y gives

$$y = \frac{2x + 12 \pm \sqrt{(-2x - 12)^2 - 4(2x^2 + 8x + 36)}}{2}$$

$$= x + 6 \pm \sqrt{4x - x^2}.$$

We now draw the graphs of the equations

$$y_1 = x + 6 \quad \text{and} \quad y_2 = \pm\sqrt{4x - x^2}.$$

The locus of the first equation is a line. By squaring and then completing the square in the x-terms, we reduce the second equation to $(x - 2)^2 + y^2 = 4$. The graph is a circle of radius 2 and center at $(2, 0)$. The line and the circle are drawn in Fig. 4–7. The point D on the graph of the original equation is obtained by adding the ordinates AB and AC; that is, AC is extended by a length equal to AB. The addition of ordinates for this purpose must be algebraic. Thus MN is negative, and the point Q is found by measuring downward from P so that $PQ = MN$. By plotting a sufficient number of points in this manner the desired graph can be constructed.

EXAMPLE 2. Determine the nature of the graph of the equation

$$2x^2 + 7xy + 3y^2 + x - 7y - 6 = 0.$$

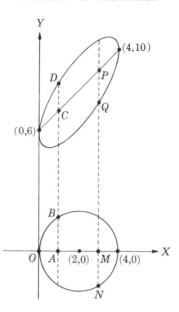

FIGURE 4–7

Solution. We find $B^2 - 4AC = 49 - 4(2)(3) = 25 > 0$. Hence the locus is a hyperbola or two intersecting lines. To decide between these two possibilities, we solve the equation for x in terms of y. Thus

$$2x^2 + (7y + 1)x + (3y^2 - 7y - 6) = 0,$$

$$x = \frac{-(7y + 1) \pm \sqrt{(7y + 1)^2 - 8(3y^2 - 7y - 6)}}{4}$$

$$= \frac{-7y - 1 \pm \sqrt{25y^2 + 70y + 49}}{4}$$

$$= \frac{-7y - 1 \pm (5y + 7)}{4} = \frac{-y + 3}{2}, \qquad -3y - 2.$$

Since x is equal to rational expressions in y, we see that the left member of the given equation can be expressed in the factored form

$$(2x + y - 3)(x + 3y + 2) = 0.$$

If the coordinates of a point make one of these factors equal to zero, they make the product equal to zero and therefore satisfy the original equation. Hence the graph consists of the two lines whose equations are

$$2x + y - 3 = 0 \quad \text{and} \quad x + 3y + 2 = 0.$$

Exercise 4–4

Assuming that equations 1 through 8 represent nondegenerate conics, classify each by computing $B^2 - 4AC$.

1. $2x^2 - 4xy + 8y^2 + 7 = 0$

2. $3x^2 + xy + x - 4 = 0$

3. $2xy - x + y - 3 = 0$

4. $x^2 + 5xy + 15y^2 = 1$

5. $x^2 - y^2 + 4 = 0$

6. $x^2 - 2xy + y^2 + 3x = 0$

7. $3x^2 + 6xy + 5y^2 - x + y = 0$

8. $4x^2 - 3xy + y^2 + 13 = 0$

Sketch the graph of each equation 9 through 16 by the addition of ordinates method.

9. $y = x \pm \sqrt{x}$

10. $y = 6 - x \pm \sqrt{4 - x^2}$

11. $y = 2x \pm \sqrt{5 + 6x - x^2}$

12. $y^2 - 2xy + 2x^2 - 1 = 0$

13. $y^2 - 2xy + x^2 - 4x - 12 = 0$

14. $y^2 - 4xy + 5x^2 - 1 = 0$

15. $y^2 - 4xy + 3x^2 + 1 = 0$

16. $y^2 + 2xy - 3x^2 + 4 = 0$

Compute $B^2 - 4AC$ in each equation 17 through 24. Then solve for one of the variables in terms of the other and tell whether the locus is a conic, a degenerate conic, or there is no locus.

17. $x^2 - xy - 2y^2 + x - 2y = 0$

18. $y^2 - 4xy + 5x^2 - 2x + 1 = 0$

19. $2x^2 - 2xy + y^2 = 0$

20. $x^2 - 2xy + y^2 + 2x - 2y = 3$

21. $4x^2 + 4xy + y^2 = 4x + 2y - 1$

22. $y^2 - 6xy + 8x^2 + 1 = 0$

23. $y^2 - 8xy + 17x^2 + 4 = 0$

24. $4y^2 - 12xy + 10x^2 + 2x + 1 = 0$

25. Work out all steps in showing $B'^2 - 4A'C' = B^2 - 4AC$. Show also that $A' + C' = A + C$.

Assume in problems 26 through 30 that the locus of

$$Ax^2 + Bxy + Cy^2 + Dx + Ey + F = 0$$

is a nondegenerate conic.

26. If A and C have opposite signs, prove that the locus is a hyperbola.

27. If $B \neq 0$ and either A or C is zero, prove that the locus is a hyperbola.

28. If both D and E are zero, prove that the locus is not a parabola.

29. If both D and E are zero, prove that the center of the conic is at the origin.

30. If the center of the conic is at the origin, prove that both D and E are zero.

CHAPTER 5

ALGEBRAIC CURVES

5–1 Introduction. An equation in which all terms are of the form $ax^m y^n$, where a is a constant and each exponent is a positive integer or zero, is an *algebraic equation* in x and y. Such an equation is also called a *polynomial*, or *rational integral*, *equation*. The sum of the exponents of x and y in any term is the degree of the term. The term or terms of highest degree determine the degree of the equation. Thus

$$y = \pm \frac{x}{\sqrt{x^2 - 1}}, \quad \text{or} \quad x^2 y^2 - y^2 = x^2$$

is an algebraic equation whose degree is four.

We considered first-degree equations in Chapter 2 and second-degree equations in Chapters 3 and 4. In this chapter we attack the problem of drawing the graphs of equations of a degree higher than two. The point-by-point method of constructing a graph is tedious except for simple equations. The task can often be lightened, however, by first discovering certain characteristics of the graph as revealed by the equation. We have already discussed the concepts of symmetry and extent of a curve. These topics occur in Sections 3–4 and 3–6 and should be carefully restudied. There are two other helpful ideas which we wish to introduce before drawing the graphs of particular equations.

5–2 Intercepts and asymptotes. The abscissa of a point where a curve touches or crosses the x-axis is called an *x-intercept*, and the ordinate of a point where a curve touches or crosses the y-axis is called a *y-intercept*. To find the x-intercepts of the graph of an equation, we set $y = 0$ and solve for x. Similarly, we set $x = 0$ and solve for y to find the y-intercepts. Thus the x-intercepts of the equation $y = (x^2 - 1)(x - 2)^2$ are -1, 1, and 2, and the y-intercept is -4.

The graphs of some equations have no points in common with an axis; for other equations there may be few or many intercepts. The intercepts are often easily determined, and are of special significance in many problems.

If the distance of a point from a straight line approaches zero as the point moves indefinitely far from the origin along a curve, then the line is called an *asymptote* of the curve. In drawing the graph of an equation it is well to determine the asymptotes, if any. They are often easily found and facilitate the graphing. The utility of the asymptotes in draw-

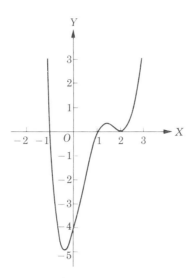

FIGURE 5-1

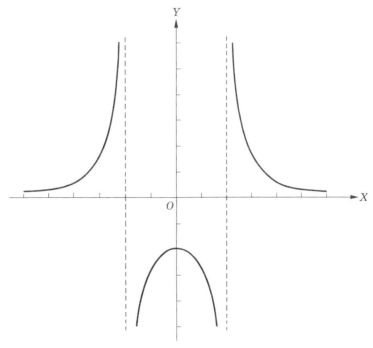

FIGURE 5-2

ing a hyperbola has already been demonstrated (Section 3–10). Here, however, we shall deal mainly with curves whose asymptotes, if any, are either horizontal or vertical.

EXAMPLE 1. Examine the equation and draw the graph of

$$y = (x^2 - 1)(x - 2)^2.$$

Solution. The three tests for symmetry (Section 3–4) reveal that the graph does not have symmetry with respect to either axis or the origin. The x-intercepts are -1, 1, and 2, and the y-intercept is -4. These points greatly facilitate the graphing. As x increases beyond 2, the y-values increase rapidly (Fig. 5–1). If x has a value between 1 and 2, the equation shows that y is positive because both factors $x^2 - 1$ and $(x - 2)^2$ are then positive. If x has a value between -1 and 1, the factor $x^2 - 1$ is negative, and the curve is below the x-axis. As x takes values to the left of $x = -1$, the y-values become large. With the preceding information we can quickly sketch the curve. The plotting of a few points other than the intercepts makes possible a rather accurate graph.

EXAMPLE 2. Examine the equation and draw the graph of

$$x^2 y - 4y = 8.$$

Solution. The y-intercept is -2. But if we set $y = 0$, there is obviously no value of x which will satisfy the equation. Hence there is no x-intercept. The graph has symmetry with respect to the y-axis but not with respect to the x-axis. The part of the graph to the right of the y-axis may first be determined and then the other drawn by the use of symmetry.

Solving the equation for y gives

$$y = \frac{8}{x^2 - 4}. \tag{1}$$

Note the right member of the equation. We see that it is negative for $-2 < x < 2$, and the graph in this range is below the x-axis. Further, if x has a value slightly less than 2, the denominator is near zero. Then the fraction, which is equal to y, has a numerically large value. As x increases still closer to 2, the corresponding values of y can be made to increase numerically without limit. If, however, x approaches 2 through values greater than 2, the values of y are positive and increase without limit. Hence the line $x = 2$ is an asymptote of the curve both below and above the x-axis. We remark that x may be assigned values arbitrarily near 2. But the value 2 is prohibited because division by zero is not defined.

x	0	1	1.5	1.9	1.99	1.999
y	-2	-2.7	-4.6	-20.5	-200	-2005

To examine for a horizontal asymptote, we note Eq. (1) and let x become large without limit. The corresponding values of y approach zero, and $y = 0$ is therefore an asymptote. This asymptote also becomes evident when the given equation is solved for x. Taking the positive roots, we get

$$x = 2 \sqrt{\frac{y + 2}{y}}.$$

In this form we see that as y approaches zero through positive values, x increases without limit. It shows that $y = 0$ is an asymptote and also reveals the excluded values of y. Since the radicand is not to be negative, the values $-2 < y < 0$ are excluded.

The graph is constructed in Fig. 5–2.

In the preceding problem the asymptotes are evident when the equation is solved for each variable in terms of the other. For equations which are thus readily solvable, we state the following rules:

1. *Solve the given equation for y in terms of x. If the result is a fraction whose denominator contains x, set each real linear factor of the denominator equal to zero. This gives the vertical asymptotes.*

2. *Solve the given equation for x in terms of y. If the result is a fraction whose denominator contains y, set each real linear factor of the denominator equal to zero. This gives the horizontal asymptotes.*

5–3 Horizontal asymptotes. Solving an equation for x to test for a horizontal asymptote is not always practicable or even possible. Accordingly, we develop an alternative plan for equations in which y is equal to the quotient of two polynomials in x. Consider, for example, the equation

$$y = \frac{3x^3 - 2x^2 + x - 5}{2x^3 + 4x^2 - 8x - 1},$$

where the numerator and denominator are of the same degree. To determine the behavior of the right member as x takes numerically large values, we divide the numerator and denominator by x^3. This gives

$$y = \frac{3 - (2/x) + (1/x^2) - (5/x^3)}{2 + (4/x) - (8/x^2) - (1/x^3)}.$$

If now x is assigned a numerically large value, positive or negative, each term after the first term of both numerator and denominator is close to zero. Hence the value of the fraction is close to $\frac{3}{2}$. Further, the value can be made as near $\frac{3}{2}$ as desired by assigning x a sufficiently large value. We conclude, then, that $y = \frac{3}{2}$ is a horizontal asymptote.

Suppose next that the degree of the numerator is less than the degree of the denominator, as in

$$y = \frac{3x^2 - 5x + 6}{2x^3 + 7x^2 + 5} = \frac{(3/x) - (5/x^2) + (6/x^3)}{2 + (7/x) + (5/x^3)}.$$

Clearly, for large values of x, the numerator is close to 0 and the denominator is close to 2. The fraction can be made arbitrarily close to 0 by taking x large enough. Consequently, $y = 0$ is an asymptote.

Finally, we let the degree of the numerator be greater than that of the denominator, as in

$$y = \frac{x^3 - 3x + 1}{3x^2 + 4x + 5} = \frac{x - (3/x) + (1/x^2)}{3 + (4/x) + (5/x^2)}.$$

In this case the value of y will exceed, numerically, any chosen value when x is sufficiently large.

We generalize this discussion by employing the equation

$$y = \frac{Ax^n + \text{(terms of lower degree)}}{Bx^m + \text{(terms of lower degree)}}.$$

There are three possibilities here, depending on the relative values of m and n.

1. If $m = n$, $y = A/B$ is a horizontal asymptote.
2. If $m > n$, $y = 0$ is a horizontal asymptote.
3. If $m < n$, there is no horizontal asymptote.

EXAMPLE. Draw the graph of

$$y = \frac{(x + 3)(x - 1)}{(x + 1)(x - 2)}.$$

Solution. The x-intercepts are -3 and 1, and the y-intercept is $\frac{3}{2}$. The lines $x = -1$ and $x = 2$ are vertical asymptotes. The numerator and denominator of the fraction are quadratic and the coefficient of x^2 in each is unity. Hence $y = 1$ is a horizontal asymptote. Since there are two vertical asymptotes, the graph consists of three separate parts. To aid in sketching, we examine the given equation to determine the signs of y to the right and left of each vertical asymptote and to the right and left of each x-intercept. In this examination the notations $(+)$ and $(-)$ indicate the signs of the factors of the numerator and denominator for the specified values of x.

When $x < -3$, the signs are $\dfrac{(-)(-)}{(-)(-)}$, and hence $y > 0$.

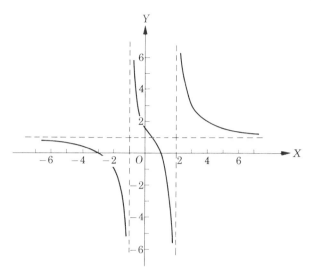

FIGURE 5–3

When $-3 < x < -1$, the signs are $\dfrac{(+)(-)}{(-)(-)}$, and hence $y < 0$.

When $-1 < x < 1$, the signs are $\dfrac{(+)(-)}{(+)(-)}$, and hence $y > 0$.

When $1 < x < 2$, the signs are $\dfrac{(+)(+)}{(+)(-)}$, and hence $y < 0$.

When $x > 2$, the signs are $\dfrac{(+)(+)}{(+)(+)}$, and hence $y > 0$.

The asymptotes, the signs of y in the various intervals, and just a few plotted points in addition to the intercepts allow us to draw a good graph (Fig. 5–3).

EXERCISE 5–1

Find the x-intercepts in equations 1 through 12. Determine the sign of y to the left of the smallest intercept, between consecutive intercepts, and to the right of the largest intercept. Then sketch the curve.

1. $y = x(x^2 - 4)$ 2. $y = x(4 - x^2)$
3. $y = (x - 1)^2(x - 3)$ 4. $y = (x + 2)(x - 3)^2$
5. $y = x^2(4 - x)$ 6. $y = x(x + 3)^2$
7. $y = x^4 - 16$ 8. $y = (x^2 - 4)(x - 1)^2$
9. $y = x^3(1 - x)$ 10. $y = x(1 - x)^3$
11. $y = (x - 1)^2(x + 1)^2$ 12. $y = (x^2 - 4)(x^2 - 1)$

Discuss each equation 13 through 34 with regard to intercepts, symmetry, extent of graph, and horizontal and vertical asymptotes. Draw the asymptotes and sketch the curve.

13. $y = \dfrac{2}{x}$

14. $y = \dfrac{x+3}{x}$

15. $y = \dfrac{x+2}{x+1}$

16. $y = \dfrac{x-3}{x-1}$

17. $y = \dfrac{4}{x^2-1}$

18. $y = \dfrac{8}{x^3}$

19. $y = \dfrac{x-1}{x^2-4}$

20. $y = \dfrac{x+1}{x^2-9}$

21. $y = \dfrac{4}{x^2+1}$

22. $y = \dfrac{x}{x^2+1}$

23. $y = \dfrac{3}{(x-2)^2}$

24. $y = \dfrac{x}{(x+1)^2}$

25. $y = \dfrac{2x-3}{(x-1)^2}$

26. $y = \dfrac{x+3}{(x-2)^2}$

27. $y = \dfrac{x^2-4}{x^2+4}$

28. $y = \dfrac{x^2+4}{x^2-4}$

29. $y = \dfrac{x^2-9}{x^2-16}$

30. $y = \dfrac{x^2-16}{x^2-9}$

31. $y = \dfrac{(x-2)(x+1)}{x(x-4)}$

32. $y = \dfrac{(x-3)(x+1)}{x(x-2)}$

33. $y = \dfrac{(x-1)(x^2+1)}{(x-2)(x+1)^2}$

34. $y = \dfrac{(2x+1)(x-3)^2}{(x-4)(x-1)^2}$

5–4 Irrational equations. In this section we consider equations in which y is equal to the square root of a polynomial in x or the square root of the quotient of two polynomials. The procedure for constructing the graphs is like that of the previous section.

EXAMPLE 1. Draw the graph of

$$y = \sqrt{x(x^2 - 16)}.$$

Solution. The x-intercepts are 0, ± 4. The permissible values of x are those for which the radicand is not negative. The radicand is positive when $-4 < x < 0$ and also when $x > 4$. The radicand is negative when $x < -4$ and when $0 < x < 4$; hence these values must be excluded. This information and the few plotted points are sufficient for drawing the graph (Fig. 5–4).

x	-3	-2	-1	4.5	5
y (approx.)	4.6	4.9	3.9	4.4	6.7

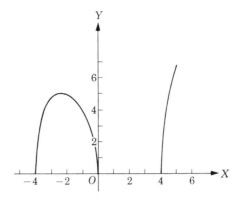

FIGURE 5-4

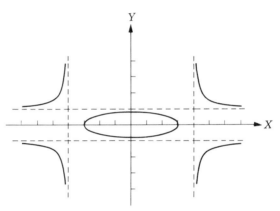

FIGURE 5-5

EXAMPLE 2. Draw the graph of

$$y^2 = \frac{x^2 - 9}{x^2 - 16}.$$

Solution. The graph is symmetric with respect to both axes. Hence we can draw the part in the first quadrant and readily finish the construction by the use of symmetry. The positive x-intercept is 3, and the positive y-intercept is $\frac{3}{4}$. The line $x = 4$ is a vertical asymptote, and the line $y = 1$ is a horizontal asymptote. We observe that y^2 is positive when $0 \leq x < 3$ and when $x > 4$. But y^2 is negative when x has a value between 3 and 4; hence these values must be excluded. From the analysis of the given equation, we sketch the graph (Fig. 5–5). Somewhat greater accuracy can be had by plotting the points indicated in the accompanying table.

x	1	2	4.2	5	6	7
y (approx.)	0.7	0.6	2.3	1.3	1.2	1.1

Exercise 5–2

Sketch the graph of each equation.

1. $y = \sqrt{x(x^2 - 4)}$ 2. $y = \sqrt{x(9 - x^2)}$

3. $y = -\sqrt{x^2(x - 1)}$ 4. $y = -\sqrt{x^3(1 - x)}$

5. $y = \sqrt{x^2(x + 2)}$ 6. $y = \sqrt{x(x - 1)(x + 1)^2}$

7. $y = \sqrt{x(x + 1)(x - 2)^2}$ 8. $y = \sqrt{x^2(2 - x)(3 - x)}$

9. $y = \sqrt{\dfrac{x}{x^2 - 4}}$ 10. $y = \sqrt{\dfrac{2x}{x^2 + 1}}$

11. $y = \sqrt{\dfrac{1}{1 + x^2}}$ 12. $y = \sqrt{\dfrac{x(x - 3)}{x - 1}}$

13. $y = \sqrt{\dfrac{x(x - 2)}{x^2 - 1}}$ 14. $y = \sqrt{\dfrac{x^2 - 1}{x^2 - 4}}$

15. $y^2 = \dfrac{4}{x + 3}$ 16. $y^2 = \dfrac{x^2}{x^2 - 4}$

17. $y^2 = \dfrac{4}{x^2 + 9}$ 18. $y^2 = \dfrac{x^2}{x^2 + 4}$

19. $y^2 = \dfrac{x^2 - 16}{x^2 - 9}$ 20. $y^2 = \dfrac{x(x - 1)}{x^2 - 4}$

21. $y^2 = \dfrac{x(x - 2)}{x - 1}$ 22. $y^2 = \dfrac{x(x + 1)}{x - 1}$

23. $y^2 = \dfrac{(x + 1)^2}{x^3}$ 24. $y^2 = \dfrac{(x - 2)^2(x - 3)}{x^4}$

25. $y^2 = \dfrac{x^2 - 9}{(x + 4)^2}$ 26. $y^2 = \dfrac{9 - x^2}{(x - 4)^2}$

27. $y^2 = \dfrac{x(x^2 - 1)}{x^2 - 4}$ 28. $y^2 = \dfrac{(x^2 - 1)(x + 2)}{x^2 - 9}$

5–5 Slant asymptotes. When y is equal to the quotient of two polynomials in x where the degree of the numerator exceeds that of the denominator by unity, the graph will usually have a slant asymptote.
The simplest case arises when the numerator is quadratic and the denominator is linear.

EXAMPLE 1. Draw the graph of $2xy - x^2 + 6x - 4y - 10 = 0$.

Solution. The test, $B^2 - 4AC$ of Section 4–4, indicates that the curve is a
hyperbola. On solving for y and performing a division, we get

$$y = \frac{x^2 - 6x + 10}{2x - 4} = \frac{1}{2}x - 2 + \frac{1}{x - 2}.$$

Clearly, $x = 2$ is a vertical asymptote. As x increases numerically, the ordi-

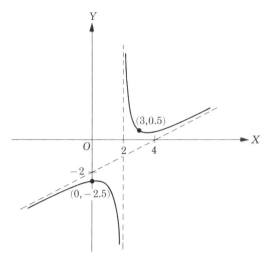

FIGURE 5-6

nate of the hyperbola approaches the ordinate of the line $y = \frac{1}{2}x - 2$. The difference of the two ordinates can be made arbitrarily near zero by taking x numerically large enough. Hence the line $y = \frac{1}{2}x - 2$ is an asymptote. The asymptotes and just a few plotted points furnish a guide for drawing the graph (Fig. 5-6).

EXAMPLE 2. Draw the graph of $2x^2y - x^3 - 8xy + 8x^2 - 20x + 8y + 14 = 0$.

Solution. We solve this equation for y and have

$$y = \frac{1}{2}x - 2 + [1/(x - 2)^2].$$

The asymptotes are the lines $y = \frac{1}{2}x - 2$ and $x - 2 = 0$. The graph is constructed in Fig. 5-7.

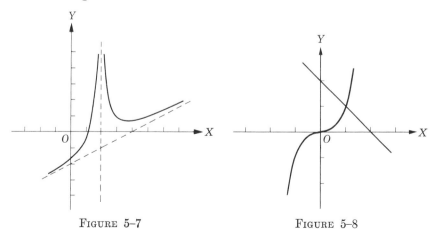

FIGURE 5-7   FIGURE 5-8

5–6 Graph of an equation in factored form. Equations sometimes appear with one member equal to zero and the other member expressed as the product of factors in terms of x and y. When an equation is in this form, its graph can be more simply obtained by first setting each of the factors equal to zero. If the coordinates of a point make one of the factors equal to zero, they make the product equal to zero and therefore satisfy the given equation. On the other hand, the coordinates of a point which make no factor equal to zero do not satisfy the equation. Hence the graph of the given equation consists of the graphs of the equations formed by setting each of the factors of the nonzero member equal to zero.

Illustration. The graph of $(3x - y - 1)(y^2 - 9x) = 0$ consists of the line $3x - y - 1 = 0$ and the parabola $y^2 - 9x = 0$.

5–7 Intersections of graphs. If the graphs of two equations in two variables have a point in common, then, from the definition of a graph, the coordinates of the point satisfy each equation separately. Hence the point of intersection gives a pair of real numbers which is a simultaneous solution of the equations. Conversely, if the two equations have a simultaneous real solution, then their graphs have the corresponding point in common. Thus simultaneous real solutions of two equations in two unknowns can be obtained graphically by reading the coordinates of their points of intersection. Because of the imperfections in the process, the results thus found are usually only approximate. If the graphs have no point of intersection, there is no real solution. In simple cases, the solutions, both real and imaginary, can be found by algebraic processes.

EXAMPLE. Find the points of intersection of the graphs of

$$y = x^3, \qquad y = 2 - x.$$

Solution. The graphs (Fig. 5–8) intersect in one point whose coordinates are $(1, 1)$.

Eliminating y between the equations yields

$$x^3 + x - 2 = 0, \qquad \text{or} \qquad (x - 1)(x^2 + x + 2) = 0,$$

whence

$$x = 1, \qquad \frac{-1 + \sqrt{-7}}{2}, \qquad \frac{-1 - \sqrt{-7}}{2}.$$

The corresponding values of y are obtained from the linear equation. The solutions, real and imaginary, are

$$(1, 1); \qquad \left(\frac{-1 + \sqrt{-7}}{2}, \frac{5 - \sqrt{-7}}{2} \right); \qquad \left(\frac{-1 - \sqrt{-7}}{2}, \frac{5 + \sqrt{-7}}{2} \right).$$

The graphical method gives only the real solution.

Exercise 5–3

Draw the asymptotes and sketch the graph of each equation in problems 1 through 14.

1. $xy - x^2 + 2 = 0$
2. $xy + x^2 - 3 = 0$
3. $x^2 - xy + x + 1 = 0$
4. $x^2 + xy + 2x - 1 = 0$
5. $x^2 - xy + x - y + 2 = 0$
6. $x^2 - xy + 3x - 2y + 1 = 0$
7. $2x^2 + 2xy + 3x - 6y + 5 = 0$
8. $2x^2 - 2xy - x + y - 2 = 0$
9. $x^2y - x^3 - 1 = 0$
10. $x^2y - x^3 + 1 = 0$
11. $x^2y - x^3 - 4xy + 12x + 4y - 14 = 0$
12. $x^2y - x^3 - 4xy + 11x + 4y - 16 = 0$
13. $x^2y - x^3 - x^2 - x + y - 2 = 0$
14. $x^2y - x^3 - x^2 - x + y = 0$

Describe the graphs of the equations in problems 15 through 20.

15. $(x^2 + y^2)(x - y) = 0$
16. $(x^2 + y^2 + 1)(2x - 3y) = 0$
17. $xy(x + y - 2) = 0$
18. $2x^3 + 3xy^2 = 5x$
19. $x^3y + xy^3 = 4xy$
20. $x^2y - 9y^2 = 0$

Construct the graph of each pair of equations and estimate the coordinates of any points of intersection. Check by obtaining the solutions algebraically.

21. $x + 2y = 7,$
    $3x - 2y = 5$
22. $x^2 + y^2 = 13,$
    $3x - 2y = 0$
23. $x^2 - 4y = 0,$
    $y^2 - 6x = 0$
24. $x^2 + y^2 = 16,$
    $y^2 - 6x = 0$
25. $y = x^3 - 4x,$
    $y = x + 4$
26. $x^2 - y^2 = 9,$
    $x^2 + y^2 = 16$
27. $x^2 + 4y^2 = 25,$
    $4x^2 - 7y^2 = 8$
28. $y = x^3 + 3x^2 - x - 3,$
    $y = x + 5$

CHAPTER 6

TRANSCENDENTAL CURVES

6–1 Introduction. In the preceding chapters we have studied algebraic equations. In this chapter we shall introduce equations which are not algebraic, but are classed as *transcendental*. The most common transcendental equations, and those which we shall consider, are trigonometric, inverse trigonometric, exponential, and logarithmic equations. Equations of this kind are of extreme importance; they are used extensively in physics, engineering, probability, and statistics.

6–2 Graphs of trigonometric functions. Before constructing the graphs of the trigonometric functions, we point out a property which these functions possess. A trigonometric function is not changed in value when the angle is increased or decreased by an integral multiple of 2π radians. For this reason the functions are said to be *periodic*. The sine function, for example, satisfies the equations

$$\sin x = \sin (x + 2\pi) = \sin (x + 2n\pi),$$

where x is any angle in radians and n is an integer. Thus the values of the sine of an angle recur in intervals of 2π radians. This recurrence does not take place in smaller intervals, and hence 2π is defined as the period of the sine function. This is also the period of the cosine, secant, and cosecant of an angle. The period of the tangent and cotangent of an angle is π. For these functions we have the identities

$$\tan x = \tan (x + \pi)$$

and

$$\cot x = \cot (x + \pi).$$

In drawing the graph of a trigonometric function, advantage should be taken of its periodic nature. If the graph is obtained for an interval equal to its period, then this part of the graph can be reproduced in other intervals to the right and left. To plot points for drawing the curve over an interval of one period, the values of the function corresponding to values of the angle can be obtained from a table of trigonometric functions (see Table II of the Appendix).

109

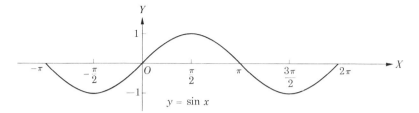

FIGURE 6–1

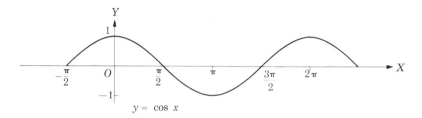

FIGURE 6–2

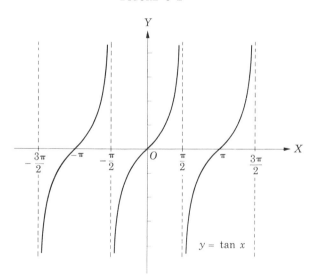

FIGURE 6–3

Figures 6–1 and 6–2 show the graphs of $y = \sin x$ and $y = \cos x$. Each of these curves crosses the x-axis after every π radians of x-values. The ordinates of each vary from -1 to 1. These are called the *extreme* values, and the constant 1 is called the *amplitude*.

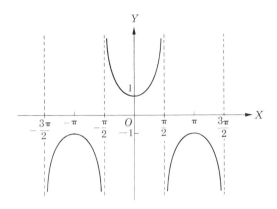

FIGURE 6–4

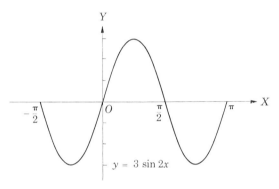

FIGURE 6–5

The tangent curve (Fig. 6–3) crosses the x-axis at integral multiples of π radians and has asymptotes at odd integral multiples of $\frac{1}{2}\pi$ radians. Amplitude is not defined for the tangent.

The secant curve (Fig. 6–4) has no x-intercepts. The asymptotes occur after every π radians of x-values.

We next consider the function $a \sin bx$, where a and b are constants. Since the extreme values of $\sin bx$ are -1 and 1, the extreme values of $a \sin bx$ are $-a$ and a. The amplitude is equal to the absolute value of a. To find the period, we determine how much x changes in producing a change of 2π in the angle bx. As x varies from 0 to $2\pi/b$, the angle bx increases from 0 to 2π. Hence the period of $\sin bx$ is $2\pi/b$. As an illustration, $3 \sin 2x$ has an amplitude of 3 and a period of π. The graph of $y = 3 \sin 2x$ is drawn in Fig. 6–5.

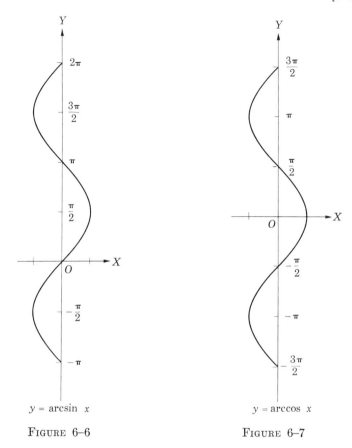

$y = \arcsin \; x$ $y = \arccos \; x$

FIGURE 6-6   FIGURE 6-7

6-3 Inverse trigonometric functions. The graphs of inverse trigonometric functions may be obtained readily from the graphs of the direct
functions. To draw the graph of $y = \arcsin x$, for example, we recall
that the equations

$$y = \arcsin x \qquad \text{and} \qquad x = \sin y$$

express the same relation between x and y. Hence the graphs of these
two equations must coincide. The equations

$$x = \sin y \qquad \text{and} \qquad y = \sin x$$

have x and y interchanged. The graph of $y = \sin x$ (Fig. 6-1) winds
along the x-axis. We conclude, therefore, that the graph of $x = \sin y$
is a curve of the same form winding along the y-axis. The graph of
$x = \sin y$, or $y = \arcsin x$, is shown in Fig. 6-6.

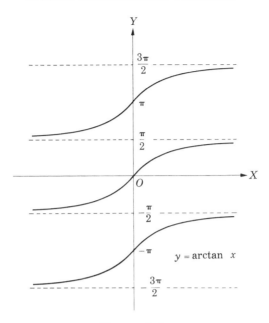

FIGURE 6–8

The graphs of each of the other inverse functions can be found similarly from the graph of the direct function by reversing the roles of x and y. Figures 6–7 and 6–8 show the graphs of $y = \arccos x$ and $y = \arctan x$.

EXERCISE 6–1

Find the period of each function in problems 1 through 12. Give the amplitudes of the sine and cosine functions.

1. $\cos 3x$
2. $\sin \frac{1}{2}x$
3. $\sin \frac{1}{3}x$
4. $2 \cos 4x$
5. $\tan 5x$
6. $\cot \frac{1}{4}x$
7. $\sec 6x$
8. $\cos 7x$
9. $\tan \frac{3}{4}x$
10. $3 \cos \pi x$
11. $2 \sin \frac{1}{2}\pi x$
12. $\sec (\frac{1}{2}x + \frac{1}{2}\pi)$

Sketch the graph of each equation in problems 13 through 24.

13. $y = 3 \cos x$
14. $y = 2 \sin x$
15. $y = \sin 3x$
16. $y = \cos 2x$
17. $y = \tan 2x$
18. $y = \cot x$
19. $y = 3 \sin \frac{1}{2}x$
20. $y = 4 \tan \frac{2}{3}x$
21. $y = 4 \sin \frac{3}{2}x$
22. $y = \tan \frac{1}{2}x$
23. $y = \csc x$
24. $y = 5 \sin 4x$

Draw the graphs of the inverse trigonometric equations in problems 25 through 30.

25. $y = 2 \arccos x$
26. $y = 3 \arcsin x$
27. $y = 2 \arctan x$
28. $y = \frac{1}{2} \arccos \frac{1}{2}x$
29. $y = 3 \arcsin \frac{1}{2}x$
30. $y = \frac{1}{2} \arctan 2x$

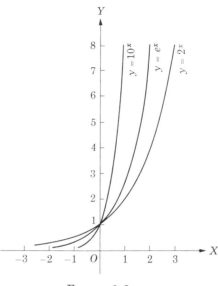

FIGURE 6–9

6–4 Exponential curves. An equation in which a variable appears in an exponent is called an *exponential equation*. The corresponding graph is known as an *exponential curve*. The equations

$$y = 2^x, \quad y = e^x, \quad \text{and} \quad y = 10^x$$

are exponential equations. Each could be made more general by replacing the exponent by a less simple expression in x.

The letter e in the second equation stands for an irrational number approximately equal to 2.71828. This number is of great importance in the theory and applications of mathematics.

The graph of $y = e^x$ can be drawn by using Table III (see Appendix) to find values of y for assigned values of x. Corresponding values of y in the equations $y = 2^x$ and $y = 10^x$ are simply obtained when x is an integer. To determine other pairs of values a table of logarithms can be used. Figure 6–9 has the graph of the three equations drawn in the same coordinate system for purposes of comparison.

6–5 Logarithmic curves. If a is a positive number different from 1 and y is any real number in the equation $a^y = x$, then y is called the logarithm of x to the base a. This relation may be written symbolically as $y = \log_a x$. Thus the two equations

$$a^y = x \quad \text{and} \quad y = \log_a x$$

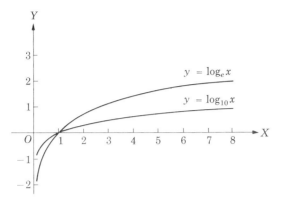

FIGURE 6–10

express the same relation among the numbers a, x, and y. The first is in exponential form and the second in logarithmic form. Since the base a is positive, a^y also has a positive value. Hence we shall consider the logarithms of positive numbers only.

Since a logarithmic equation can be changed to an exponential equation, it appears that logarithmic and exponential curves must be closely related. To see the relation, we note that the logarithmic equation $y = \log_a x$ is equivalent to, and therefore has the same graph as, $x = a^y$. Now the equations

$$x = a^y \qquad \text{and} \qquad y = a^x$$

are alike except that x and y play reverse roles. Hence their graphs must have the same form but different positions relative to the coordinate axes.

The most frequently used bases for logarithms are the numbers 10 and e. A table of logarithms can be used for drawing the curve corresponding to a logarithmic equation employing either of these bases. Corresponding values of x and y for the equations

$$y = \log_{10} x \qquad \text{and} \qquad y = \log_e x$$

are here tabulated with the logarithmic values rounded off to one decimal place. They should be verified by referring to the tables in the Appendix. The graphs are drawn in Fig. 6–10

x	0.01	0.1	0.2	0.5	0.8	1	2	4	8	10
$\log_{10} x$	−2.0	−1.0	−0.7	−0.3	−0.1	0	0.3	0.6	0.9	1.0
$\log_e x$	−4.6	−2.3	−1.6	−0.7	−0.2	0	0.7	1.4	2.1	2.3

Sketch the graphs of the following equations.

1. $y = 4^x$ 2. $y = 4^{-x}$ 3. $y = 2e^x$
4. $y = e^{2x}$ 5. $y = e^{x^2}$ 6. $y = e^{-x^2}$
7. $y = 2^{2x-1}$ 8. $y = 2^{x^2-x}$ 9. $y = xe^x$
10. $y = 3 \log_{10} x$ 11. $y = 2 \log_e x$ 12. $y = \log_{10} (-x)$
13. $y = \log_e (-x)$ 14. $y = \log_{10} 4x$ 15. $y = \log_e x^2$
16. $y = \log_2 x$ 17. $y = \log_{10} (x - 3)$

18. Show that the graph of $y = \log_a bx$ is the graph of $y = \log_a x$ shifted vertically a distance of $\log_a b$.

19. Show that the graph of $y = \log_a x^2$ can be obtained by doubling each ordinate of $y = \log_a x$.

20. If \$100 is invested at 2% per year compounded continuously, the accumulated amount y at the end of x years is given by the equation

$$y = 100e^{0.02x}.$$

Sketch the graph of this equation and from the graph estimate the accumulated amount at the end of (a) 3 yr, (b) 6 yr, (c) 9 yr. Estimate also the time required for the original investment to double.

6–6 Graph by addition of ordinates. The method called addition of ordinates can sometimes be applied efficiently to draw the graph of a transcendental equation. The process is exactly that used in Section 4–5 and is illustrated by the following example.

EXAMPLE 1. Sketch the graph of the equation

$$y = \sqrt{x} + \sin x.$$

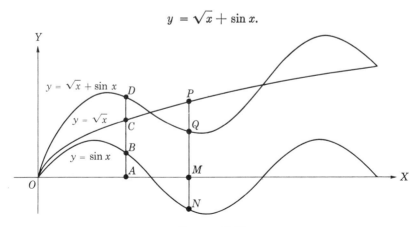

FIGURE 6–11

Solution. We first draw the graphs of

$$y = \sqrt{x} \quad \text{and} \quad y = \sin x.$$

The locus of the first of these equations is the upper half of the parabola $y^2 = x$, and the second yields the sine curve; both are familiar and easily sketched. The two curves are shown in Fig. 6–11. The point D on the graph of the given equation is obtained by adding the ordinates AB and AC. That is, AC is extended by a length equal to AB. The addition of ordinates for this purpose must be algebraic. Thus MN is negative and the point Q is found by measuring downward from P so that $PQ = MN$. By plotting a sufficient number of points in this way the desired graph can be drawn.

EXERCISE 6–3

Sketch the graph of each of the following equations by the addition of ordinates method.

1. $y = x + \sin x$
2. $y = x - \cos x$
3. $y = \sqrt{x} + \cos x$
4. $y = \sin x + \cos x$
5. $y = \sin x + \cos 2x$
6. $y = 2 \sin x + \sin 2x$
7. $y = x + \log_{10} x$
8. $y = x + e^x$
9. $y = \frac{1}{2}(e^x + e^{-x})$
10. $y = e^x + \log_{10} x$

CHAPTER 7

POLAR COORDINATES

7–1 Introduction. There are various types of coordinate systems. The rectangular system with which we have been dealing is probably the most important. In it a point is located by its distances from two perpendicular lines. We shall introduce in this chapter a coordinate system in which the coordinates of a point in a plane are its distance from a fixed point and its direction from a fixed line. The coordinates given in this way are called *polar coordinates*. The proper choice of a coordinate system depends on the nature of the problem at hand. For some problems either the rectangular or the polar system may be satisfactory; usually, however, one of the two is preferable. And in some situations it is advantageous to use both systems, shifting from one to the other.

7–2 Polar coordinate system. The reference frame in the polar coordinate system is a half-line drawn from some point in the plane. In Fig. 7–1 a half-line is represented by OA. The point O is called the *origin* or *pole* and OA the *polar axis*. The position of any point P in the plane is definitely determined by the distance OP and the angle AOP. The segment OP, denoted by ρ, is referred to as the *radius vector;* the angle AOP, denoted by θ, is called the *vectorial angle*. The coordinates of P are then written as (ρ, θ).

It is customary to regard polar coordinates as signed quantities. The vectorial angle, as in trigonometry, is defined as positive or negative according as it is measured counterclockwise or clockwise from the polar axis. The ρ-coordinate is defined as positive if measured from the pole along the terminal side of θ and negative if measured along the terminal side extended through the pole.

A given pair of polar coordinates definitely locates a point. For example, the coordinates $(3, 30°)$ determine one particular point. To plot the

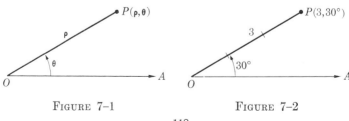

FIGURE 7–1   FIGURE 7–2

118

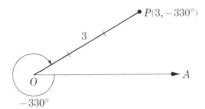

FIGURE 7–3

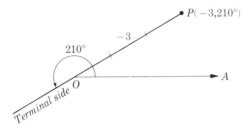

FIGURE 7–4

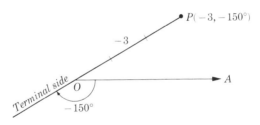

FIGURE 7–5

point, we first draw the terminal side of a 30° angle measured counter-clockwise from OA (Fig. 7–2) and then lay off three units along the terminal side. While this pair of coordinates defines a particular point, there are other coordinate values which define this same point. This is evident, since the vectorial angle may have 360° added or subtracted repeatedly without changing the point represented. Additional coordinates of the point may be obtained also by using a negative value for the distance coordinate. Restricting the vectorial angle to values numerically less than 360°, we see (Figs. 7–2 through 7–5) that the following pairs of coordinates define the same point:

$$(3, 30°), \quad (3, -330°), \quad (-3, 210°), \quad (-3, -150°).$$

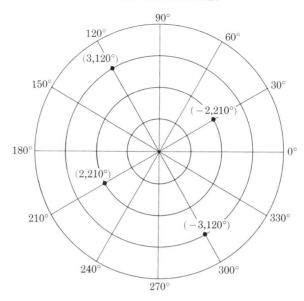

FIGURE 7–6

Points can be plotted conveniently on polar coordinate paper which has equally spaced circles with their centers at the pole and equally spaced radial lines through the pole (Fig. 7–6). The ρ-coordinate is the same at all points of a circle. A radial line consists of the terminal side of an angle and the extension of the side through the pole. The points on the terminal side correspond to positive values of ρ and those on an extension of the side correspond to negative values of ρ, as the plotted points illustrate. The ρ-coordinate is, of course, zero at the pole. Consequently, the coordinates of the pole are $(0, \theta)$, where θ may be any angle.

EXERCISE 7–1

In problems 1 through 4 plot each of the points corresponding to the given pair of coordinates. Write three other pairs of polar coordinates for the point, restricting the vectorial angles to numerical values not exceeding 360°.

1. (a) $(3, 60°)$, (b) $(6, -30°)$, (c) $(2, 180°)$, (d) $(0, 10°)$
2. (a) $(5, 210°)$, (b) $(4, 0°)$, (c) $(-6, 135°)$, (d) $(-2, -180°)$
3. (a) $(-1, \frac{5}{6}\pi)$, (b) $(-3, \frac{4}{3}\pi)$, (c) $(-4, \pi)$, (d) $(4, -\frac{3}{2}\pi)$
4. (a) $(2, 300°)$, (b) $(-2, -225°)$, (c) $(-3, 315°)$, (d) $(3, -345°)$

5. Where are the points for which (a) $\rho = 4$, (b) $\rho = -4$, (c) $\rho = 0$, (d) $\theta = 45°$, (e) $\theta = -90°$, (f) $\theta = 0°$, (g) $\theta = \pi$?

6. Where are the points for which (a) $\rho = \frac{3}{2}$, (b) $\rho = -2$, (c) $\theta = -\pi$, (d) $\theta = -135°$, (e) $\theta = \frac{3}{4}\pi$, (f) $\theta = \frac{5}{6}\pi$, (g) $\theta = 30°$?

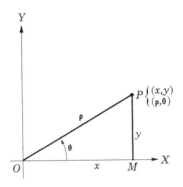

FIGURE 7–7

7–3 Relations between rectangular and polar coordinates. As we have mentioned, it is often advantageous in the course of a problem to shift from one coordinate system to another. For this purpose we shall derive transformation formulas which express polar coordinates in terms of rectangular coordinates, and vice versa. In Fig. 7–7 the two systems are placed so that the origins coincide and the polar axis lies along the positive x-axis. Then a point P has the coordinates (x, y) and (ρ, θ). From the triangle OMP, we have

$$\cos \theta = \frac{x}{\rho} \quad \text{and} \quad \sin \theta = \frac{y}{\rho},$$

and hence

$$x = \rho \cos \theta, \tag{1}$$

$$y = \rho \sin \theta. \tag{2}$$

To obtain ρ and θ in terms of x and y, we write

$$\rho^2 = x^2 + y^2 \quad \text{and} \quad \tan \theta = \frac{y}{x};$$

whence, solving for ρ and θ,

$$\rho = \pm\sqrt{x^2 + y^2}, \tag{3}$$

$$\theta = \arctan \frac{y}{x}. \tag{4}$$

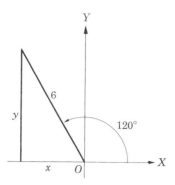

FIGURE 7–8

These four equations enable us to transform the coordinates of a point, and therefore the equation of a locus, from one system to the other. The θ-coordinate as given by Eq. (4) is not single-valued. Hence it is necessary to select a proper value for θ when applying the formula to find this coordinate of a point. See Example 2.

EXAMPLE 1. Find the rectangular coordinates of the point defined by the polar coordinates (6, 120°).

Solution. Using the Eqs. (1) and (2), we have (Fig. 7–8)

$$x = \rho \cos \theta = 6 \cos 120° = -3,$$
$$y = \rho \sin \theta = 6 \sin 120° = 3\sqrt{3}.$$

The required coordinates are $(-3, 3\sqrt{3})$.

EXAMPLE 2. Express the rectangular coordinates $(-2, -2)$ in terms of polar coordinates

Solution. Equations (3) and (4) give

$$\rho = \sqrt{x^2 + y^2} = 2\sqrt{2} \quad \text{and} \quad \theta = \arctan \frac{y}{x} = \arctan 1.$$

Since the point is in the third quadrant, we select $\theta = 225°$. Hence the pair of coordinates $(2\sqrt{2}, 225°)$ is a polar representation of the given point.

EXAMPLE 3. Find the polar coordinate equation corresponding to $2x - 3y = 5$.

Solution. Substituting for x and y gives

$$2(\rho \cos \theta) - 3(\rho \sin \theta) = 5 \quad \text{or} \quad \rho(2 \cos \theta - 3 \sin \theta) = 5.$$

EXAMPLE 4. Transform the equation $\rho = 4 \sin \theta$ to rectangular coordinates.

Solution. Since $\rho = \sqrt{x^2 + y^2}$ and $\sin \theta = y/\rho = y/\sqrt{x^2 + y^2}$, we substitute in the given equation and obtain

$$\sqrt{x^2 + y^2} = \frac{4y}{\sqrt{x^2 + y^2}},$$

or

$$x^2 + y^2 = 4y.$$

The required equation, as well as the original equation, represents a circle.

EXERCISE 7–2

1. Derive the transformation formulas of Eqs. (1) through (4) from a figure in which the terminal side is in the (a) second quadrant, (b) third quadrant, (c) fourth quadrant.

Find the rectangular coordinates of the following points.

2. $(4, 90°)$	3. $(3\sqrt{2}, 45°)$	4. $(7, 0°)$
5. $(0, 180°)$	6. $(-8, 270°)$	7. $(-1, -60°)$
8. $(6, 150°)$	9. $(4\sqrt{2}, -135°)$	10. $(9, 180°)$

Find nonnegative polar coordinates of the following points.

11. $(0, 3)$	12. $(3, 0)$	13. $(0, 0)$
14. $(-1, 0)$	15. $(0, -5)$	16. $(\sqrt{2}, \sqrt{2})$
17. $(6\sqrt{3}, -6)$	18. $(-2\sqrt{3}, 2)$	19. $(3, -4)$
20. $(-4, 3)$	21. $(5, 12)$	22. $(-5, -12)$

Transform the following equations to the corresponding polar coordinate equations.

23. $x = 3$	24. $y = -4$	25. $2x - y = 3$
26. $3x + y = 0$	27. $y = x$	28. $Ax + By = D$
29. $x^2 + y^2 = 16$	30. $xy = a^2$	
31. $x^2 + y^2 - 2x + 2y = 0$	32. $x^2 - y^2 = a^2$	
33. $y^2 = 4x$	34. $(x^2 + y^2)^2 = 2a^2xy$	

Transform the following equations to the corresponding rectangular coordinate equations.

35. $\rho = 4$ 36. $\theta = 0°$	37. $\theta = 45°$
38. $\rho = 2 \sin \theta + 2 \cos \theta$	39. $\rho = 6 \sin \theta - 4 \cos \theta$
40. $\rho = 8 \cos \theta$	41. $\rho = 8 \sin \theta$
42. $\rho \cos \theta = 6$	43. $\rho \sin \theta = 6$
44. $\rho^2 \cos 2\theta = a^2$	45. $\rho^2 \sin 2\theta = a^2$

46. $\rho = \dfrac{3}{1 + \cos \theta}$ 47. $\rho = \dfrac{3}{2 + \cos \theta}$

48. $\rho = \dfrac{2}{1 - 2 \cos \theta}$ 49. $\rho = \dfrac{2}{3 \sin \theta + 4 \cos \theta}$

50. $\rho = \dfrac{5}{2 \sin \theta - \cos \theta}$ 51. $\rho = \dfrac{1}{\cos \theta - 3 \sin \theta}$

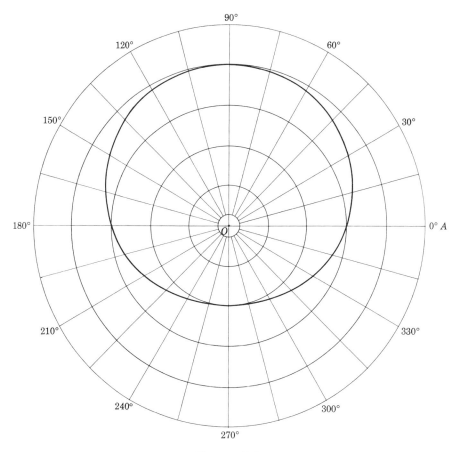

FIGURE 7–9

7–4 Graphs of polar coordinate equations. The definition of a graph in polar coordinates and the technique of its construction are essentially the same as those of an equation in rectangular coordinates.

DEFINITION. *The graph of an equation in polar coordinates consists of all the points which have coordinates satisfying the equation.*

We shall first consider comparatively simple equations and obtain their graphs by preparing tables of corresponding values of the variables. Following this preliminary encounter with polar coordinates, we shall consider certain aids by which tracing a curve can be facilitated.

EXAMPLE 1. Draw the graph of $\rho = 3 + \sin \theta$.

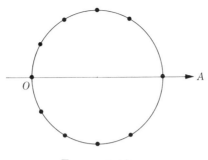

FIGURE 7–10

Solution. We assign certain values to θ in the interval 0° to 360° and prepare the following table.

θ	0°	30°	45°	60°	90°	120°	150°	180°
ρ	3	3.5	3.7	3.9	4	3.9	3.5	3

θ	210°	225°	240°	270°	300°	315°	330°	360°
ρ	2.5	2.3	2.1	2	2.1	2.3	2.5	3

By plotting these points and drawing a curve through them the graph of Fig. 7–9 is obtained.

EXAMPLE 2. Draw the graph of $\rho = 4 \cos \theta$.

Solution. We first prepare a table of corresponding values of ρ and θ.

θ	0°	30°	45°	60°	75°
ρ	4	3.5	2.8	2.0	1.0

θ	90°	120°	135°	150°	180°
ρ	0	−2.0	−2.8	−3.5	−4

This table yields the graph in Fig. 7–10. We did not extend the table to include values of θ in the interval 180° to 360°, since values of θ in this range would merely repeat the graph already obtained. For example, the point (−3.5, 210°) is on the graph, but this point is also defined by the coordinates (3.5, 30°).

The graph appears to be a circle. This surmise is verified by transforming the equation to rectangular coordinates. The transformed equation is $(x - 2)^2 + y^2 = 4$.

EXERCISE 7–3

Draw the graphs of the following equations. In the equations involving trigonometric functions, points plotted at 30° intervals will suffice, with a few exceptions.

1. $\rho = 5$ 2. $\rho = -5$ 3. $\theta = 120°$

4. $\theta = 180°$ 5. $\rho = 1 - \cos \theta$ 6. $\rho = 1 - \sin \theta$

7. $\rho = 2 + \cos \theta$ 8. $\rho = 2 - \sin \theta$ 9. $\rho = 10 \sin \theta$

10. $\rho = 2a \cos \theta$ 11. $\rho = \tan \theta$ 12. $\rho = \sec \theta$

13. $\rho = \dfrac{10}{2 + \sin \theta}$ 14. $\rho = \dfrac{8}{2 - \cos \theta}$ 15. $\rho = \dfrac{1}{1 + \cos \theta}$

16. $\rho = \dfrac{1}{1 - \sin \theta}$ 17. $\rho = \dfrac{1}{1 - 2 \sin \theta}$ 18. $\rho = \dfrac{1}{1 + 2 \sin \theta}$

19. $\rho = 10 \sin^2 \theta$ 20. $\rho = 10 \cos^2 \theta$ 21. $\rho = 10 \sec^2 \theta$

22. $\rho = 4 \sin \theta - 4 \cos \theta$ 23. $\rho = 8 \sin \theta + 6 \cos \theta$

7–5 Aids in graphing polar coordinate equations. We have seen that the examination of an equation in rectangular coordinates may reveal short cuts to the construction of its graph. In the same way, certain features of a graph in polar coordinates can often be discovered by an analysis of its equation. It is better, for economy of time, to wrest useful information from an equation and thus keep at a minimum the tedious point-by-point plotting in sketching a graph. We shall discuss and illustrate a few simple devices employed in tracing polar curves.

Variation of ρ with θ. Many equations are sufficiently simple so that the way in which ρ varies as θ increases is evident. Usually a range of θ-values from 0° to 360° yields the complete graph. However, we shall find exceptions to this rule. By observing the equation and letting θ increase through its range, the graph can be visualized. A rough sketch may then be made with a few pencil strokes. To illustrate this situation, we use the equation

$$\rho = 3(1 + \sin \theta).$$

If θ starts at 0° and increases in 90°-steps to 360°, it is a simple matter to see how ρ varies in each 90°-interval. This variation is represented in the diagram. The graph (Fig. 7–11) is a heart-shaped curve called the *cardioid*.

As θ increases from	$\sin \theta$ varies from	ρ varies from
0° to 90°	0 to 1	3 to 6
90° to 180°	1 to 0	6 to 3
180° to 270°	0 to -1	3 to 0
270° to 360°	-1 to 0	0 to 3

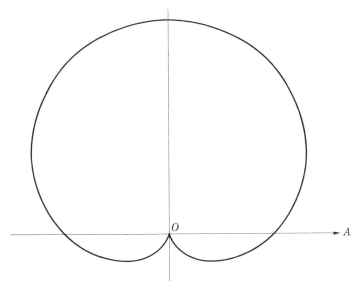

FIGURE 7–11

Tangent lines at the origin. If ρ shrinks to zero as θ approaches and takes a fixed value θ_0, then the line $\theta = \theta_0$ is tangent to the curve at the origin. Intuitively, this statement seems correct; it can be proved. In the preceding equation, $\rho = 3(1 + \sin\theta)$, the value of ρ diminishes to zero as θ increases to 270°. Hence the curve is tangent to the vertical line at the origin (Fig. 7–11).

To find the tangents to a curve at the origin, set $\rho = 0$ in the equation and solve for the corresponding values of θ.

Symmetry. We shall give tests for symmetry with respect to the pole, the polar axis, and the vertical line $\theta = 90°$. From Fig. 7–12, the following tests are evident.

1. *If the equation is unchanged when ρ is replaced by $-\rho$ or when θ is replaced by $180° + \theta$, the graph is symmetric with respect to the pole.*
2. *If the equation is unchanged when θ is replaced by $-\theta$, the graph is symmetric with respect to the polar axis.*
3. *If the equation is unchanged when θ is replaced by $180° - \theta$, the graph is symmetric with respect to the vertical line $\theta = 90°$.*

These tests will be found helpful. When any of the tests is satisfied in an equation, the symmetry is certain. On the other hand, the failure of a test does not disprove the symmetry in question. This is unlike the

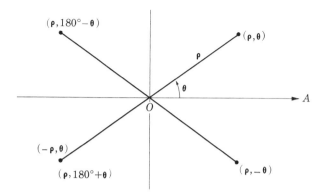

FIGURE 7–12

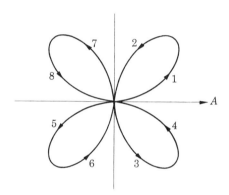

FIGURE 7–13

analogous situation in rectangular coordinates and is a consequence of the fact that a point has more than one polar coordinate representation. For example, replacing ρ by $-\rho$, the equation

$$\rho = \sin 2\theta$$

becomes

$$-\rho = \sin 2\theta.$$

This does not establish symmetry with respect to the pole. But substituting $180° + \theta$ for θ yields

$$\rho = \sin 2(180° + \theta) = \sin (360° + 2\theta) = \sin 2\theta,$$

which proves the symmetry with respect to the pole.

Continuing with the equation

$$\rho = \sin 2\theta,$$

we see that it does not satisfy tests 2 and 3. But it is sufficient to obtain the graph for θ from $0°$ to $180°$, and then to complete the drawing by the known symmetry with respect to the pole. Since we have a trigonometric function of 2θ, it is convenient to consider the variation of ρ as θ increases in steps of $45°$. The diagram indicates this variation. From it we see

θ	2θ	$\sin 2\theta$, or ρ
$0° \rightarrow 45°$	$0° \rightarrow 90°$	$0 \rightarrow 1$
$45° \rightarrow 90°$	$90° \rightarrow 180°$	$1 \rightarrow 0$
$90° \rightarrow 135°$	$180° \rightarrow 270°$	$0 \rightarrow -1$
$135° \rightarrow 180°$	$270° \rightarrow 360°$	$-1 \rightarrow 0$

the values of θ corresponding to the zero value of ρ, and therefore conclude that the graph is tangent to the polar axis and the vertical line at the origin. The completed graph (Fig. 7–13) exhibits all three types of symmetry. Because of its shape, the graph is called a *four-leaved rose*. The barbs and numbers indicate how a point would move in tracing the curve as θ increases from $0°$ to $360°$.

Excluded values. Frequently we shall meet equations in which certain values of the variables are excluded. For example, $\rho^2 = a^2 \sin \theta$ places restrictions on both ρ and θ. The values of ρ are in the range $-a$ to a, and θ cannot have a value which makes $\sin \theta$ negative since ρ would then be imaginary. In particular, the angles between $180°$ and $360°$ are excluded. The graph, however, extends into the third and fourth quadrants for other values of θ because the equation satisfies the test for symmetry with respect to the origin.

Intercepts. The points at which a curve touches or cuts the horizontal and vertical lines through the pole are called *intercept* points; they are sometimes quite helpful in drawing the graph of a polar equation. The intercept points can be found by using the values $0°$, $90°$, $180°$, $270°$, or angles coterminal with these, for θ and finding the corresponding values of ρ. In this way, for example, we find that the intercept points of $\rho = 3 + \sin \theta$ are $(3, 0°)$, $(4, 90°)$, $(3, 180°)$, and $(2, 270°)$. The intercept points of $\rho = 2\theta$ are limitless in number. They occur at $\theta = n\pi$ and $\theta = (n + \frac{1}{2})\pi$, where n is any integer, positive, negative, or zero.

We remark, however, that a curve may pass through the origin at angles other than a quadrantal angle. The test for this situation, as already stated, is to find the values of θ when $\rho = 0$.

7–6 Special types of equations. There are several types of polar co-ordinate equations whose graphs have been given special names. We consider a few of these equations.

The graphs of equations of the forms

$$\rho = a \sin n\theta \quad \text{and} \quad \rho = a \cos n\theta,$$

where n is a positive integer, are called *rose curves*. The graph of a rose curve consists of equally spaced closed loops extending from the origin. The number of loops, or leaves, depends on the integer n. If n is odd, there are n leaves; if n is even, there are $2n$ leaves. Figure 7–13 pictures a four-leaved rose.

The graph of an equation of the form

$$\rho = b + a \sin \theta \quad \text{or} \quad \rho = b + a \cos \theta$$

is called a *limaçon*. The shape of the graph depends on the relative values of a and b. If $a = b$, the limaçon is called a cardioid from its heartlike shape, as illustrated in Fig. 7–11. If the numerical value of b is greater than that of a, the graph is a curve surrounding the origin (Fig. 7–9). An interesting feature is introduced in the graph when a is numerically greater than b. The curve then has an inner loop. To show this, we draw the graph of $\rho = 2 + 4 \cos \theta$. Replacing θ by $-\theta$ leaves the equation unchanged, since $\cos (-\theta) = \cos \theta$. Hence there is symmetry with respect to the polar axis. Setting $\rho = 0$ gives

$$2 + 4 \cos \theta = 0,$$
$$\cos \theta = -\tfrac{1}{2},$$
$$\theta = 120°, 240°.$$

The lines $\theta = 120°$ and $\theta = 240°$ are tangent to the curve at the origin. The diagram indicates the variation of ρ as θ increases from $0°$ to $180°$.

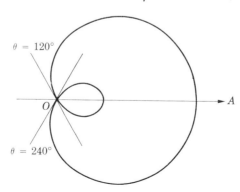

FIGURE 7–14

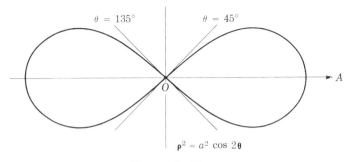

$$\rho^2 = a^2 \cos 2\theta$$

FIGURE 7–15

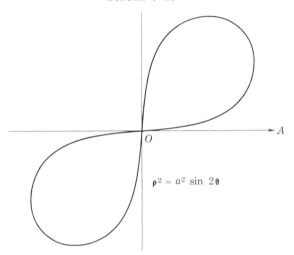

$$\rho^2 = a^2 \sin 2\theta$$

FIGURE 7–16

The graph is shown in Fig. 7–14; the lower half of the large loop and the upper half of the small loop were drawn by the use of symmetry.

θ	$\cos \theta$	ρ
$0° \rightarrow 90°$	$1 \rightarrow 0$	$6 \rightarrow 2$
$90° \rightarrow 120°$	$0 \rightarrow -\frac{1}{2}$	$2 \rightarrow 0$
$120° \rightarrow 180°$	$-\frac{1}{2} \rightarrow -1$	$0 \rightarrow -2$

The graphs of the equations

$$\rho^2 = a^2 \sin 2\theta \qquad \text{and} \qquad \rho^2 = a^2 \cos 2\theta$$

are *lemniscates* (Figs. 7–15 and 7–16) of. In each these equations, ρ ranges

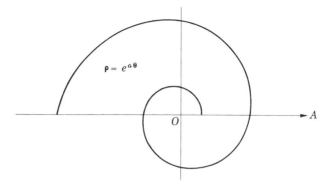

FIG. 7–17. Logarithmic Spiral.

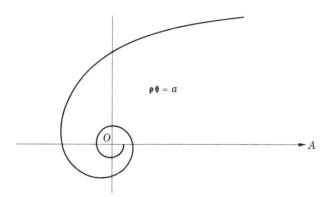

FIG. 7–18. Reciprocal Spiral.

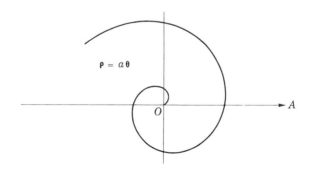

FIG. 7–19. Spiral of Archimedes.

from $-a$ to a; values of θ which make the right member negative are excluded. In the first equation θ may not take a value between 90° and 180° or between 270° and 360°. In the second the excluded intervals are $45° < \theta < 135°$ and $225° < \theta < 315°$.

Discussing further the equation

$$\rho^2 = a^2 \cos 2\theta,$$

we observe that its graph is symmetric with respect to the pole, the polar axis, and the vertical line through the pole. As θ increases from 0° to 45°, the positive values of ρ vary from a to 0 and the negative values from $-a$ to 0. Hence this interval for θ gives rise to the upper half of the right loop and the lower half of the left loop of the graph (Fig. 7–15). Either of these half loops combined with the known symmetries is sufficient for completing the graph.

Finally, the equations $\rho = e^{a\theta}$, $\rho\theta = a$, and $\rho = a\theta$ are examples of *spirals*. Their graphs for $a > 0$ and $\theta \geq 0°$ are shown in Figs. 7–17 to 7–19.

EXERCISE 7–4

1. Observe that (ρ, θ) and $(-\rho, 180° - \theta)$ are symmetric with respect to the polar axis, and that (ρ, θ) and $(-\rho, -\theta)$ are symmetric with respect to the line $\theta = 90°$. On the basis of this information, state two tests for the symmetry of the graph of an equation. Apply the tests to the equation $\rho = \sin 2\theta$.

Sketch the graph of each of the following equations. First examine the equation to find properties which are helpful in tracing the graph. Where the literal constant a occurs, assign to it a convenient positive value. In the spirals 25 through 29 use radian measure for θ.

2. $\rho = 4(1 - \cos \theta)$

3. $\rho = 6(1 - \sin \theta)$

4. $\rho = a(1 + \cos \theta)$

5. $\rho = 5 - 2 \sin \theta$

6. $\rho = 10 - 5 \cos \theta$

7. $\rho = 8 + 4 \cos \theta$

8. $\rho = 8 \cos 2\theta$

9. $\rho = a \sin 2\theta$

10. $\rho = 6 \sin 3\theta$

11. $\rho = 4 \cos 3\theta$

12. $\rho = 2 \sin 5\theta$

13. $\rho = 2 \cos 5\theta$

14. $\rho = 4 - 8 \cos \theta$

15. $\rho = 6 - 3 \sin \theta$

16. $\rho = 4 + 8 \cos \theta$

17. $\rho = 6 + 3 \sin \theta$

18. $\rho = a \cos 4\theta$

19. $\rho = a \sin 4\theta$

20. $\rho^2 = 9 \cos 2\theta$

21. $\rho^2 = 16 \sin 2\theta$

22. $\rho^2 = -a^2 \cos 2\theta$

23. $\rho^2 = -a^2 \sin 2\theta$

24. $\rho^2 = a^2 \cos \theta$

25. $\rho = 2\theta$

26. $\rho\theta = 4$

27. $\rho = e^\theta$

28. $\rho^2\theta = a$ (lituus)

29. $\rho^2 = a^2\theta$ (parabolic spiral)

30. $\rho = \sin \frac{1}{2}\theta$

31. $\rho = \cos \frac{1}{2}\theta$

32. $\rho = 3 \sec \theta + 4$

33. $\rho = 6 \sec \theta - 6$

7–7 Polar equations of lines and conics. The equations of lines and conics can be obtained in polar coordinates by transforming the rectangular coordinate equations of these loci. The equations can also be derived directly. We shall derive the polar coordinate equation of a line in general position and the equations of the conic sections in special positions.

In Fig. 7–20 the segment OR is drawn perpendicular to the line L. We denote the length of this segment by p and the angle which it makes with the polar axis by ω. The coordinates of a variable point on the line are (ρ, θ). From the right triangle ORP, we have

$$\frac{p}{\rho} = \cos(\theta - \omega)$$

or

$$\rho \cos(\theta - \omega) = p. \tag{1}$$

This equation holds for all points of the line. If P is chosen below OA, then the angle ROP is equal to $(\omega + 2\pi - \theta)$. Although this angle is not equal to $(\theta - \omega)$, we do have $\cos(\omega + 2\pi - \theta) = \cos(\omega - \theta) = \cos(\theta - \omega)$. In a similar way, the equation could be derived for the line L in any other position and not passing through the origin.

Equation (1) is called the *polar normal form* of the equation of a straight line. For lines perpendicular to the polar axis $\omega = 0°$ or $180°$, and for lines parallel to the polar axis $\omega = 90°$ or $270°$. Substituting these values for ω, we have the special forms

$$\rho \cos \theta = \pm p \tag{2}$$

and

$$\rho \sin \theta = \pm p. \tag{3}$$

The θ-coordinate is constant for points on a line passing through the origin. Hence the equation of a line through the origin with inclination α is

$$\theta = \alpha. \tag{4}$$

Although the equation of a line through the origin can be written immediately in this form, it is worth noting that Eq. (4) is a special case of Eq. (1). By setting $p = 0$ in Eq. (1), we have $\rho \cos(\theta - \omega) = 0$, $\cos(\theta - \omega) = 0$, $\theta - \omega = \frac{1}{2}\pi$, and $\theta = \frac{1}{2}\pi + \omega = \alpha$.

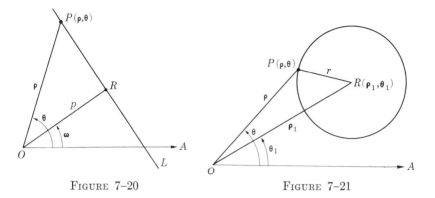

FIGURE 7–20   FIGURE 7–21

We next write the equation of a circle of radius r with center at (ρ_1, θ_1). Observing Fig. 7–21 and applying the law of cosines to the triangle ORP, we get the equation of the circle in the form

$$\rho^2 + \rho_1^2 - 2\rho\rho_1 \cos(\theta - \theta_1) = r^2. \tag{5}$$

If the center is at $(r, 0°)$, then $\rho_1 = r$ and $\theta_1 = 0°$ and the equation reduces to

$$\rho = 2r \cos \theta. \tag{6}$$

If the center is at $(r, 90°)$, the equation becomes

$$\rho = 2r \sin \theta. \tag{7}$$

We use the focus-directrix property of conics (Section 3–7) to derive their equations in polar coordinates. The equations can be obtained in simple forms if the focus and origin coincide and the directrix is parallel or perpendicular to the polar axis. In Fig. 7–22 the directrix DE is per-

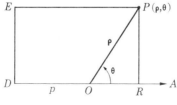

FIGURE 7–22

pendicular to the polar axis and to the left of O. If we indicate the eccentricity by e and the length of DO by p, we have for any point $P(\rho, \theta)$ of the conic

$$\frac{OP}{EP} = e.$$

But the numerator $OP = \rho$, and the denominator $EP = DR = DO + OR = p + \rho \cos \theta$. Hence $\rho/(p + \rho \cos \theta) = e$, and solving for ρ, we get

$$\rho = \frac{ep}{1 - e \cos \theta}. \tag{8}$$

When the focus is at the pole and the directrix is p units to the right of the pole, the equation is

$$\rho = \frac{ep}{1 + e \cos \theta}. \tag{9}$$

If the focus is at the pole and the directrix is parallel to the polar axis, the equation is

$$\rho = \frac{ep}{1 + e \sin \theta} \tag{10}$$

or

$$\rho = \frac{ep}{1 - e \sin \theta}, \tag{11}$$

depending on whether the directrix is p units above or below the pole.

An equation in any of the forms (8) through (11) represents a parabola if $e = 1$, an ellipse if e is between 0 and 1, and a hyperbola if e is greater than 1. In any case the graph can be sketched immediately. Having observed the type of conic from the value of e, the next step is to find the points where the curve cuts the polar axis, the extension of the axis through O, and the line through the pole perpendicular to the polar aixs. These are called the *intercept points*, and may be obtained by using the values 0°, 90°, 180°, and 270° for θ. Only three of these values can be used for a parabola, since one of them would make the denominator zero. The intercept points are sufficient for a rough graph. For increased accuracy a few additional points should be plotted.

EXAMPLE. Sketch the graph of $\rho = 15/(3 - 2 \cos \theta)$.

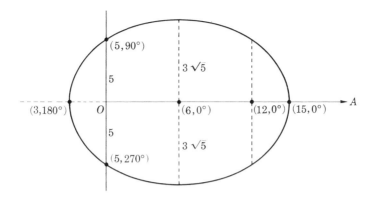

FIGURE 7–23

Solution. The equation takes the form of Eq. (8) when the numerator and denominator of the right member are divided by 3. This produces

$$\rho = \frac{5}{1 - (\frac{2}{3}) \cos \theta} \, .$$

In this form we observe that $e = \frac{2}{3}$, and hence the graph is an ellipse. Substituting 0°, 90°, 180°, and 270° in succession for θ in the original equation, we find the intercept points to be

$$(15, 0°), \qquad (5, 90°), \qquad (3, 180°), \qquad \text{and} \qquad (5, 270°).$$

These points are plotted in Fig. 7–23. The points $(15, 0°)$ and $(3, 180°)$ are vertices and the other intercept points are the ends of a latus rectum. The center, midway between the vertices, is at $(6, 0°)$. The length of the major axis $2a = 18$, and $a = 9$. The distance between the center and the focus at O is $c = 6$; hence $b^2 = a^2 - c^2 = 81 - 36 = 45$, and $b = 3\sqrt{5}$.

EXERCISE 7–5

1. From a figure find the equation of the line perpendicular to the polar axis and (a) 3 units to the right of the pole, (b) 3 units to the left of the pole. Compare your results with formula (2).

2. From a figure find the equation of the line parallel to the polar axis and (a) 3 units below the axis, (b) 3 units above the axis. Check your results with Eq. (3).

3. Show that Eq. (1) can be reduced to the form

$$\rho = \frac{C}{A \cos \theta + B \sin \theta} \, .$$

Assign convenient values to θ and find the coordinates of two points on the line represented by each equation in problems 4 through 9. Plot the points and draw the line.

4. $\rho = \dfrac{1}{\cos \theta + 2 \sin \theta}$

5. $\rho = \dfrac{4}{2 \cos \theta - \sin \theta}$

6. $\rho = \dfrac{-10}{2 \cos \theta + 5 \sin \theta}$

7. $\rho = \dfrac{-12}{3 \cos \theta - 2 \sin \theta}$

8. $\rho = \dfrac{3}{\sin \theta - 6 \cos \theta}$

9. $\rho = \dfrac{-4}{2 \sin \theta + 3 \cos \theta}$

Write the polar equation of the line described in each problem 10 through 15.

10. The horizontal line through the point $(2, 90°)$
11. The horizontal line through the point $(-2, 90°)$
12. The vertical line through the point $(-4, 0°)$
13. The vertical line through the point $(3, -\pi)$
14. The line tangent to the circle $\rho = 2$ at the point $(2, 60°)$
15. The line tangent to the circle $\rho = 4$ at the point $(4, 225°)$

Give the polar coordinates of the center and the radius of the circle defined by each equation 16 through 21.

16. $\rho = 8 \cos \theta$ 17. $\rho = 6 \sin \theta$ 18. $\rho = -10 \sin \theta$
19. $\rho = -4 \cos \theta$ 20. $\rho = 12 \cos \theta$ 21. $\rho = -7 \sin \theta$

Find the polar equation of the circle in each problem 22 through 30.

22. Center at $(3, 0°)$ and radius 3   23. Center at $(4, 0°)$ and radius 4
24. Center at $(6, 90°)$ and radius 6   25. Center at $(-5, 0°)$ and radius 5
26. Center at $(-8, 90°)$ and radius 8
27. Center at $(4, 0°)$ and radius 2   28. Center at $(4, 90°)$ and radius 2
29. Center at $(5, 45°)$ and radius 5   30. Center at $(6, 60°)$ and radius 6

Sketch the conic defined by each equation in problems 31 through 42.

31. $\rho = \dfrac{4}{1 - \cos \theta}$

32. $\rho = \dfrac{6}{1 + \sin \theta}$

33. $\rho = \dfrac{9}{2 + 2 \cos \theta}$

34. $\rho = \dfrac{10}{3 - 3 \sin \theta}$

35. $\rho = \dfrac{12}{2 - \cos \theta}$

36. $\rho = \dfrac{12}{2 + \sin \theta}$

37. $\rho = \dfrac{16}{4 + 3 \cos \theta}$

38. $\rho = \dfrac{15}{5 - 4 \sin \theta}$

39. $\rho = \dfrac{8}{1 - 2 \cos \theta}$

40. $\rho = \dfrac{10}{2 + 3 \cos \theta}$

41. $\rho = \dfrac{15}{3 + 5 \sin \theta}$

42. $\rho = \dfrac{18}{3 - 4 \sin \theta}$

7–8 Intersections of polar coordinate curves. A simultaneous real solution of two equations in rectangular coordinates represents a point of intersection of their graphs. Conversely, the coordinates of a point of intersection yield a simultaneous solution. In polar coordinates, however, this converse statement does not always hold. This difference in the two systems is a consequence of the fact that a point has more than one pair of polar coordinates. As an illustration, consider the equations $\rho = -2$, $\rho = 1 + \sin \theta$ and the two pairs of coordinates $(2, 90°)$, $(-2, 270°)$. The equation $\rho = -2$ is satisfied by the second pair of coordinates but not by the first. The equation $\rho = 1 + \sin \theta$ is satisfied by the first pair of coordinates but not by the second. The two pairs of coordinates, however, determine the same point. Although the two curves pass through this point, no pair of coordinates of the point satisfies both equations. The usual process of solving two equations simultaneously does not yield an intersection point of this kind. The graphs of the equations, of course, show all intersections.

EXAMPLE 1. Solve simultaneously and sketch the graphs of

$$\rho = 6 \sin \theta \qquad \text{and} \qquad \rho = 6 \cos \theta.$$

Solution. Equating the right members of the equations, we have

$$6 \sin \theta = 6 \cos \theta,$$
$$\tan \theta = 1,$$
$$\theta = 45°, 225°,$$
$$\rho = 3\sqrt{2}, -3\sqrt{2}.$$

The coordinates $(3\sqrt{2}, 45°)$ and $(-3\sqrt{2}, 225°)$ define the same point. The graphs (Fig. 7–24) show this point, and show also that both curves pass through

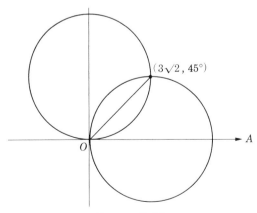

FIGURE 7–24

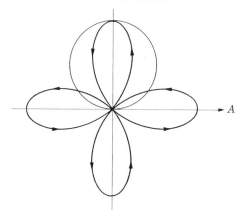

FIGURE 7–25

the origin. The coordinates $(0, 0°)$ satisfy the first equation and $(0, 90°)$ satisfy the second equation. But the origin has no pair of coordinates which satisfies both equations.

EXAMPLE 2. Solve simultaneously and draw the graphs of

$$\rho = 4 \sin \theta \quad \text{and} \quad \rho = 4 \cos 2\theta.$$

Solution. Eliminating ρ and using the trigonometric identity $\cos 2\theta = 1 - 2 \sin^2 \theta$, we obtain

$$4 \sin \theta = 4(1 - 2 \sin^2 \theta),$$
$$2 \sin^2 \theta + \sin \theta - 1 = 0,$$
$$(2 \sin \theta - 1)(\sin \theta + 1) = 0,$$
$$\sin \theta = \tfrac{1}{2}, -1,$$
$$\theta = 30°, 150°, 270°,$$
$$\rho = 2, \quad 2, \quad -4.$$

The solutions are $(2, 30°)$, $(2, 150°)$, and $(-4, 270°)$. Figure 7–25 shows that the curves also cross at the origin, but the origin has no pair of coordinates which satisfies both equations.

EXERCISE 7–6

In each of the following problems solve the equations simultaneously and sketch their graphs. Extraneous solutions are sometimes introduced in the solving process. For this reason all results should be checked.

1. $\rho = 2 \cos \theta,$
   $\rho = 1$

2. $\rho = 4 \sin \theta,$
   $\rho = 2$

3. $\rho = 6 \cos \theta,$
   $\rho \cos \theta = 3$

4. $\rho = a(1 + \sin \theta),$
   $\rho = 2a \sin \theta$

5. $\rho = a(1 + \cos \theta)$,
   $\rho = a(1 - \cos \theta)$

6. $\rho \cos \theta = 1$,
   $\rho = 2$

7. $\rho^2 = 4 \cos \theta$,
   $\rho = 2$

8. $\rho = 1 + \sin \theta$,
   $\rho = 1 + \cos \theta$

9. $\rho = \dfrac{2}{1 + \cos \theta}$,
   $3\rho \cos \theta = 2$

10. $\rho = \dfrac{3}{4 - 3 \cos \theta}$,
    $\rho = 3 \cos \theta$

11. $\rho = 2 \sin \theta + 1$,
    $\rho = \cos \theta$

12. $\rho^2 = a^2 \sin 2\theta$,
    $\rho = a\sqrt{2} \cos \theta$

13. $\rho = 2 \sin \frac{1}{2}\theta$,
    $\theta = 60°$

14. $\rho = \sin^2 \theta$,
    $\rho = \cos^2 \theta$

15. $\rho = 2 \sin \frac{1}{2}\theta$,
    $\rho = 1$

16. $\rho = 1 - \sin \theta$,
    $\rho = \cos 2\theta$

17. $\rho = 4 + \cos \theta$,
    $\rho \cos \theta = -3$

18. $\rho = 4 - \sin \theta$,
    $\rho \sin \theta = 3$

19. $\rho = 2 \cos \theta + 1$,
    $\rho \cos \theta = 1$

20. $\rho = \dfrac{2}{\sin \theta + \cos \theta}$,
    $\rho = \dfrac{2}{1 - \cos \theta}$

CHAPTER 8

PARAMETRIC EQUATIONS

8–1 Introduction. Relations between x and y up to this point have been expressed by equations involving these variables. Another way of defining a relation between x and y is to use two equations in which each variable is expressed separately in terms of a third variable. The third variable is called a *parameter*, and the equations are called *parametric equations*. Equations of this kind are of considerable importance; the mathematical treatment of many problems is facilitated by their use.

The equations

$$x = t - 1 \quad \text{and} \quad y = 2t + 3,$$

for example, are parametric equations, and t is the parameter. The equations define a locus. If a value is assigned to t, corresponding values are determined for x and y. The pair of values for x and y constitute a point of the locus. The complete locus consists of all points determined in this way as t varies through all its values. We can eliminate t between the equations and obtain an equation involving x and y. Thus solving either equation for t and substituting in the other, we get

$$2x - y + 5 = 0.$$

The locus of this equation, which is also the locus of the parametric equations, is a straight line.

Often the parameter can be eliminated, as illustrated here, to obtain a direct relation between x and y. Sometimes, however, the process is not easy or possible because the parameter is included in a complicated way. The equations

$$x = t^5 + \log t \quad \text{and} \quad y = t^3 + \tan t$$

illustrate this statement.

It is sometimes helpful in solving a problem to change an equation in x and y to parametric form. We illustrate this process with the equation

$$x^2 + 2x + y = 4,$$

which defines a parabola. If we substitute $2t$ for x and solve the resulting

142

equation for y, we get $y = 4 - 4t - 4t^2$. Hence the parametric equations

$$x = 2t \quad \text{and} \quad y = 4 - 4t - 4t^2$$

also represent the parabola. It is evident that other representations could be obtained by equating x to other expressions in t. Again, this procedure is inconvenient or perhaps impossible in equations which contain both variables in a complicated way.

The parameter as used in this chapter plays a different role from the parameter which we discussed in Section 2–5. Here the parameter is a variable, and a curve is determined by letting the parameter vary. In contrast, the parameter in a linear equation in x and y gives rise to a family of curves (lines). A line is determined by each value assigned to the parameter.

8–2 Parametric equations of the circle and ellipse. To find a parametric representation of the circle of radius a and center at the origin, we select for the parameter the angle θ indicated in Fig. 8–1. We have at once

$$x = a \cos \theta \quad \text{and} \quad y = a \sin \theta.$$

If we let θ increase from $0°$ to $360°$, the point (x, y) defined by these equations starts at $(a, 0)$ and moves counterclockwise around the circle. By letting θ change directly with the time t so that $\theta = kt$, the equations become

$$x = a \cos kt \quad \text{and} \quad y = a \sin kt.$$

These equations give the location of the moving point at any time. The speed of the point is constant.

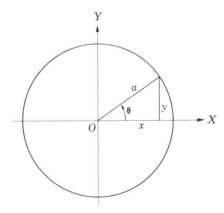

FIGURE 8–1

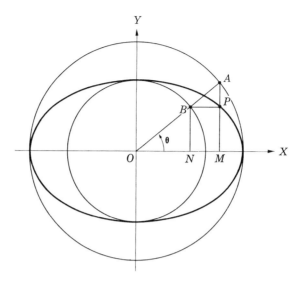

FIGURE 8–2

The equations $x = a \cos \theta$ and $y = b \sin \theta$ represent an ellipse. This statement can be verified by eliminating the parameter θ. Writing the equations as

$$\frac{x}{a} = \cos \theta \qquad \text{and} \qquad \frac{y}{b} = \sin \theta,$$

squaring both members of each equation, and adding, we get

$$\frac{x^2}{a^2} + \frac{y^2}{b^2} = 1.$$

From this result we see that the parametric equations represent an ellipse, and we are able to interpret the quantities a and b. The geometric significance of θ can be seen in Fig. 8–2. The concentric circles are of radii a and b. The terminal side of θ cuts the circles at A and B. The intersection of the vertical line through A and the horizontal line through B gives a point of the ellipse. For this point P, we have

$$x = OM = OA \cos \theta = a \cos \theta,$$
$$y = MP = NB = OB \sin \theta = b \sin \theta.$$

Hence as θ varies, P moves along an ellipse. The ellipse is traced by letting θ vary through 360°. If θ starts at 0° and increases to 360°, the point P starts at $(a, 0)$ and traces the ellipse in a counterclockwise direction.

8–3 Graph of parametric equations. We proceed next to the problem of constructing the graph defined by two parametric equations. The method is straightforward. We first assign to the parameter a set of values and compute the corresponding values of x and y. The plotted points (x, y) furnish a guide for drawing the graph. Usually only a few plotted points are necessary. This is especially true when certain properties of the graph, such as the extent, the intercepts, and the asymptotes, are apparent from the equations.

An alternative procedure is to eliminate the parameter and construct the graph of the resulting equation. In some cases, however, the graph of the parametric equations and the graph of the corresponding rectangular equation do not coincide throughout. Example 3 illustrates such a case.

EXAMPLE 1. Sketch the graph of the parametric equations

$$x = 2 + t \quad \text{and} \quad y = 3 - t^2.$$

Solution. The table is the result of assigning to t the indicated values and finding the corresponding values of x and y. The curve drawn through the points (x, y), as determined by the table, constitutes a part of the graph (Fig. 8–3).

t	-3	-2	-1	0	1	2	3
x	-1	0	1	2	3	4	5
y	-6	-1	2	3	2	-1	-6

By inspecting the equations, we see that x may have any real value and that y may have any value not exceeding 3. Hence the graph extends indefinitely far into the third and fourth quadrants.

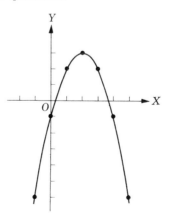

FIGURE 8–3

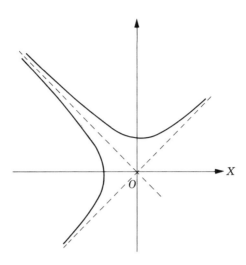

FIGURE 8–4

We next eliminate the parameter to obtain a rectangular equation. Solving the first equation for t and substituting in the second, we get

$$(x - 2)^2 = -(y - 3).$$

The graph is a parabola with vertex at $(2, 3)$, and it opens downward.

EXAMPLE 2. Construct the graph of $(x + y)^3 = 2y(x + y)^2 - 8$.

Solution. It would be tedious indeed to find points of the graph by assigning values to one variable and solving for the other. We seek then a parametric representation of the graph. As pointed out earlier, there are different possible representations. The occurrence of $x + y$ in both members of the given equation leads us to try the substitution $x + y = 2t$. This substitution permits us to express y in terms of t and then x in terms of t. Thus we have the equations

$$x = \frac{t^3 - 1}{t^2} \quad \text{and} \quad y = \frac{t^3 + 1}{t^2}.$$

By means of these equations, points of the graph can be easily found by assigning values to t. The graph (Fig. 8–4) has the indicated asymptotes. This can be verified by examining the parametric equations for numerically large positive and negative values of t and values of t near zero. We have, by addition and subtraction,

$$x + y = 2t \quad \text{and} \quad x - y = -2/t^2.$$

From the second of these equations, we see that $x - y$ is near zero when t is numerically large. From the given equations, we see that x and y are positive

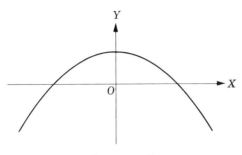

FIGURE 8–5

and large when t is positive and large, and x and y are negative and numerically large when t is negative and numerically large. We conclude, then, that $x - y = 0$ is an asymptote to the graph in both the first and third quadrants. We next observe that when t is near zero, $x + y$ is near zero, x is negative and numerically large, and y is positive and large. Hence the part of the line $x + y = 0$ in the second quadrant is an asymptote of the graph.

EXAMPLE 3. Construct the graph defined by the equations

$$x = 2 \sin \theta \quad \text{and} \quad y = \cos^2 \theta.$$

Solution. Let us first find the direct relation between x and y. From the first equation, we have $x^2/4 = \sin^2 \theta$. This equation and the second given equation yield

$$\frac{x^2}{4} + y = 1,$$

and, consequently,

$$x^2 = -4(y - 1).$$

The graph of this equation is the parabola drawn in Fig. 8–5. We note, however, that the graph of the parametric equations does not include the part of the parabola below the x-axis. This results from the fact that the values of x are restricted to the range -2 to 2 and those of y from 0 to 1.

EXERCISE 8–1

Sketch the graph from the parametric equations in each problem 1 through 22. Then compare the graph with that of the rectangular equation obtained by eliminating the parameter.

1. $x = 2t, y = 3t$ 2. $x = 1 + t, y = 4 - 3t$
3. $x = 2 \sin^2 \theta, y = 2 \cos^2 \theta$
4. $x = 1 + 3 \sin^2 \theta, \quad y = 1 + 3 \cos^2 \theta$

5. $x = \tan^2 \theta, y = \sec^2 \theta$ 6. $x = 5 \sin \theta, y = 5 \cos \theta$

7. $x = t, y = t^3$ 8. $x = t^2, y = t^3$

9. $x = t^2, y = 4t$ 10. $x = t + 3, y = t^2 - 2$

11. $x = 1 + 2t, y = 2 - t^2$ 12. $x = 6t^{-1}, y = t$

13. $x = t + 3, y = 1/t^3$ 14. $x = 1/t^2, y = 2t^2$

15. $x = \dfrac{2}{1 + t^2}, y = \dfrac{2t}{1 + t^2}$ 16. $x = \dfrac{2t^2}{1 + t^2}, y = \dfrac{t}{1 + t^2}$

17. $x = 4 \cos \theta, y = 3 \sin \theta$ 18. $x = \sin^2 \theta, y = 2 \cos \theta$

19. $x = \cos 2\theta, y = 2 \sin \theta$ 20. $x = 2 + 5 \sin \theta, y = 2 - 3 \cos \theta$

21. $x = \sec \theta, y = \tan \theta$ 22. $x = 2 \sin 2\theta, y = 2 \sin^2 \theta$

Using the accompanying relation, express each rectangular equation in problems 23 through 28 in parametric form. Sketch the graph from the parametric equations.

23. $x^2 + xy - 1 = 0, x = t^{-1}$

24. $xy - 4x - 2y - 4 = 0, x = t - 1$

25. $x^2 - 2xy + y^2 - 4x + 5y = 0, x - y = t$

26. $(x + y)^3 - 2y(x + y)^2 + 8 = 0, x + y = 2/t$

27. $x^3 + y^3 - 3xy = 0, y = tx$

28. $x^{1/2} + y^{1/2} = a^{1/2}, x = a \sin^4 \theta$

Use radian measure for the parameter in each problem 29 through 34 and sketch the curve. Restrict t to the interval 0 to 2π.

29. $x = t + \sin t, y = \cos t$ 30. $x = t + \sin t, y = t + \cos t$

31. $x = \tfrac{1}{10}e^t, y = \sin t$ 32. $x = 10e^{-t}, y = \sin t$

33. $x = t \sin t, y = \cos t$ 34. $x = t \sin t, y = t \cos t$

8–4 Path of a projectile.

The equations of certain curves can be determined more readily by the use of a parameter than otherwise. In fact, this is one of the principal uses of parametric equations. In the remainder of this chapter parametric equations of curves are required. These curves have interesting properties and also have important practical and theoretical applications.

We consider first the path of a projectile in air. Suppose that a body is given an initial upward velocity of v_0 feet per second in a direction which makes an angle α with the horizontal. If the resistance of the air is small and can be neglected without great error, the object will move subject to the vertical force of gravity. This means that there is no horizontal force to change the speed in the horizontal direction. Observing Fig. 8–6 with the origin of coordinates at the point where the projectile is fired, we see that the velocity in the x-direction is $v_0 \cos \alpha$. Then the distance traveled horizontally at the end of t seconds is $(v_0 \cos \alpha)t$ feet.

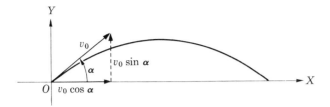

Y

v_0

$v_0 \sin \alpha$

α

O $v_0 \cos \alpha$

X

FIGURE 8–6

Now the projectile is started with a vertical component of velocity of $v_0 \sin \alpha$ feet per second. This velocity would cause the projectile to rise upward to a height of $(v_0 \sin \alpha)t$ feet in t seconds. But the effect of the pull of gravity lessens this distance. According to a formula of physics the amount to be subtracted is $\frac{1}{2}gt^2$, where g is a constant and approximately equal to 32. Hence the parametric equations of the path are

$$x = (v_0 \cos \alpha)t, \qquad y = (v_0 \sin \alpha)t - \tfrac{1}{2}gt^2. \qquad (1)$$

If we solve the first equation for t and substitute the result in the second, we obtain the equation of the path in the rectangular form

$$y = (\tan \alpha)x - \frac{gx^2}{2v_0^2 \cos^2 \alpha}. \qquad (2)$$

This equation, which is of the second degree in x and the first degree in y, represents a parabola.

EXAMPLE. A stone is thrown with a velocity of 160 ft/sec in a direction 45° above the horizontal. Find how far away the stone strikes the ground and its greatest height.

Solution. We substitute $v_0 = 160$, $\alpha = 45°$, and $g = 32$ in equations (1). This gives the parametric equations

$$x = 80\sqrt{2}\, t, \qquad y = 80\sqrt{2}\, t - 16t^2.$$

The stone reaches the ground when $y = 0$. We substitute this value for y in the second equation and find $t = 5\sqrt{2}$ sec as the time of flight. The value of x at this time is $x = 80\sqrt{2}\,(5\sqrt{2}) = 800$ ft. We know that the stone moves along a parabola which opens downward and that a parabola is symmetric with respect to its axis. Hence the greatest height is the value of y when t is half the flight time. Substituting $t = 5\sqrt{2}/2$ in the second equation, we find $y = 200$ ft. The stone strikes the ground 800 ft from the starting point and reaches a maximum height of 200 ft.

Alternatively, we can obtain the desired results by using the rectangular equation of the path. Thus substituting for v_0, α, and y in Eq. (2), we have

$$y = x - \frac{x^2}{800}.$$

This equation, reduced to standard form, becomes

$$(x - 400)^2 = -800(y - 200).$$

The vertex, at (400, 200), is the highest point. Letting $y = 0$, we find $x = 800$. Hence the stone strikes the ground at the point (800, 0).

8–5 The cycloid. The path traced by a given point on the circumference of a circle which rolls along a line is called a *cycloid*. To derive the equation of the cycloid, we select the line as the x-axis and take the origin at a position where the tracing point is in contact with the x-axis.

In Fig. 8–7 the radius of the rolling circle is a, and P is the tracing point. In the position drawn, the circle has rolled so that CP makes an angle θ (radians) with the vertical. Since the circle rolls without slipping, the line segment OB and the arc PB are of equal length. Hence

$$OB = \text{arc } PB = a\theta.$$

Observing the right triangle PDC, we may write

$$x = OA = OB - PD = a\theta - a \sin \theta,$$
$$y = AP = BC - DC = a - a \cos \theta.$$

The equations of the cycloid in parametric form are

$$x = a(\theta - \sin \theta), \qquad y = a(1 - \cos \theta).$$

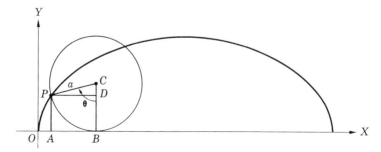

FIGURE 8–7

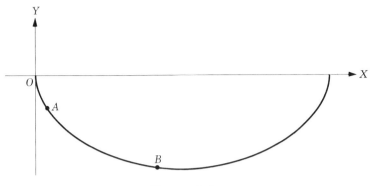

FIGURE 8–8

The result of eliminating θ from these equations is the complicated equation

$$x = a \arccos \frac{a - y}{a} \pm \sqrt{2ay - y^2}.$$

If a circle rolls beneath a line, a point of the circle would generate an inverted cycloid (Fig. 8–8). This curve has an interesting and important physical property. A body sliding without friction would move from A to B, two points on a downward part of the curve, in a shorter time than would be required along any other path connecting the two points. A proof of this property is too difficult to be included.

EXERCISE 8–2

In each problem 1 through 4 write the parametric equations of the path of the object, using $g = 32$. Write also the rectangular equation of the path and give the requested information.

1. A ball is thrown with an initial velocity of 80 ft/sec and at an angle 45° above the horizontal. How high does the ball ascend and how far away, assuming the ground to be level, does it strike the ground?

2. A projectile is fired with an initial velocity of 160 ft/sec and at an angle 30° above the horizontal. Find the coordinates of its position at the end of (a) 1 sec, (b) 3 sec, (c) 5 sec. At what times is the projectile 64 ft above the starting point?

3. A projectile is fired horizontally ($\alpha = 0°$) from a building 64 ft high. If the initial velocity is v_0 ft/sec, find how far downward and how far horizontally the projectile travels in 2 sec.

4. A pitcher throws a baseball horizontally with an initial velocity of 108 ft/sec. If the point of release is 6 ft above the ground, at what height does the ball reach the home plate, 60.5 ft from the pitcher's box?

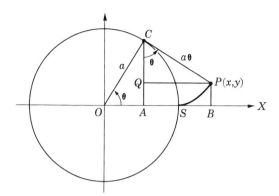

FIGURE 8-9

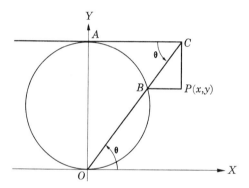

FIGURE 8-10

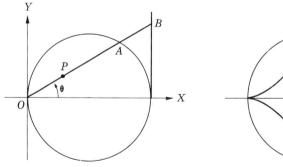

FIGURE 8-11

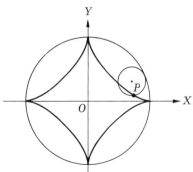

FIGURE 8-12

5. A circle of radius a rolls along a line. A point on a radius, b units from the center, describes a path. Paralleling the derivation in Section 8–5, show that the path is represented by the equations

$$x = a\theta - b \sin \theta, \qquad y = a - b \cos \theta.$$

The curve is called a *curtate cycloid* if $b < a$ and a *prolate cycloid* if $b > a$.

6. Sketch the curve of the equations in problem 5, taking $a = 4$ and $b = 3$. Sketch the curve if $a = 4$ and $b = 6$.

7. A circle of radius 4 rolls along a line and makes a revolution in 2 sec. A point, starting downward on a vertical radius, moves from the center to the circumference along the radius at a rate of 2 ft/sec. Find the equations of the path of the point.

8. The end of a thread kept in the plane of a circle describes a path called the *involute* of the circle, as it is unwound tautly from the circle. Use Fig. 8–9 to show that the parametric equations of the involute are

$$x = a(\cos \theta + \theta \sin \theta), \qquad y = a(\sin \theta - \theta \cos \theta).$$

9. In Fig. 8–10 a circle of radius a is tangent to the two parallel lines OX and AC. The line OC cuts the circle at B, and $P(x, y)$ is the intersection of a horizontal line through B and a vertical line through C. Show that the equations of the locus of P, as C moves along the upper tangent, are

$$x = 2a \cot \theta, \qquad y = 2a \sin^2 \theta.$$

This curve is called the *witch of Agnesi*. Show that its rectangular equation is

$$y = \frac{8a^3}{x^2 + 4a^2}.$$

10. In Fig. 8–11, $OP = AB$. Show that the equations of the path traced by P, as A moves around the circle, are

$$x = 2a \sin^2 \theta, \qquad y = 2a \sin^2 \theta \tan \theta.$$

The curve is called the *cissoid of Diocles*. The rectangular equation is

$$y^2 = \frac{x^3}{2a - x}.$$

11. The path traced by a given point on the circumference of a circle of radius $\frac{1}{4}a$ as it rolls inside and along a circle of radius a is called a *hypocycloid of four cusps*. Use Fig. 8–12 to obtain the parametric equations

$$x = a \cos^3 \theta, \qquad y = a \sin^3 \theta.$$

CHAPTER 9

CURVE FITTING

9–1 Equation corresponding to empirical data. In previous chapters we have found equations of curves which satisfy given geometric conditions. In each case all points of the curve were definitely fixed by the prescribed conditions. We now take up a different and more difficult aspect of the problem of finding equations representing known information. The problem is not primarily of geometric interest, but one in which analytic geometry is fruitful in aiding the scientist. Experimental scientists make observations and measurements of various kinds of natural phenomena. Measurements in an investigation often represent two variable quantities which are related. In many situations the study can be advanced through an equation which expresses the relation, or an approximate relation, between the variables in question. The equation can then be used to compute corresponding values of the variables other than those obtained by measurement. The equation is called an *empirical equation*, and the process employed is called *curve fitting*.

Suppose, for example, that various loads are placed at the mid-point of a beam supported at its ends. If for each load we measure the deflection of the beam at its mid-point, then we obtain a series of corresponding values. One value of each pair is the load and the other the deflection produced by the load. The table lists readings where x stands for the load in pounds and y for the deflection in inches. The pairs of values are plotted as points in Fig. 9–1. The points lie almost in a straight line

x	100	120	140	160	180	200
y	0.45	0.55	0.60	0.70	0.80	0.85

and suggest that the deflection is proportional to the load; that is, an equation of the form

$$y = mx + b$$

gives the relation, or an approximate relation, between the load and the deflection. Since the points are not exactly in a straight line, no linear equation can be satisfied by all pairs of the readings. We are then faced with the problem of selecting a particular linear equation. A line could be drawn by sight so that it passes quite close to each point. It is desirable, however, to follow some procedure which will locate a definite

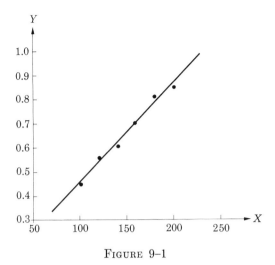

FIGURE 9–1

line. In the next section we shall discuss a method of determining a line which is called the *best fitting line* for a set of data.

If the points representing a set of data are not approximately in a straight line, a linear equation will not express well the relation between the variables; then it would be necessary to seek some nonlinear relation. Although numerous nonlinear equations are used in curve fitting, we shall deal only with the forms

$$y = ax^b,$$
$$y = a \cdot 10^{bx},$$
$$y = a \log x + b.$$

We shall refer to these equations as the *power formula*, the *exponential formula*, and the *logarithmic formula*. Many physical relations approximately obey one of these types of equations. The equations are advantageous because of their simplicity and because the constants a and b are easily determined.

9–2 Method of least squares. Suppose that we have given n points in a plane whose coordinates are (x_1, y_1), (x_2, y_2), . . . , (x_n, y_n). We define the *residual* of each of the points relative to a curve as the ordinate of the point minus the ordinate of the curve for the same x-value. The totality of residuals may be examined to determine if the curve is a good fit to the points. A curve is considered a good fit if each of the residuals is small. Since some of the residuals could be positive and others negative, their sum might be near zero for a curve which is a poor fit to the

points. Hence the sum of the residuals would not furnish a reliable measure of the accuracy of fit. For this reason we shall deal with the squares
of the residuals, thus avoiding negative quantities. If the sum of the
squares of the residuals is small, we would know that the curve passes
close to each of the n points. The better fitting of two curves of the same
type is the one for which the sum of the squares of the residuals is smaller.
The best fitting curve of a given type is the one for which the sum of
the squares of the residuals is a minimum.

Starting with the simplest situation, we shall show how to determine
the best fitting line to the n given points. We write the linear equation

$$y = mx + b,$$

where values are to be found for m and b so that the sum of the squares
of the residuals of the n points is a minimum. The residual of the point
(x_1, y_1) is $y_1 - (mx_1 + b)$. The quantity y_1 is the ordinate of the point,
and $(mx_1 + b)$ is the ordinate of the line when $x = x_1$. Hence the residuals of the points are

$$y_1 - (mx_1 + b), y_2 - (mx_2 + b), \ldots, y_n - (mx_n + b),$$

and their squares are

$$y_1^2 - 2mx_1y_1 - 2y_1b + m^2x_1^2 + 2mx_1b + b^2,$$
$$y_2^2 - 2mx_2y_2 - 2y_2b + m^2x_2^2 + 2mx_2b + b^2,$$
$$\vdots$$
$$y_n^2 - 2mx_ny_n - 2y_nb + m^2x_n^2 + 2mx_nb + b^2.$$

We use the following notation to express the sum of these expressions in
a convenient form.

$$\sum x = x_1 + x_2 + \cdots + x_n,$$
$$\sum x^2 = x_1^2 + x_2^2 + \cdots + x_n^2,$$
$$\sum xy = x_1y_1 + x_2y_2 + \cdots + x_ny_n.$$

Denoting the sum of the squares of the residuals by R, we have

$$R = \sum y^2 - 2m\sum xy - 2b\sum y + m^2\sum x^2 + 2mb\sum x + nb^2. \quad (1)$$

We note that all quantities in the right member of this equation are
fixed in value except for m and b. For example, $\sum y^2$ is not a variable; it
stands for the sum of the squares of the ordinates of the n fixed points.

Our problem now is to determine values for m and b which make R a
minimum. The expression for R contains the first and second powers of

both m and b. If, however, we treat b as an unspecified constant, then the variables in the equation are R and m. Since R appears linearly and m quadratically, the graph of the equation is a parabola. Choosing the m-axis as horizontal and the R-axis as vertical, we see that the parabola would have a vertical axis. Further, the parabola opens upward because R, being the sum of squared expressions, is not negative. Consequently, the least value of R is the ordinate of the vertex. Hence R takes the least possible value when m is equal to the abscissa of the vertex of the parabola. We can find the abscissa of the vertex by writing Eq. (1) in standard form (Section 3–3). In this way it can be shown that R has its least value when

$$m\sum x^2 + b\sum x - \sum xy = 0.$$

Similarly, we can consider m as a constant and obtain the equation

$$m\sum x + nb - \sum y = 0.$$

Solving the two preceding equations simultaneously for m and b, we obtain

$$m = \frac{n\sum xy - \sum x\sum y}{n\sum x^2 - (\sum x)^2}, \quad b = \frac{\sum x^2\sum y - \sum x\sum xy}{n\sum x^2 - (\sum x)^2}. \tag{2}$$

These formulas enable us to compute m and b for the line of best fit to a set of given points. We illustrate their use in an example.

EXAMPLE. Find the line of best fit to the data plotted in Fig. 9–1.

Solution. The six pairs of corresponding x- and y-values are listed in Section 9–1. We use these data to compute the sums appearing in Eq. (2) and obtain

$$\sum x = 100 + 120 + 140 + 160 + 180 + 200 = 900,$$
$$\sum y = 0.45 + 0.55 + 0.60 + 0.70 + 0.80 + 0.85 = 3.95,$$
$$\sum x^2 = 100^2 + 120^2 + 140^2 + 160^2 + 180^2 + 200^2 = 142{,}000,$$
$$\sum xy = 100(.45) + 120(.55) + 140(.60) + 160(.70) + 180(.80) + 200(.85)$$
$$= 621.$$

These results, substituted in Eq. (2) for m and b, yield

$$m = \frac{6(621) - 900(3.95)}{6(142{,}000) - 900^2} = \frac{171}{42{,}000} = 0.0041,$$
$$b = \frac{142{,}000(3.95) - 900(621)}{42{,}000} = 0.048.$$

Using these values for m and b, we find the equation of the line of best fit to the data to be

$$y = 0.0041x + 0.048.$$

This equation gives approximately the relation between the load and deflection and holds for loads which do not bend the beam beyond its elastic limits. The deflection produced by a load of 400 pounds, for example, is $y = 0.0041(400) + 0.048 = 1.69$ inches. The data and the line are shown graphically in Fig. 9–1.

EXERCISE 9–1

Find the equation of the line of best fit to the sets of points in problems 1 and 2. Plot the points and draw the line.

1. $(1, 8), (4, 6), (5, 5), (8, 3), (9, 2), (11, 1)$
2. $(-2, -10), (0, -5), (1, 0), (2, 5), (4, 8)$

3. The length y (in.) of a coiled spring under various loads x (lb) are recorded in the table. Find the line of best fit, $y = mx + b$, for these measurements. Use the resulting equation to find the length of the spring when the load is 17 lb.

x	10	20	30	40	50
y	11.0	12.1	13.0	13.9	15.1

4. A business showed net profits at the end of each year for 4 years as follows:

Year	1	2	3	4
Profit	$10,000	$12,000	$13,000	$15,000

Determine the best linear fit and predict the profit for the 5th year.

5. The population N of a city at the end of each decade t for 5 decades is shown in the table. Find the line of best fit, $N = mt + b$, for these data. Predict the population at the end of the 6th decade.

t	1	2	3	4	5
N	8,000	9,000	10,100	11,400	13,700

6. The relation between the total amount of heat H in a pound of saturated steam at T degrees centigrade is $H = mT + b$. Determine m and b for the best linear fit to these data.

T	50	70	90	110
H	623	627	632	636

9–3 The power formula. Proceeding to nonlinear fits, we consider first the equation

$$y = ax^b.$$

The common logarithms of the members of the equation yield

$$\log y = b \log x + \log a.$$

This equation, being linear in $\log x$ and $\log y$, suggests the plotting of the points $(\log x, \log y)$. If the points so obtained lie approximately on a line, the power formula is applicable to the set of data. The procedure then is to determine a and b for the best linear fit to the points $(\log x, \log y)$. The substitution of the values thus determined in the equation $y = ax^b$ gives a best-power fit to the data.

A test of the applicability of a power formula can be made quickly by the use of logarithmic coordinate paper which has its horizontal and vertical rulings placed at distances $\log 2$, $\log 3$, $\log 4$, and so on, from the origin. The original data plotted on this kind of paper are equivalent to plotting the logarithms on regular coordinate paper. The following example illustrates the power-formula method and the use of the special coordinate paper.

EXAMPLE. The relation between the pressure p and the volume V of a confined gas is given by

$$p = aV^b,$$

when the gas neither receives nor loses heat. Determine a and b for the data contained in the table.

V (cu ft)	9.80	6.72	4.53	4.16	3.36	2.83
p (lb/in²)	3	6	9	12	15	18

Solution. The given data are plotted on logarithmic paper in Fig. 9–2. The points are approximately in a straight line, and therefore indicate that an equation of the power type is suitable for representing the data.

We form the following table by replacing each number of the above data by its common logarithm.

$\log V$	0.9912	0.8274	0.6561	0.6191	0.5263	0.4518
$\log p$	0.4771	0.7782	0.9542	1.0792	1.1761	1.2553

The equation corresponding to this transformed data is

$$\log p = b \log V + \log a.$$

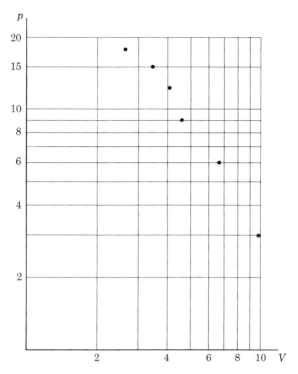

FIGURE 9–2

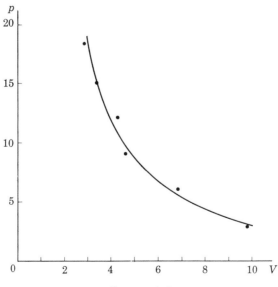

FIGURE 9–3

To obtain the best linear fit to the new data, we employ Eq. (2), Section 9–2, using log V for x and log p for y. The first formula yields the coefficient of log V and the second yields the constant term log a. We have the following sums:

$$\sum \log V = 4.0719,$$
$$\sum (\log V)^2 = 2.9619,$$
$$\sum \log p = 5.7201,$$
$$\sum (\log V)(\log p) = 3.5971.$$

Substituting these values and $n = 6$, we get

$$b = \frac{6(3.5971) - 4.0719(5.7201)}{6(2.9619) - (4.0719)^2} = -1.43,$$

$$\log a = \frac{2.9619(5.7201) - 4.0719(3.5961)}{6(2.9619) - (4.0719)^2} = 1.9272,$$

$$a = 84.6.$$

Making these substitutions for a and b, we have

$$p = 84.6 \cdot V^{-1.43}.$$

The graph of this equation and the points representing the original data are shown in Fig. 9–3.

EXERCISE 9–2

In problems 1 and 2 assume the form $y = ax^b$ and determine a and b for the best fit.

1.

x	2	3	5	7
y	1	4	20	50

2.

x	1	2	3	4
y	0.5	3.0	6.8	10.0

3. A body falls s feet in t seconds. Show that the form $t = as^b$ is applicable to the recorded data and determine a and b for the best fit.

s	4	10	16	25	36
t	0.51	0.79	1.01	1.24	1.49

4. If R is the air resistance in pounds against an automobile traveling at V miles per hour, show that the form $R = aV^b$ is applicable to the measurements in the table and find a and b for the best fit.

V	10	20	30	40	50
R	7	24	65	120	180

5. Corresponding measurements of the volume and pressure of steam are given in the table. Find the best fit of the form $p = aV^n$ to these data.

V	9	5	2.4	2.1	1
p	5	10	30	40	100

9–4 Exponential and logarithmic formulas. We saw in the preceding section that the power form can be reduced to a linear form. Similarly, the exponential and logarithmic forms are reducible to linear forms.

We take the common logarithm of each member of the equation

$$y = a \cdot 10^{bx}$$

and get

$$\log y = bx + \log a.$$

Here $\log y$ is expressed linearly in terms of x. Hence the exponential formula is applicable to a set of data if the points $(x, \log y)$ are in close proximity to a straight line. When this occurs, the procedure is to determine a and b so that $bx + \log a$ is the best linear fit to the set of points $(x, \log y)$.

Semilogarithmic paper may be used to determine whether the exponential formula is adequate to represent the given data. This paper has the usual scale along the x-axis and the logarithmic scale along the positive y-axis.

Passing finally to the logarithmic formula

$$y = a \log x + b,$$

we see that the equation is linear in y and $\log x$. We consider the points $(\log x, y)$. If these are about in a straight line, then a and b should be found for a linear fit to the points. The values thus obtained should be substituted in the logarithmic equation.

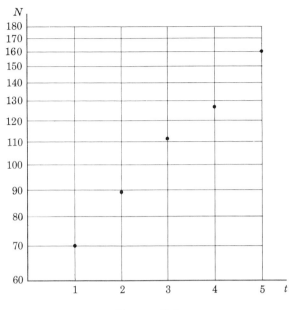

FIGURE 9–4

EXAMPLE. The number of bacteria N per unit volume in a culture after t hours is given by the table for several values of t. Show that $N = a \cdot 10^{bt}$ may represent the data and find values for a and b.

t	1	2	3	4	5
N	70	88	111	127	160

Solution. The given data, plotted on semilogarithmic paper, yield points almost collinear (Fig. 9–4). This indicates that the data can be approximated by an exponential formula. Hence we transform the given data by taking the logarithm of each N.

t	1	2	3	4	5
$\log N$	1.845	1.945	2.045	2.104	2.204

We compute the following sums:

$$\sum t = 15, \qquad \sum t^2 = 55,$$
$$\sum \log N = 10.143, \qquad \sum t(\log N) = 31.306.$$

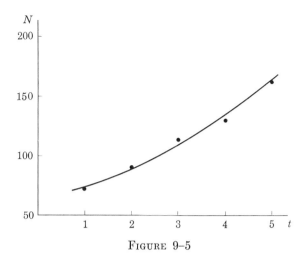

FIGURE 9–5

Using these values in Eq. (2), Section 9–2, we get

$$b = \frac{5(31.306) - 15(10.143)}{5(55) - 15^2} = \frac{4.385}{50} = 0.0877,$$

$$\log a = \frac{55(10.143) - 15(31.306)}{50} = 1.766,$$

$$a = 58.3.$$

We obtain the equation $N = 58.3 \cdot 10^{0.0877t}$. The graph and the given data are shown in Fig. 9–5.

EXERCISE 9–3

In problems 1 through 3 find best fits of the type indicated.

1.

x	-3	-1	1	3	5
y	0.8	1.5	2.7	4.9	9.0

$y = a \cdot 10^{bx}$

2.

x	0	1	2	3	5
y	3.0	2.5	2.1	1.6	1.1

$y = a \cdot 10^{bx}$

3.

x	$\frac{1}{2}$	1	3	5	8
y	0	3.1	7.8	9.9	12

$y = a \log x + b$

4. The bacteria count N per unit volume in a certain culture at the end of t hours was estimated as in the table. Find the best relation of the form $N = a \cdot 10^{bt}$.

t	0	2	4	6	8
N	10	16	25	40	63

5. The temperature T (degrees C) of a cooling body at time t (min) was measured as recorded. Find an exponential formula of best fit for T in terms of t.

t	0	1	2	3	4	5
T	100	79	63	50	40	32

6. The atmospheric pressure p in pounds per square inch at a height h in thousands of feet is shown in the table. Express p exponentially in terms of h.

h	0	5	10	15	20
p	14.6	12.1	10.1	8.4	7.0

7. The horsepower P required for the speeds V in knots for a certain ship are recorded in the table. Find the best fit to the data of the form $V = a \log P + b$.

P	2000	4000	7000	12000
V	12	13	14	15

CHAPTER 10

SPACE COORDINATES AND SURFACES

10–1 Space coordinates. In our study thus far, we have dealt with equations in two variables and have pictured equations in a plane coordinate system. When we introduce a third variable, a plane will not suffice for the illustration of an equation. For this purpose our coordinate system is extended to three dimensions.

Let OX, OY, and OZ be three mutually perpendicular lines (Fig. 10–1) which constitute the x-, y-, and z-axes. In this drawing, and others which we shall make, the y- and z-axes are in the plane of the page, and the x-axis is to be visualized as perpendicular to the page. The z-axis may be regarded as vertical and the others as horizontal. The axes, in pairs, determine three mutually perpendicular planes, XOY, XOZ, and YOZ, called *coordinate planes*. They are designated, respectively, the xy-, xz-, and yz-planes. They divide space into eight regions, called *octants*.

We next establish a number scale on each axis with the point O as the origin. The position of a point P in this coordinate system is determined by its distances from the coordinate planes. The distance of P from the yz-plane is called the *x-coordinate*, the distance from the xz-plane the *y-coordinate*, and the distance from the xy-plane the *z-coordinate*. The coordinates of a point are written in the form (x, y, z). We observe that three given distances definitely locate a point. To plot the point

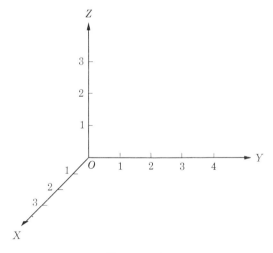

FIGURE 10–1

166

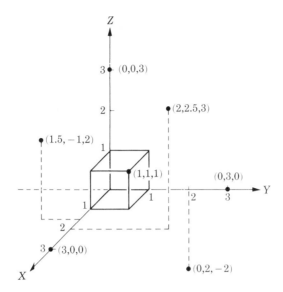

FIGURE 10–2

$(1.5, -1, 2)$, for example, we go 1.5 units from the origin along the positive x-axis, then 1 unit to the left parallel to the y-axis, and finally 2 units upward parallel to the z-axis. The signs of the coordinates determine the octant in which a point lies. Points whose coordinates are all positive are said to belong to the *first octant;* the other octants are not customarily assigned numbers. If a point is on a coordinate axis, two of its coordinates are zero.

In plotting points and drawing figures, we shall make unit distances on the y- and z-axes equal. A unit distance on the x-axis will be represented by an actual length of about 0.7 of a unit. The x-axis will be drawn at an angle of 135° with the y-axis. This position of the x-axis and the foreshortening in the x-direction aid in visualizing space figures. Look at the cube and the plotted points in Fig. 10–2.

10–2 The locus of an equation. The locus of an equation in a three-dimensional system is defined exactly as it is in a two-dimensional system.

DEFINITION. *The locus of an equation consists of all the points, and only those points, whose coordinates satisfy the given equation.*

In the two-dimensional system we found lines and curves as the loci of equations. In three dimensions the locus of an equation is a *surface.* There are equations whose loci, in three dimensions, are space curves (curves not lying in a plane). We are excluding space curves from consideration. We have observed, of course, that some two-dimensional equations have no loci, and that others consist of one or more isolated points. Similarly, there are exceptional cases in a three-dimensional system. However, we shall be interested in equations whose loci exist and are surfaces.

10–3 Cylindrical surfaces. We shall begin our study of loci by considering equations in one and two variables. As a further restriction, we shall use equations of only the first and second degrees. The loci of equations of this class are comparatively easy to determine.

To find the locus of the equation

$$y = 4,$$

for example, we observe that the equation is satisfied by giving y the value 4. Since the equation does not contain x or z, no restrictions are placed on these variables; hence the locus consists of all points which have the y-coordinate equal to 4. The locus is obviously the plane parallel to the xz-plane and 4 units to the right.

Passing now to a linear equation in two variables, we choose for illustration the equation

$$2x + 3z = 6.$$

In the xz-plane this equation represents a line. Consider now a plane through this line and parallel to the y-axis (Fig. 10–3). Any point $P(x, y, z)$ on this plane has a point on the line with the same x- and z-coordinates. Hence the coordinates of P satisfy the given equation. We conclude, therefore, that the plane is the locus of the equation.

The two examples illustrate the correctness of the following statement:

The locus of a first-degree equation in one or two variables is a plane and the plane is parallel to the axis of each missing variable.

Take now the equation

$$x^2 + (y - 2)^2 = 4.$$

In the xy-plane the locus of this equation is a circle of radius 2 with the center on the positive y-axis 2 units from the origin (Fig. 10–4). Let $(x, y, 0)$ be the coordinates of any point of the circle. Then the point (x, y, z), where z is any real number, satisfies the equation. Thus we see that the locus of the given equation is a surface generated by a line which moves so that it keeps parallel to the z-axis and intersects the circle. The surface therefore is a right circular cylinder which is symmetric with

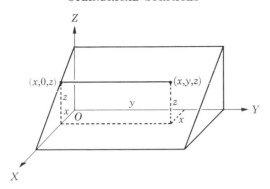

FIGURE 10–3

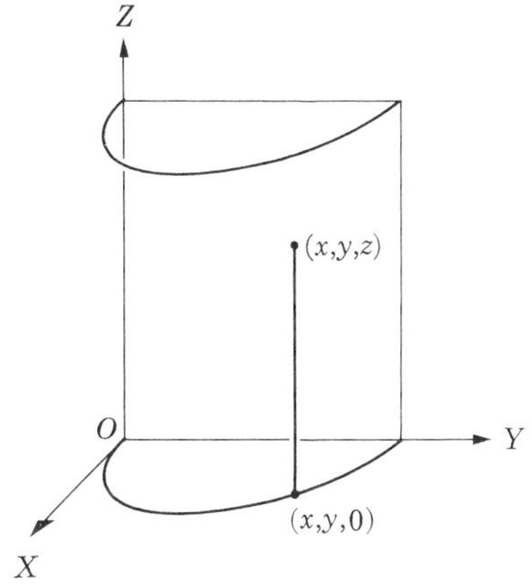

FIGURE 10–4

respect to the yz-plane. In the figure, only the part of the surface in the first octant is indicated.

A surface generated by a line which moves so that it keeps parallel to a fixed line and intersects a fixed curve in a plane is called a *cylindrical surface* or *cylinder*. The curve is called the *directrix*, and the generating line in any position is called an *element* of the cylinder. In accordance with this definition, a plane is a special case of a cylinder with a straight line as the directrix. Hence the locus of each of the three equations which we have considered is a cylinder.

It is easy to generalize the preceding discussion to apply to equations in two variables, even without restriction to the degree, and establish the following theorem.

THEOREM. *The locus of an equation in two variables is a cylinder whose elements are parallel to the axis of the missing variable.*

EXERCISE 10–1

1. Draw the coordinate axes and plot the points: $A(0, 0, 2)$, $B(0, 2, 0)$, $C(2, 0, 0)$, $D(2, 3, 0)$, $E(3, 2, 4)$, $F(-2, 0, 4)$, $G(-1, -1, -1)$, $H(2, 1, -2)$.

2. Draw a cube which has the origin and the point $(4, 4, 4)$ as opposite corners. Write the coordinates of the other corners.

3. Draw the edges of a box which has four of its vertices located at the points $(0, 0, 0)$, $(3, 0, 0)$, $(0, 2, 0)$, and $(0, 0, 2)$. Write the coordinates of the other vertices.

4. Draw the rectangular parallelepiped which has three of its faces in the coordinate planes and the points $(0, 0, 0)$ and $(4, 5, 3)$ as the ends of a diagonal. Write the coordinates of the vertices.

Describe the surface corresponding to each equation 5 through 24 and make a sketch of the surface.

5. $x = 0$	6. $y = 0$	7. $z = 0$
8. $z = 5$	9. $z = -5$	10. $x + y = 4$
11. $3x + 4z = 12$	12. $2y + z = 6$	13. $x + z = 0$
14. $2x - y = 0$	15. $3y - z = 6$	16. $z - 4x = 8$
17. $x^2 + y^2 = 4$	18. $(y - 2)^2 + z^2 = 1$	19. $x^2 = 9z$
20. $y^2 = 4z$	21. $(x - 2)^2 = 8y$	22. $4x^2 + 9y^2 = 36$
23. $x^2 + z^2 - 4x - 6z + 9 = 0$	24. $x^2 + 4y^2 - 4x - 32y = 64$	

10–4 The general linear equation. In rectangular coordinates of two dimensions we found that a linear equation, in either one or two variables, represents a line. In our three-dimensional system we might, by analogy, surmise that linear equations in one, two, or three variables represent surfaces of the same type. The surmise is correct. At this point, however, we merely state the fact as a theorem and reserve the proof for the next chapter.

THEOREM. *The locus, in three dimensions, of the equation*

$$Ax + By + Cz + D = 0,$$

where the constants A, B, and C are not all zero, is a plane.

The location of a plane represented by a linear equation can be determined by finding the lines in which the plane intersects the coordinate planes. These intersections, as well as the intersections which any surface makes with the coordinate planes, are called *traces*.

Consider the equation

$$3x + 4y + 6z = 12.$$

The trace of the locus on the yz-plane has the x-coordinate equal to zero.

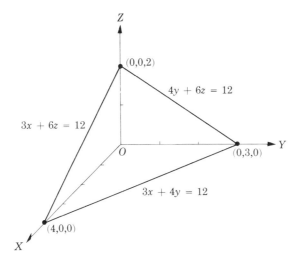

FIGURE 10–5

Hence we set $x = 0$ in the given equation and have

$$4y + 6z = 12$$

as the equation of the trace on the yz-plane. The equations of the traces on the xz- and xy-planes are

$$3x + 6z = 12 \quad \text{and} \quad 3x + 4y = 12.$$

Figure 10–5 shows segments of the traces. The segments form a triangle which may be used to picture the plane.

10–5 Second-degree equations. The locus of an equation of the second degree is called a *quadric surface*. It is not easy to determine the characteristics and location of a quadric surface corresponding to an equation. A term of the second degree in equations which we shall consider will arise from the square of a variable and not the product of two variables. The loci of equations of this type are more easily studied.

The main device in examining the locus of an equation consists of observing the intersections of the surface by the coordinate planes and planes parallel to them. The idea of symmetry, as in a two-dimensional system, may be used to advantage. If x can be replaced by $-x$ without changing the equation, there is symmetry with respect to the yz-plane. Corresponding statements apply for the other variables and coordinate planes.

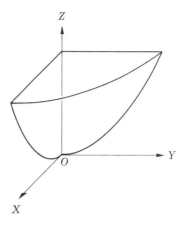

FIGURE 10–6

To illustrate the method, we examine the equation

$$x^2 + y^2 = 4z.$$

The surface is symmetric with respect to the yz- and xz-planes. Negative values must not be assigned to z; thus no part of the surface is below the xy-plane. When $z = 0$, then $x = 0$ and $y = 0$. Sections made by planes parallel to the xy-plane are circles. This is evident if we substitute a positive value for z. The plane $z = 1$, for example, cuts the surface in the circle

$$x^2 + y^2 = 4.$$

Circles of greater radii are obtained as the intersecting plane is taken farther and farther from the xy-plane. We next substitute $y = 0$ in the given equation and get

$$x^2 = 4z.$$

Hence the trace in the xz-plane is a parabola. Similarly, the trace in the yz-plane is the parabola $y^2 = 4z$.

We now have sufficient information to form a mental picture of the surface. As a matter of interest, though, we observe that sections parallel to the xz- and yz-planes are parabolas. When $x = 4$, for example, we find that the other coordinates must satisfy the equation

$$y^2 = 4(z - 4).$$

The coordinates of the vertex of this parabola are $(4, 0, 4)$. Figure 10–6 shows a sketch of the surface in the first octant. The complete surface is symmetric with respect to the xz- and yz-planes and can be easily visualized.

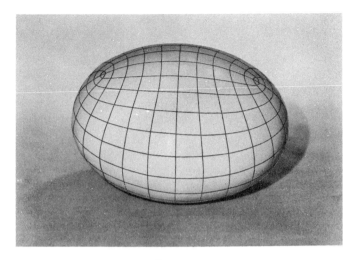

ELLIPSOID

10-6 Quadric surfaces. We shall now discuss a number of second-degree, or quadratic, equations which are said to be in standard forms. The study of these equations and their loci, though presently of only geometric interest, furnish information and experience which will prove helpful in other mathematical situations, particularly in the calculus.

A. The ellipsoid. The locus of the equation

$$\frac{x^2}{a^2} + \frac{y^2}{b^2} + \frac{z^2}{c^2} = 1$$

is called an *ellipsoid.* We see at once that the surface is symmetric with respect to each coordinate plane. By setting one of the variables at a time equal to zero, we find the trace equations to be

$$\frac{x^2}{a^2} + \frac{y^2}{b^2} = 1, \qquad \frac{x^2}{a^2} + \frac{z^2}{c^2} = 1, \qquad \frac{y^2}{b^2} + \frac{z^2}{c^2} = 1.$$

The traces are all ellipses. Next we assign to x a definite nonzero value, $x = x_0$, and write the given equation as

$$\frac{y^2}{b^2} + \frac{z^2}{c^2} = 1 - \frac{x_0^2}{a^2}.$$

This equation shows that sections made by planes parallel to the yz-plane

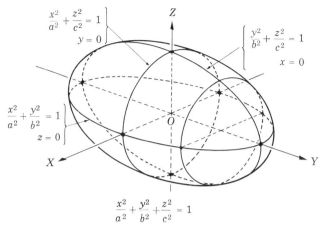

$$\frac{x^2}{a^2} + \frac{z^2}{c^2} = 1$$
$$y = 0$$

$$\frac{y^2}{b^2} + \frac{z^2}{c^2} = 1$$
$$x = 0$$

$$\frac{x^2}{a^2} + \frac{y^2}{b^2} = 1$$
$$z = 0$$

$$\frac{x^2}{a^2} + \frac{y^2}{b^2} + \frac{z^2}{c^2} = 1$$

FIGURE 10–7

are ellipses. Further, the elliptic sections decrease in size as the intersecting plane moves farther from the yz-plane. When the moving plane reaches a distance a from the yz-plane, the equation of the section becomes

$$\frac{y^2}{b^2} + \frac{z^2}{c^2} = 0,$$

and the intersection, therefore, is a point. Each of the planes $x = a$ and $x = -a$ contains one point of the ellipsoid; all other points of the surface lie between these planes.

We could have a similar discussion with respect to sections parallel to each of the other coordinate planes. Elliptic sections are obtained for values of z between $-c$ and c, and for values of y between $-b$ and b.

By the method of sections we obtain a clear mental picture of the ellipsoid and a guide for making a sketch (Fig. 10–7).

If two of the three quantities a, b, and c are equal, the sections parallel to one of the coordinate planes are circles. Taking $a = b$ and choosing a permissible value z_0 for z, we have the equation

$$x^2 + y^2 = a^2 \left(1 - \frac{z_0^2}{c^2}\right).$$

Thus we see that planes parallel to the xy-plane cut the surface in circles. The ellipsoid in this instance could be generated by revolving the xz- or the yz-trace about the z-axis. A surface generated by revolving a curve about a straight line is a *surface of revolution*. Finally, if $a = b = c$, the ellipsoid is a sphere.

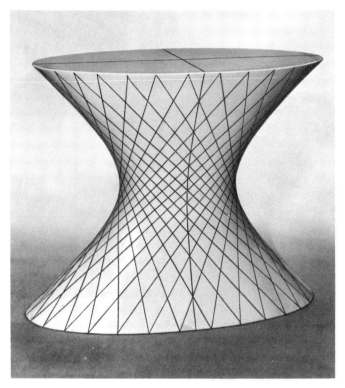

Hʏᴘᴇʀʙᴏʟᴏɪᴅ ᴏꜰ ᴏɴᴇ ꜱʜᴇᴇᴛ.

B. *The hyperboloid of one sheet.* The surface represented by the equation

$$\frac{x^2}{a^2} + \frac{y^2}{b^2} - \frac{z^2}{c^2} = 1$$

is called a *hyperboloid of one sheet* (Fig. 10–8). The surface is symmetric with respect to each of the coordinate planes. Setting $z = 0$, we get the equation

$$\frac{x^2}{a^2} + \frac{y^2}{b^2} = 1.$$

Hence the xy-trace is an ellipse. If we replace z in the given equation by a fixed value z_0, we obtain

$$\frac{x^2}{a^2} + \frac{y^2}{b^2} = 1 + \frac{z_0^2}{c^2}.$$

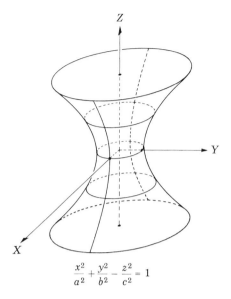

$$\frac{x^2}{a^2} + \frac{y^2}{b^2} - \frac{z^2}{c^2} = 1$$

FIGURE 10–8

This equation shows that sections parallel to the xy-plane are ellipses and that the sections increase in size as the intersecting plane $z = z_0$ recedes from the origin. If $a = b$, the sections are circles, and the surface is a surface of revolution.

The traces in the xz- and yz-planes, respectively, are the hyperbolas

$$\frac{x^2}{a^2} - \frac{z^2}{c^2} = 1 \quad \text{and} \quad \frac{y^2}{b^2} - \frac{z^2}{c^2} = 1.$$

The sections parallel to the xz- and yz-planes are likewise hyperbolas.

Each of the equations

$$\frac{x^2}{a^2} - \frac{y^2}{b^2} + \frac{z^2}{c^2} = 1 \quad \text{and} \quad -\frac{x^2}{a^2} + \frac{y^2}{b^2} + \frac{z^2}{c^2} = 1$$

represents a hyperboloid of one sheet. The first encloses the y-axis and the second the x-axis.

C. *The hyperboloid of two sheets.* The surface represented by

$$\frac{x^2}{a^2} - \frac{y^2}{b^2} - \frac{z^2}{c^2} = 1$$

is called a *hyperboloid of two sheets.* The surface possesses symmetry with

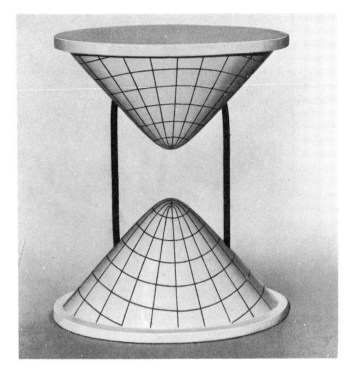

HYPERBOLOID OF TWO SHEETS.

respect to each coordinate plane. By setting each variable in turn equal to zero, we get the equations

$$\frac{x^2}{a^2} - \frac{y^2}{b^2} = 1, \qquad \frac{x^2}{a^2} - \frac{z^2}{c^2} = 1, \qquad -\frac{y^2}{b^2} - \frac{z^2}{c^2} = 1.$$

The first two equations illustrate that the xy- and xz-traces are hyperbolas. The third shows us there is no trace in the yz-plane. The sections made by the plane $x = x_0$ is given by the equation

$$\frac{y^2}{b^2} + \frac{z^2}{c^2} = \frac{x_0^2}{a^2} - 1.$$

This equation represents a point or an ellipse according as the numerical value of x_0 is equal to or greater than a. Hence the locus of the given equation consists of two separate parts. Sections parallel to the xz- and xy-planes are hyperbolas. If $b = c$, the sections parallel to the yz-plane are circles, and, in this case, the hyperboloid of two sheets is a surface of revolution.

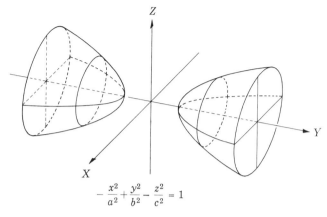

$$-\frac{x^2}{a^2}+\frac{y^2}{b^2}-\frac{z^2}{c^2} = 1$$

FIGURE 10–9

Hyperboloids of two sheets are also represented by the equations

$$-\frac{x^2}{a^2}-\frac{y^2}{b^2}+\frac{z^2}{c^2} = 1 \qquad \text{and} \qquad -\frac{x^2}{a^2}+\frac{y^2}{b^2}-\frac{z^2}{c^2} = 1.$$

The surface corresponding to this last equation is pictured in Fig. 10–9.

D. *The elliptic paraboloid.* The locus of the equation

$$\frac{x^2}{a^2}+\frac{y^2}{b^2} = cz$$

is called an *elliptic paraboloid.* The xy-trace, obtained by setting $z = 0$, is the origin. The surface, except for the origin, is above the xy-plane when $c > 0$ and below the xy-plane when $c < 0$. A plane parallel to the xy-plane and cutting the surface makes an elliptic section which increases in size as the plane recedes from the origin. The traces in the xz- and yz-planes, respectively, are the parabolas

$$\frac{x^2}{a^2} = cz \qquad \text{and} \qquad \frac{y^2}{b^2} = cz.$$

From this information, the surface (Fig. 10–10) can be readily visualized.

If $a = b$, the sections parallel to the xy-plane are circles. In this example the surface is obtainable by rotating either the xz- or the yz-trace about the z-axis.

Elliptic paraboloids are also represented by the equations

$$\frac{x^2}{a^2}+\frac{z^2}{c^2} = by \qquad \text{and} \qquad \frac{y^2}{b^2}+\frac{z^2}{c^2} = ax.$$

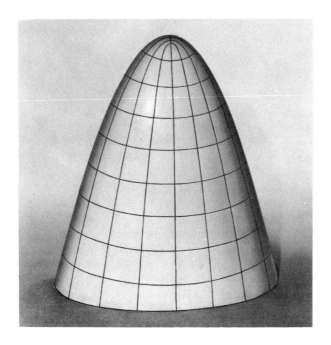

ELLIPTIC PARABOLOID

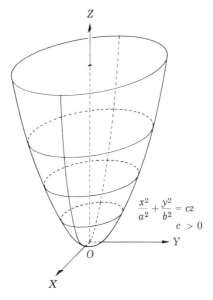

$$\frac{x^2}{a^2} + \frac{y^2}{b^2} = cz$$
$$c > 0$$

FIGURE 10-10

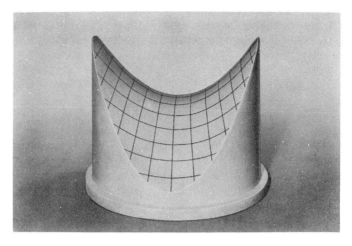

HYPERBOLIC PARABOLOID

E. The hyperbolic paraboloid. The locus of the equation

$$\frac{x^2}{a^2} - \frac{y^2}{b^2} = cz$$

is called a *hyperbolic paraboloid*. The surface is symmetric with respect to the yz- and the xz-planes. The xy-trace is given by the equation

$$\frac{x^2}{a^2} - \frac{y^2}{b^2} = 0 \qquad \text{or} \qquad \left(\frac{x}{a} + \frac{y}{b}\right)\left(\frac{x}{a} - \frac{y}{b}\right) = 0.$$

This equation represents a pair of lines intersecting at the origin. The section made by the plane $z = z_0$ is the hyperbola

$$\frac{x^2}{a^2} - \frac{y^2}{b^2} = cz_0.$$

The transverse axis of the hyperbola is parallel to the x-axis when the right member of this equation is positive, and parallel to the y-axis when the right member is negative. Sections by planes parallel to the xz-plane and the yz-plane are the parabolas

$$\frac{x^2}{a^2} = cz \qquad \text{and} \qquad -\frac{y^2}{b^2} = cz.$$

The preceding analysis suggests that the hyperbolic paraboloid is a saddle-shaped surface. Further aid in visualizing the surface may be had from Fig. 10–11.

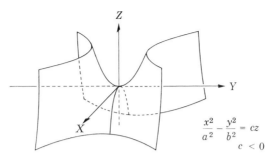

$$\frac{x^2}{a^2} - \frac{y^2}{b^2} = cz$$
$$c < 0$$

FIGURE 10–11

A hyperbolic paraboloid is also represented by each of the equations

$$\frac{x^2}{a^2} - \frac{z^2}{c^2} = by \qquad \text{and} \qquad \frac{y^2}{b^2} - \frac{z^2}{c^2} = ax.$$

F. *The elliptic cone.* The locus of the equation

$$\frac{x^2}{a^2} + \frac{y^2}{b^2} = \frac{z^2}{c^2}$$

is an *elliptic cone* (Fig. 10–12). Setting x, y, and z in turn equal to zero,

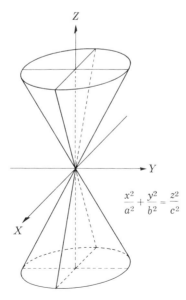

$$\frac{x^2}{a^2} + \frac{y^2}{b^2} = \frac{z^2}{c^2}$$

FIGURE 10-12

we have the trace equations

$$\frac{x^2}{a^2} + \frac{y^2}{b^2} = 0, \qquad \frac{x^2}{a^2} = \frac{z^2}{c^2}, \qquad \frac{y^2}{b^2} = \frac{z^2}{c^2}.$$

The equations reveal that the xy-trace is the origin, and that each of the other traces is a pair of lines intersecting at the origin.

Sections parallel to the xy-plane are ellipses, and those parallel to the other coordinate planes are hyperbolas.

For an instance in which $a = b$, the cone is a right circular cone.

Elliptic cones are also represented by the equations

$$\frac{x^2}{a^2} + \frac{z^2}{c^2} = \frac{y^2}{b^2} \qquad \text{and} \qquad \frac{y^2}{b^2} + \frac{z^2}{c^2} = \frac{x^2}{a^2}.$$

Exercise 10–2

Draw the traces on the coordinate planes.

1. $2x + 3y + 4z = 12$
2. $2x + y + 2z = 4$
3. $x - 4y + z = 4$
4. $2x + 3y - z = 6$
5. $x + y - z = 0$
6. $x - y - z = 0$

Identify and sketch each quadric surface. If preferred, make the sketch in the first octant only and state the symmetry with respect to the coordinate planes.

7. $\dfrac{x^2}{9} + \dfrac{y^2}{4} + \dfrac{z^2}{16} = 1$

8. $\dfrac{x^2}{9} + \dfrac{y^2}{9} + \dfrac{z^2}{4} = 1$

9. $x^2 + y^2 + z^2 = 16$

10. $x^2 + y^2 + 4z^2 = 4$

11. $\dfrac{x^2}{9} + \dfrac{y^2}{16} - \dfrac{z^2}{4} = 1$

12. $\dfrac{x^2}{4} - \dfrac{y^2}{4} + \dfrac{z^2}{9} = 1$

13. $x^2 + y^2 - z^2 = 16$

14. $x^2 - y^2 - z^2 = 16$

15. $\dfrac{x^2}{16} - \dfrac{y^2}{9} - \dfrac{z^2}{4} = 1$

16. $\dfrac{y^2}{4} - \dfrac{z^2}{9} - \dfrac{x^2}{9} = 1$

17. $\dfrac{x^2}{9} + \dfrac{y^2}{4} = 2z$

18. $\dfrac{x^2}{4} + \dfrac{z^2}{1} = 3y$

19. $y^2 + z^2 = 4x$

20. $x^2 - y^2 = 4z$

21. $\dfrac{x^2}{9} - \dfrac{y^2}{16} = \dfrac{z}{4}$

22. $\dfrac{x^2}{4} - \dfrac{z^2}{4} = 2y$

23. $\dfrac{x^2}{16} + \dfrac{y^2}{9} = \dfrac{z^2}{4}$

24. $\dfrac{y^2}{4} + \dfrac{z^2}{4} = x^2$

CHAPTER 11

VECTORS AND PLANES AND LINES

11–1 Vectors. There are two special kinds of physical quantities which are dealt with extensively in physics and in mathematics. One kind has magnitude only, and the other has magnitude and direction. A quantity which has magnitude only is called a *scalar*. The length of an object, expressed in terms of a chosen unit of length, is a scalar; mass, time, and density are other illustrations of scalars. A quantity which has both magnitude and direction is called a *vector*. Forces, velocities, and accelerations are examples of vectors. These quantities have direction as well as magnitude.

A vector is customarily represented by an arrow. The starting point of the arrow is called the *foot* and the ending point is called the *head* or *tip*. The length of the arrow represents the magnitude of the vector, and the arrow points in the assigned direction. Thus a force, for example, could be represented graphically by an arrow pointing in the direction in which the force acts and having a length (in a convenient unit) equal to the magnitude of the force.

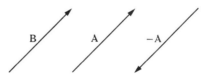

FIGURE 11–1

Two vectors are said to be equal if they are parallel, have the same magnitude (length), and point the same way. The vectors **A*** and **B** in Fig. 11–1 are equal. If a vector has the same magnitude as **A** and points in the opposite direction, it is denoted by —**A**.

As might be inferred from the definition, vectors are of great importance in physics and engineering. They are also used to much advantage in pure mathematics. The study of solid analytic geometry, in particular, is facilitated by the application of the vector concept. Our immediate objective in the introduction of vectors, however, is their use in dealing with planes and lines in space. To pursue this study, it is necessary first to consider certain operations on vectors.

---

* The **bold-faced** type indicates that the letter represents a vector.

11–2 Operations on vectors. It may be observed that a directed line segment (Section 1–2) is a vector. In numerous places we have added and subtracted directed line segments. In all these cases the vectors have had the same, or the opposite, directions. To obtain the sum or the difference of two such vectors, we have applied the usual method of adding and subtracting algebraic quantities. We now define the sum and difference of two vectors where there is no restriction as to their directions.

To find the sum of two vectors **A** and **B**, we draw from the head of **A** a vector equal to **B**. The sum of **A** and **B** is then defined as the vector drawn from the foot of **A** to the head of **B** (Fig. 11–2).

Since the opposite sides of a parallelogram are equal and parallel, it may be seen from Fig. 11–3 that the sum of two vectors is independent of the order in which they are added. That is,

$$\mathbf{A} + \mathbf{B} = \mathbf{B} + \mathbf{A}.$$

Hence vectors are said to be *commutative* with respect to addition.

The sum of three vectors **A**, **B**, and **C** may be obtained by adding **C** to **A** + **B**. It is easy to show geometrically that the sum of three or more vectors is independent of the order of addition. For example,

$$\mathbf{A} + \mathbf{B} + \mathbf{C} = (\mathbf{A} + \mathbf{B}) + \mathbf{C} = \mathbf{A} + (\mathbf{B} + \mathbf{C}).$$

This is called the *associative law* of addition.

To subtract the vector **B** from the vector **A**, we first draw the vectors from a common origin (Fig. 11–4). Then the vector extending from the tip of **B** to the tip of **A** and pointing toward the tip of **A** is defined as the difference **A** − **B**. The triangle formed by the vectors **B**, **A** − **B**, and **A** shows that

$$\mathbf{B} + (\mathbf{A} - \mathbf{B}) = \mathbf{A}.$$

That is, **A** − **B** is the vector which added to **B** gives **A**.

According to the definition of subtraction, the length of **A** − **A** is zero. A vector of length zero is said to be a *zero vector*.

The product of a scalar m and a vector **A**, expressed by $m\mathbf{A}$, is a vector m times as long as **A**, and has the direction of **A** if m is positive, and the opposite direction if m is negative. If $m = 0$, the product is a zero vector. If $m = -1$, the product is $-\mathbf{A}$. (See Fig. 11–5.)

If m and n are scalars, the sum of $m\mathbf{A}$ and $n\mathbf{A}$ is a vector $m + n$ times as long as **A**. This is expressed by

$$m\mathbf{A} + n\mathbf{A} = (m + n)\mathbf{A}. \tag{1}$$

The vectors **A** and **B** and **A** + **B** form the sides of a triangle (Fig. 11–2). If each of these vectors is multiplied by a scalar m, then $m\mathbf{A}$, $m\mathbf{B}$, and

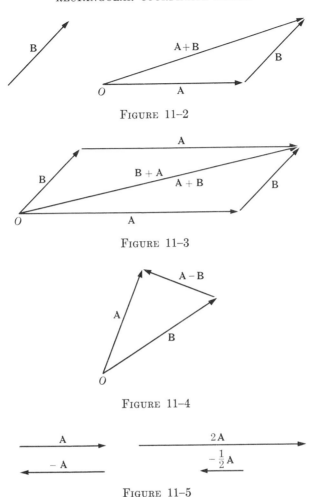

FIGURE 11–2

FIGURE 11–3

FIGURE 11–4

FIGURE 11–5

$m(\mathbf{A} + \mathbf{B})$ form a similar triangle, and hence

$$m(\mathbf{A} + \mathbf{B}) = m\mathbf{A} + m\mathbf{B}. \qquad (2)$$

Equations (1) and (2) show that vectors and scalars obey the *distributive law* of multiplication.

11–3 Vectors in a rectangular coordinate plane. Vectors are conveniently dealt with when they are expressed as the sum of vectors parallel to the coordinate axes. The letters **i** and **j** are usually employed to represent vectors of unit length from the origin to the points $(1, 0)$ and $(0, 1)$, respectively. Any vector in the plane can be expressed as the sum of a

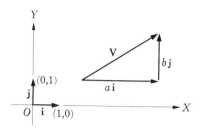

FIGURE 11-6

scalar times **i** and a scalar times **j**. Thus the vector **V** (Fig. 11-6) may be written as

$$\mathbf{V} = a\mathbf{i} + b\mathbf{j}.$$

The vectors $a\mathbf{i}$ and $b\mathbf{j}$ are called *components* of **V**. The vector $a\mathbf{i}$ is the *x*-component, and $b\mathbf{j}$ is the *y*-component.

The length of a vector **V**, also called the magnitude or absolute value, is denoted by $|\mathbf{V}|$. Accordingly $|a\mathbf{i}| = |a|$ and $|b\mathbf{j}| = |b|$ since **i** and **j** are each of unit length. If $\mathbf{V} = a\mathbf{i} + b\mathbf{j}$, we have, by the Pythagorean theorem,

$$|\mathbf{V}| = \sqrt{a^2 + b^2}.$$

The quotient of **V** and $|\mathbf{V}|$ is a vector of unit length in the direction of **V**; a vector is called a *unit vector* if its length is unity.

The length of $\mathbf{V} = 3\mathbf{i} - 4\mathbf{j}$, for example, is

$$|\mathbf{V}| = \sqrt{9 + 16} = 5, \quad \text{and} \quad \frac{\mathbf{V}}{|\mathbf{V}|} = \frac{3\mathbf{i} - 4\mathbf{j}}{5} = \frac{3}{5}\mathbf{i} - \frac{4}{5}\mathbf{j}$$

is a unit vector having the same direction as $3\mathbf{i} - 4\mathbf{j}$.

If the vectors $\mathbf{V}_1$ and $\mathbf{V}_2$, in terms of components, are

$$\mathbf{V}_1 = a_1\mathbf{i} + b_1\mathbf{j}, \quad \mathbf{V}_2 = a_2\mathbf{i} + b_2\mathbf{j},$$

then

$$\mathbf{V}_1 + \mathbf{V}_2 = (a_1 + a_2)\mathbf{i} + (b_1 + b_2)\mathbf{j}.$$

Thus the sum is a vector whose *x*- and *y*-components are the sums of the *x*- and *y*-components, respectively, of the two given vectors.

Similarly, we have

$$\mathbf{V}_1 - \mathbf{V}_2 = (a_1 - a_2)\mathbf{i} + (b_1 - b_2)\mathbf{j}.$$

EXAMPLE 1. Vectors are drawn from the origin to the points $A(3, -2)$ and $B(1, 5)$. Indicating these vectors by $\overrightarrow{OA} = \mathbf{A}$ and $\overrightarrow{OB} = \mathbf{B}$, find $\mathbf{A} + \mathbf{B}$ and $\mathbf{A} - \mathbf{B}$.

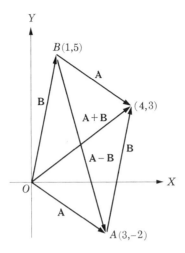

FIGURE 11–7

Solution. The vectors (Fig. 11–7) are

$$\mathbf{A} = 3\mathbf{i} - 2\mathbf{j}, \qquad \mathbf{B} = \mathbf{i} + 5\mathbf{j}.$$

Their sum is

$$\mathbf{A} + \mathbf{B} = 4\mathbf{i} + 3\mathbf{j},$$

and their difference is

$$\mathbf{A} - \mathbf{B} = 2\mathbf{i} - 7\mathbf{j}.$$

The coordinates of the head of $\mathbf{A} + \mathbf{B}$ are (4, 3). The foot of the vector $\mathbf{A} - \mathbf{B}$, in the figure, is not at the origin. A vector equal to $\mathbf{A} - \mathbf{B}$ with its foot at the origin would have (2, -7) as the coordinates of its head.

EXAMPLE 2. Find the vector from the origin to the point two-thirds of the way from $A(1, 3)$ to $B(4, -3)$.

Solution. The required vector is equal to the vector from the origin to A plus two-thirds of the vector from the point A to the point B. Indicating the vectors from the origin to A and B by $\mathbf{A}$ and $\mathbf{B}$, respectively, we have

$$\mathbf{A} = \mathbf{i} + 3\mathbf{j},$$
$$\mathbf{B} = 4\mathbf{i} - 3\mathbf{j},$$
$$\mathbf{B} - \mathbf{A} = 3\mathbf{i} - 6\mathbf{j}.$$

Hence the required vector $\mathbf{V}$ is

$$\mathbf{V} = \mathbf{i} + 3\mathbf{j} + \tfrac{2}{3}(3\mathbf{i} - 6\mathbf{j})$$
$$= 3\mathbf{i} - \mathbf{j}.$$

EXERCISE 11–1

In problems 1 through 4 find the sum of the vectors from the origin to the given points. Also subtract the second vector from the first. Draw all vectors.

1. $A(2, 3)$, $B(-4, 5)$ 2. $A(5, 0)$, $B(0, 4)$
3. $A(3, -2)$, $B(-1, -4)$ 4. $A(6, 7)$, $B(-5, -5)$

Determine a unit vector having the direction of the vector in each problem 5 through 10.

5. $3\mathbf{i} + 4\mathbf{j}$ 6. $3\mathbf{i} - 12\mathbf{j}$ 7. $12\mathbf{i} - 5\mathbf{j}$
8. $2\mathbf{i} - 3\mathbf{j}$ 9. $\mathbf{i} + 2\mathbf{j}$ 10. $4\mathbf{i} + 3\mathbf{j}$

Find the length of each vector 11 through 16 and the cosine of the angle which the vector makes with the positive x-axis.

11. $\mathbf{i} + \mathbf{j}$ 12. $-\mathbf{i} + 3\mathbf{j}$ 13. $\mathbf{i} + 0\mathbf{j}$
14. $0\mathbf{i} + 3\mathbf{j}$ 15. $-3\mathbf{i} + 2\mathbf{j}$ 16. $5\mathbf{i} + 12\mathbf{j}$

17. Find the vector from the origin to the mid-point of the vector $\overrightarrow{P_1 P_2}$ joining $P_1(3, 6)$ and $P_2(5, -8)$.

18. Find the vectors from the origin to the trisection points of the vector $\overrightarrow{P_1 P_2}$ joining the points $P_1(-3, 4)$ and $P_2(12, -5)$.

11–4 Vectors in space. In the three-dimensional rectangular coordinate system, the unit vectors from the origin to the points $(1, 0, 0)$, $(0, 1, 0)$, and $(0, 0, 1)$ are denoted, respectively, by $\mathbf{i}$, $\mathbf{j}$, and $\mathbf{k}$. Any vector in space can be expressed in terms of these unit vectors. Thus the vector from the origin to the point $A(a, b, c)$ is

$$\overrightarrow{OA} = \mathbf{A} = a\mathbf{i} + b\mathbf{j} + c\mathbf{k}.$$

The vectors $a\mathbf{i}$, $b\mathbf{j}$, and $c\mathbf{k}$ are the x-, y-, and z-components of the vector $\mathbf{A}$. The length of the vector $\mathbf{A}$ may be obtained by using the lengths of the sides of the right triangles OCA and ODC (Fig. 11–8). From the Pythag-

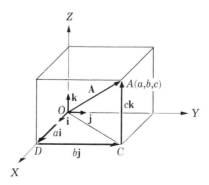

FIGURE 11–8

orean relation, we derive

$$(OA)^2 = (OC)^2 + (CA)^2$$
$$= (OD)^2 + (DC)^2 + (CA)^2$$
$$= a^2 + b^2 + c^2.$$

Hence the length of **A** is

$$|\mathbf{A}| = \sqrt{a^2 + b^2 + c^2}.$$

The vector from $P_1(x_1, y_1, z_1)$ to $P_2(x_2, y_2, z_2)$ in Fig. 11–9 has the components $(x_2 - x_1)\mathbf{i}$, $(y_2 - y_1)\mathbf{j}$, $(z_2 - z_1)\mathbf{k}$. Hence it is expressed by

$$\overrightarrow{P_1P_2} = (x_2 - x_1)\mathbf{i} + (y_2 - y_1)\mathbf{j} + (z_2 - z_1)\mathbf{k}.$$

The length of the vector $\overrightarrow{P_1P_2}$, or the distance d between the points P_1 and P_2, is

$$d = \sqrt{(x_2 - x_1)^2 + (y_2 - y_1)^2 + (z_2 - z_1)^2}.$$

EXAMPLE 1. Write the equation of the sphere whose center is at $(-2, 4, -1)$ and whose radius is 6.

Solution. By the preceding distance formula, if $P(x, y, z)$ is a point of the sphere, then

$$(x + 2)^2 + (y - 4)^2 + (z + 1)^2 = 36.$$

This is the desired equation because all points of the sphere, and only those points, satisfy the equation.

EXAMPLE 2. The points $A(1, -2, 3)$, $B(-4, 5, 6)$, and $C(5, 7, 0)$ are vertices of a triangle. Express the sides as vectors and find the length of each side.

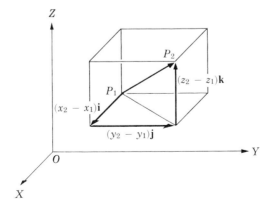

FIGURE 11–9

Solution. The vectors from the origin to the given points are

$$\overrightarrow{OA} = \mathbf{A} = \mathbf{i} - 2\mathbf{j} + 3\mathbf{k},$$
$$\overrightarrow{OB} = \mathbf{B} = -4\mathbf{i} + 5\mathbf{j} + 6\mathbf{k},$$
$$\overrightarrow{OC} = \mathbf{C} = 5\mathbf{i} + 7\mathbf{j}.$$

The sides, expressed as vectors, are

$$\overrightarrow{AB} = \mathbf{B} - \mathbf{A} = -5\mathbf{i} + 7\mathbf{j} + 3\mathbf{k},$$
$$\overrightarrow{BC} = \mathbf{C} - \mathbf{B} = 9\mathbf{i} + 2\mathbf{j} - 6\mathbf{k},$$
$$\overrightarrow{CA} = \mathbf{A} - \mathbf{C} = -4\mathbf{i} - 9\mathbf{j} + 3\mathbf{k}.$$

The lengths of the vectors are

$$|\overrightarrow{AB}| = \sqrt{(-5)^2 + 7^2 + 3^2} = \sqrt{83},$$
$$|\overrightarrow{BC}| = \sqrt{9^2 + 2^2 + (-6)^2} = 11,$$
$$|\overrightarrow{CA}| = \sqrt{(-4)^2 + (-9)^2 + 3^2} = \sqrt{106}.$$

EXERCISE 11–2

Find the distance between the points A and B in each problem 1 through 4.

1. $A(-3, 2, 0)$, $B(6, -4, 2)$ 2. $A(3, 1, 4)$, $B(1, -1, -2)$
3. $A(5, 7, 1)$, $B(6, -3, 2)$ 4. $A(4, 4, 0)$, $B(-2, 1, -2)$

In each problem 5 through 8 the given points are the vertices of a triangle. Determine the vectors $\overrightarrow{AB}$, $\overrightarrow{BC}$, and $\overrightarrow{CA}$ and the lengths of these vectors.

5. $A(6, 8, 1)$, $B(0, 2, 1)$, $C(0, -4, -5)$
6. $A(2, 3, -2)$, $B(-2, 1, 3)$, $C(3, 8, 0)$
7. $A(3, 3, 3)$, $B(4, 5, 5)$, $C(1, 2, 5)$
8. $A(2, 4, 5)$, $B(6, 8, -1)$, $C(-2, -2, 1)$

Determine a unit vector having the direction of the vector in each problem 9 through 12.

9. $6\mathbf{i} + 3\mathbf{j} - 6\mathbf{k}$ 10. $2\mathbf{i} - 4\mathbf{j} + 4\mathbf{k}$
11. $2\mathbf{i} - \mathbf{j} - 3\mathbf{k}$ 12. $\mathbf{i} + \mathbf{j} + \mathbf{k}$

13. Find the vectors from the origin to the mid-point and the trisection points of the line segment joining the points $(1, -3, 7)$ and $(7, 3, -2)$. What are the coordinates of the tips of these vectors?

14. Find the equation of a sphere of radius 5 and center at $(1, -2, 3)$.

15. Find the center and radius of the sphere $x^2 + y^2 + z^2 + 4x - 2y + 6z = 0$.

16. Find the coordinates of the points which divide the line segment from $(4, 5, 7)$ to $(2, 3, 5)$ into four equal parts.

17. Find the vector from the origin to the intersection of the medians of the triangle whose vertices are $A(4, 2, 1)$, $B(-5, 7, 0)$, and $C(4, -3, 5)$.

18. The line segment from $(3, 4, 6)$ to $(-1, 1, 0)$ is produced by its own length through each end. Find the coordinates of the new ends.

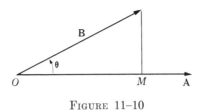

FIGURE 11–10

11–5 The scalar product of two vectors. So far we have not defined a product of two vectors. Actually there are two kinds of vector products which have arisen in physics and are extensively used. We shall define these products and make some applications to geometry.

The *scalar product* of two vectors **A** and **B**, denoted by **A** · **B**, is defined by the equation

$$\mathbf{A} \cdot \mathbf{B} = |\mathbf{A}|\,|\mathbf{B}|\,\cos\theta,$$

where θ is the angle between the vectors when drawn from a common origin (Fig. 11–10). It makes no difference whether θ is taken as positive or negative, since $\cos\theta = \cos(-\theta)$. However, we shall restrict θ to the range from 0° to 180°. The angle θ is 0° if **A** and **B** point in the same direction, and is equal to 180° if they point oppositely. The name *scalar* is used because the product is a scalar quantity. This product is also called the *dot product*, since the product is indicated by placing a dot between the two vectors.

Since $\cos 90° = 0$ and $\cos 0° = 1$, it is evident that the scalar product of two perpendicular vectors is zero, and the scalar product of two vectors in the same direction is the product of their lengths. The dot product of a vector on itself is the square of the length of the vector. That is,

$$\mathbf{A} \cdot \mathbf{A} = |\mathbf{A}|^2.$$

In the figure the point M is the foot of the perpendicular to the vector **A** drawn from the tip of **B**. The vector from O to M is called the *vector projection* of **B** on **A**. The vector projection and **A** point in the same direction, since θ is an acute angle. If θ exceeds 90°, then **A** and the vector from O to M point oppositely. The *scalar projection* of **B** on **A** is defined as $|\mathbf{B}|\cos\theta$; the sign of the scalar projection depends on $\cos\theta$. Using the idea of scalar projection of one vector on another, we can interpret the dot product geometrically as

$$\mathbf{A} \cdot \mathbf{B} = |\mathbf{A}|\,|\mathbf{B}|\,\cos\theta$$
$$= \text{(length of } \mathbf{A}\text{) times (the scalar projection of } \mathbf{B} \text{ on } \mathbf{A}\text{)}.$$

We could also say that the dot product of **A** and **B** is the length of **B** times the scalar projection of **A** on **B**.

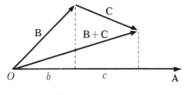

FIGURE 11–11

It follows immediately from the definition of scalar product that

$$\mathbf{A} \cdot \mathbf{B} = \mathbf{B} \cdot \mathbf{A}. \tag{1}$$

Therefore the dot product of two vectors is said to be *commutative*.

We next establish the *distributive* law from the scalar multiplication of vectors. If we let b and c stand for the scalar projections of $\mathbf{B}$ and $\mathbf{C}$ on $\mathbf{A}$, we see (Fig. 11–11) that the sum of the scalar projections of $\mathbf{B}$ and $\mathbf{C}$ on $\mathbf{A}$ is the same as the scalar projection of $(\mathbf{B} + \mathbf{C})$ on $\mathbf{A}$. Hence

$$|\mathbf{A}|(b + c) = |\mathbf{A}|b + |\mathbf{A}|c,$$

and

$$\mathbf{A} \cdot (\mathbf{B} + \mathbf{C}) = \mathbf{A} \cdot \mathbf{B} + \mathbf{A} \cdot \mathbf{C}. \tag{2}$$

Equation (2) expresses the distributive law for the multiplication of vectors. Since the dot product is commutative [Eq. (1)], we have also

$$(\mathbf{B} + \mathbf{C}) \cdot \mathbf{A} = \mathbf{B} \cdot \mathbf{A} + \mathbf{C} \cdot \mathbf{A}. \tag{3}$$

From equations (2) and (3) it may be seen that the scalar product of the sums of vectors may be carried out as in multiplying two algebraic expressions, each of which consists of more than one term. Thus, for example,

$$(\mathbf{A} + \mathbf{B}) \cdot (\mathbf{C} + \mathbf{D}) = \mathbf{A} \cdot (\mathbf{C} + \mathbf{D}) + \mathbf{B} \cdot (\mathbf{C} + \mathbf{D}).$$

If m and n are scalars, it follows that

$$(m\mathbf{A}) \cdot (n\mathbf{B}) = mn(\mathbf{A} \cdot \mathbf{B}).$$

The equation is true if either m or n is zero or either vector is equal to zero. Suppose that m and n are either both positive or both negative and that neither vector is equal to zero. Then, by definition,

$$(m\mathbf{A}) \cdot (n\mathbf{B}) = |m\mathbf{A}|\,|n\mathbf{B}|\cos\theta = mn|\mathbf{A}|\,|\mathbf{B}|\cos\theta = mn(\mathbf{A} \cdot \mathbf{B}).$$

If m and n have opposite signs,

$$(m\mathbf{A}) \cdot (n\mathbf{B}) = |m\mathbf{A}|\,|n\mathbf{B}|\cos(180° - \theta) = mn|\mathbf{A}|\,|\mathbf{B}|\cos\theta = mn(\mathbf{A} \cdot \mathbf{B}).$$

Hence the equation is true for all scalars m and n and for all vectors **A** and **B**.

If two vectors are expressed in terms of **i**, **j**, and **k**, the scalar product can be found in a simple way. Let the vectors **A** and **B** be expressed as

$$\mathbf{A} = a_1\mathbf{i} + a_2\mathbf{j} + a_3\mathbf{k},$$
$$\mathbf{B} = b_1\mathbf{i} + b_2\mathbf{j} + b_3\mathbf{k}.$$

To obtain the dot product of **A** and **B**, we first determine the dot products of the unit vectors **i**, **j**, and **k**. We have

$$\mathbf{i} \cdot \mathbf{i} = \mathbf{j} \cdot \mathbf{j} = \mathbf{k} \cdot \mathbf{k} = 1,$$
$$\mathbf{i} \cdot \mathbf{j} = \mathbf{j} \cdot \mathbf{k} = \mathbf{k} \cdot \mathbf{i} = 0.$$

Then we have

$$
\begin{aligned}
\mathbf{A} \cdot \mathbf{B} &= (a_1\mathbf{i} + a_2\mathbf{j} + a_3\mathbf{k}) \cdot (b_1\mathbf{i} + b_2\mathbf{j} + b_3\mathbf{k}) \\
&= a_1\mathbf{i} \cdot (b_1\mathbf{i} + b_2\mathbf{j} + b_3\mathbf{k}) + a_2\mathbf{j} \cdot (b_1\mathbf{i} + b_2\mathbf{j} + b_3\mathbf{k}) \\
&\quad + a_3\mathbf{k} \cdot (b_1\mathbf{i} + b_2\mathbf{j} + mb_3\mathbf{k}) \\
&= a_1b_1\mathbf{i} \cdot \mathbf{i} + 0 + 0 + 0 + a_2b_2\mathbf{j} \cdot \mathbf{j} + 0 + 0 + 0 + a_3b_3\mathbf{k} \cdot \mathbf{k}.
\end{aligned}
$$

Hence

$$\mathbf{A} \cdot \mathbf{B} = a_1b_1 + a_2b_2 + a_3b_3. \tag{4}$$

Equation (4) shows that the dot product is obtained by the simple process of adding the products of the corresponding coefficients of **i**, **j**, and **k**.

EXAMPLE 1. Determine whether the vectors

$$\mathbf{A} = 3\mathbf{i} + 4\mathbf{j} - 8\mathbf{k},$$
$$\mathbf{B} = 4\mathbf{i} - 7\mathbf{j} - 2\mathbf{k}$$

are perpendicular.

Solution. The scalar product is

$$\mathbf{A} \cdot \mathbf{B} = (3)(4) + (4)(-7) + (-8)(-2) = 0.$$

Since this product is zero, the vectors are perpendicular.

EXAMPLE 2. Vectors are drawn from the origin to the points $A(6, -3, 2)$ and $B(-2, 1, 2)$. Find the angle AOB.

Solution. Indicating $\overrightarrow{OA}$ by **A** and $\overrightarrow{OB}$ by **B**, we write

$$\mathbf{A} = 6\mathbf{i} - 3\mathbf{j} + 2\mathbf{k},$$
$$\mathbf{B} = -2\mathbf{i} + \mathbf{j} + 2\mathbf{k}.$$

To find the angle, we substitute in both members of the equation

$$\mathbf{A} \cdot \mathbf{B} = |\mathbf{A}| \, |\mathbf{B}| \cos \theta.$$

The product in the left member is $\mathbf{A} \cdot \mathbf{B} = -12 - 3 + 4 = -11$. The lengths of $\mathbf{A}$ and $\mathbf{B}$ are $|\mathbf{A}| = \sqrt{36 + 9 + 4} = 7$, $|\mathbf{B}| = \sqrt{4 + 1 + 4} = 3$. Hence

$$\cos \theta = \frac{\mathbf{A} \cdot \mathbf{B}}{|\mathbf{A}| \, |\mathbf{B}|} = \frac{-11}{21},$$

$$\theta = \arccos \frac{-11}{21} = 122° \text{ (nearest degree)}.$$

EXAMPLE 3. Find the scalar projection and the vector projection of

$$\mathbf{B} = 2\mathbf{i} - 3\mathbf{j} - \mathbf{k} \text{ on } \mathbf{A} = 3\mathbf{i} - 6\mathbf{j} + 2\mathbf{k}.$$

Solution. The scalar projection of $\mathbf{B}$ on $\mathbf{A}$ is $|\mathbf{B}| \cos \theta$, where θ is the angle between the vectors. Using the equation

$$\mathbf{A} \cdot \mathbf{B} = |\mathbf{A}| \, |\mathbf{B}| \cos \theta,$$

we have

$$|\mathbf{B}| \cos \theta = \frac{\mathbf{A} \cdot \mathbf{B}}{|\mathbf{A}|}.$$

Since $\mathbf{A} \cdot \mathbf{B} = 6 + 18 - 2 = 22$ and $|\mathbf{A}| = \sqrt{9 + 36 + 4} = 7$, it follows that

$$|\mathbf{B}| \cos \theta = \tfrac{22}{7}.$$

The scalar projection of $\mathbf{B}$ on $\mathbf{A}$ is $\tfrac{22}{7}$. Since the scalar projection is positive, the vector projection is in the direction of $\mathbf{A}$. The vector projection is, therefore, the product of the scalar projection and a unit vector in the direction of $\mathbf{A}$. This unit vector is $\mathbf{A}$ divided by its length. Hence the vector projection of $\mathbf{B}$ on $\mathbf{A}$ is

$$\frac{22}{7} \cdot \frac{3\mathbf{i} - 6\mathbf{j} + 2\mathbf{k}}{7} = \frac{22}{49}(3\mathbf{i} - 6\mathbf{j} + 2\mathbf{k}).$$

EXERCISE 11–3

Find the dot product of the vectors in each problem 1 through 4. Find also the cosine of the angle between the vectors.

1. $\mathbf{A} = 4\mathbf{i} - \mathbf{j} + 8\mathbf{k}$,
   $\mathbf{B} = 2\mathbf{i} + 2\mathbf{j} - \mathbf{k}$

2. $\mathbf{A} = 5\mathbf{i} - 3\mathbf{j} + 2\mathbf{k}$,
   $\mathbf{B} = -\mathbf{i} + 7\mathbf{j} + 13\mathbf{k}$

3. $\mathbf{A} = 10\mathbf{i} + 2\mathbf{j} + 11\mathbf{k}$,
   $\mathbf{B} = 4\mathbf{i} - 8\mathbf{j} - \mathbf{k}$

4. $\mathbf{A} = \mathbf{i} + \mathbf{j} + 2\mathbf{k}$,
   $\mathbf{B} = 8\mathbf{i} + 4\mathbf{j} + \mathbf{k}$

In problems 5 and 6 find the scalar projection and the vector projection of **B** on **A**.

5. $\mathbf{A} = \mathbf{i} - \mathbf{j} - \mathbf{k}$,
   $\mathbf{B} = 10\mathbf{i} - 11\mathbf{j} + 2\mathbf{k}$

6. $\mathbf{A} = 3\mathbf{i} + 3\mathbf{j} + \mathbf{k}$,
   $\mathbf{B} = \mathbf{i} - 2\mathbf{j} - 2\mathbf{k}$

7. Find the angle which a diagonal of a cube makes with one of its edges.

8. From a vertex of a cube, a diagonal of a face and a diagonal of the cube are drawn. Find the angle thus formed.

The points in problems 9 and 10 are vertices of a triangle. In each, determine the vector from A to B and the vector from A to C. Find the angle between these vectors. Similarly, find the other interior angles of the triangle.

9. $A(3, 4, 2)$, $B(1, 7, 1)$, $C(-2, 3, -5)$

10. $A(-2, -1, 1)$, $B(1, 0, -2)$, $C(0, -3, 1)$

11. Let α, β, and γ denote the angles which the vector $\mathbf{A} = a\mathbf{i} + b\mathbf{j} + c\mathbf{k}$ makes with the positive x-, y-, and z-axes, respectively. Using $\mathbf{A} \cdot \mathbf{i}$, $\mathbf{A} \cdot \mathbf{j}$, and $\mathbf{A} \cdot \mathbf{k}$, find $\cos \alpha$, $\cos \beta$, and $\cos \gamma$. The cosines of α, β, and γ are called the *direction cosines* of the vector $\mathbf{A}$. Show that $\cos^2 \alpha + \cos^2 \beta + \cos^2 \gamma = 1$.

11–6 The equation of a plane. We have discovered (Section 10–3) that a linear equation in one or two variables represents a plane. In Section 10–4, we stated without proof that a linear equation in three variables also represents a plane. We shall now prove that the locus of a linear equation, in one, two, or three variables, is a plane.

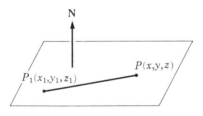

FIGURE 11–12

Suppose that a point $P_1(x_1, y_1, z_1)$ is in a given plane and that a non-zero vector

$$\mathbf{N} = A\mathbf{i} + B\mathbf{j} + C\mathbf{k}$$

is perpendicular, or normal, to the plane (Fig. 11–12). A point $P(x, y, z)$ will lie in the given plane if, and only if, the vector

$$\overrightarrow{P_1P} = (x - x_1)\mathbf{i} + (y - y_1)\mathbf{j} + (z - z_1)\mathbf{k}$$

is perpendicular to **N**. Setting the scalar product of these vectors equal to zero, we obtain the equation

$$\mathbf{N} \cdot \overrightarrow{P_1P} = 0,$$

or

$$A(x - x_1) + B(y - y_1) + C(z - z_1) = 0. \tag{1}$$

This is the equation of the plane which passes through $P_1(x_1, y_1, z_1)$ and is perpendicular to the vector $\mathbf{N} = A\mathbf{i} + B\mathbf{j} + C\mathbf{k}$. Substituting D for the constant $-Ax_1 - By_1 - Cz_1$, we write the equation in the form

$$Ax + By + Cz + D = 0. \tag{2}$$

Conversely, any linear equation of the form (2) represents a plane. Starting with this equation, we can find a point $P_1(x_1, y_1, z_1)$ whose coordinates satisfy it. Then we have

$$Ax_1 + By_1 + Cz_1 + D = 0.$$

This equation and Eq. (2) yield, by subtraction,

$$A(x - x_1) + B(y - y_1) + C(z - z_1) = 0,$$

which is of the form (1). Hence Eq. (2) represents a plane perpendicular to the vector $\mathbf{N} = A\mathbf{i} + B\mathbf{j} + C\mathbf{k}$.

THEOREM. *Any plane can be represented by a linear equation. Conversely, the locus of a linear equation is a plane.*

EXAMPLE 1.   Write the equation of the plane which contains the point $P_1(4, -3, 2)$ and is perpendicular to the vector $\mathbf{N} = 2\mathbf{i} - 3\mathbf{j} + 5\mathbf{k}$.

Solution. We use the coefficients of $\mathbf{i}$, $\mathbf{j}$, and $\mathbf{k}$ as the coefficients of x, y, and z and write the equation

$$2x - 3y + 5z + D = 0.$$

For any value of D this equation represents a plane perpendicular to the given vector. The equation will be satisfied by the coordinates of the given point if

$$8 + 9 + 10 + D = 0, \quad \text{or} \quad D = -27.$$

The required equation therefore is

$$2x - 3y + 5z - 27 = 0.$$

EXAMPLE 2.   Find the equation of the plane determined by the points $P_1(1, 2, 6)$, $P_2(4, 4, 1)$, and $P_3(2, 3, 5)$.

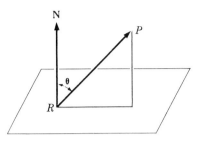

FIGURE 11–13

Solution. A vector which is perpendicular to two sides of the triangle $P_1P_2P_3$ is normal to the plane of the triangle. To find such a vector, we write

$$\overrightarrow{P_1P_2} = 3\mathbf{i} + 2\mathbf{j} - 5\mathbf{k},$$
$$\overrightarrow{P_1P_3} = \mathbf{i} + \mathbf{j} - \mathbf{k},$$
$$\mathbf{N} = A\mathbf{i} + B\mathbf{j} + C\mathbf{k}.$$

The coefficients A, B, and C are to be found so that $\mathbf{N}$ is perpendicular to each of the other vectors. Thus

$$\mathbf{N} \cdot \overrightarrow{P_1P_2} = 3A + 2B - 5C = 0,$$
$$\mathbf{N} \cdot \overrightarrow{P_1P_3} = A + B - C = 0.$$

These equations give $A = 3C$ and $B = -2C$. Choosing $C = 1$, we have $\mathbf{N} = 3\mathbf{i} - 2\mathbf{j} + \mathbf{k}$. The plane $3x - 2y + z + D = 0$ is normal to $\mathbf{N}$, and passes through the given points if $D = -5$. Hence

$$3x - 2y + z - 5 = 0.$$

EXAMPLE 3. Find the distance d from the point $P(6, 4, -1)$ to the plane $2x + 3y - 6z - 2 = 0$.

Solution. Let R be any point of the plane (Fig. 11–13). The scalar projection of the vector $\overrightarrow{RP}$ on a vector perpendicular to the plane gives the required distance. This scalar projection is obtained by taking the dot product of $\overrightarrow{RP}$ and a unit vector normal to the plane. The point $(1, 0, 0)$ is in the plane, and using this point for R, we have $\overrightarrow{RP} = 5\mathbf{i} + 4\mathbf{j} - \mathbf{k}$. Either of the vectors

$$\mathbf{N} = \pm \frac{2\mathbf{i} + 3\mathbf{j} - 6\mathbf{k}}{7}$$

is a unit vector normal to the plane. Hence

$$\mathbf{N} \cdot \overrightarrow{RP} = \pm \frac{10 + 12 + 6}{7} = \pm \frac{28}{7}.$$

We choose the ambiguous sign $+$ in order to have a positive result. Thus we get $d = 4$.

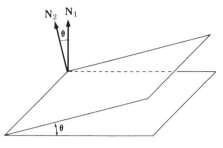

FIGURE 11–14

EXAMPLE 4. Find the angle θ between the planes $4x - 8y - z + 5 = 0$ and $x + 2y - 2z + 3 = 0$.

Solution. The angle between two planes is equal to the angle between their normals (Fig. 11–14). The vectors

$$\mathbf{N}_1 = \frac{4\mathbf{i} - 8\mathbf{j} - \mathbf{k}}{9}, \qquad \mathbf{N}_2 = \frac{\mathbf{i} + 2\mathbf{j} - 2\mathbf{k}}{3}$$

are unit vectors normal to the given planes. The dot product yields

$$\cos \theta = \mathbf{N}_1 \cdot \mathbf{N}_2 = -\tfrac{10}{27}, \qquad \text{and} \qquad \theta = 112°.$$

The planes intersect, making a pair of angles equal (approximately) to 112°, and a second pair equal to 68°. Choosing the smaller angle, we give the angle between the planes as 68°.

EXERCISE 11–4

Write the equation of the plane which satisfies the given conditions in each problem 1 through 8.

1. Perpendicular to $\mathbf{N} = 3\mathbf{i} - 2\mathbf{j} + 5\mathbf{k}$ and passes through the point $(1, 1, 2)$
2. Perpendicular to $\mathbf{N} = 4\mathbf{i} - \mathbf{j} - \mathbf{k}$ and passes through the origin
3. Parallel to the plane $2x - 3y - 4z = 5$ and passes through $(1, 2, -3)$
4. Perpendicular to the line segment $(4, 0, 6)$, $(0, -8, 2)$ at its mid-point
5. Passes through the origin and is perpendicular to the line through $(2, -3, 4)$ and $(5, 6, 0)$
6. Passes through the points $(0, 1, 2)$, $(2, 0, 3)$, $(4, 3, 0)$
7. Passes through the points $(2, -2, -1)$, $(-3, 4, 1)$, $(4, 2, 3)$
8. Passes through $(0, 0, 0)$, $(3, 0, 0)$, $(1, 1, 1)$

Use the dot product of vectors to find the distance from the given point to the given plane in each problem 9 through 12.

9. $2x - y + 2z + 3 = 0$, $(0, 1, 3)$
10. $6x + 2y - 3z + 2 = 0$, $(2, -4, 3)$
11. $4x - 2y + z - 2 = 0$, $(-1, 1, 2)$
12. $3x - 4y - 5z = 0$, $(5, -1, 3)$

13. Use vectors to show that the distance d from $P_1(x_1, y_1, z_1)$ to the plane $Ax + By + Cz + D = 0$ is

$$d = \frac{|Ax_1 + By_1 + Cz_1 + D|}{\sqrt{A^2 + B^2 + C^2}}.$$

Apply this formula to work problems 9 through 12 above.

Find the cosine of the acute angle between each pair of planes in problems 14 through 17.

14. $2x + y + z + 3 = 0$, $2x - 2y + z - 7 = 0$
15. $2x + y + 2z - 5 = 0$, $2x - 3y + 6z + 5 = 0$
16. $3x - 2y + z - 9 = 0$, $x - 3y - 9z + 4 = 0$
17. $x - 8y + 4z - 3 = 0$, $4x + 2y - 4z + 3 = 0$

18. Show that the planes

$$A_1x + B_1y + C_1z + D_1 = 0 \quad \text{and} \quad A_2x + B_2y + C_2z + D_2 = 0$$

are perpendicular if, and only if,

$$A_1A_2 + B_1B_2 + C_1C_2 = 0.$$

19. Determine the value of C so that the planes $2x - 6y + Cz = 5$ and $x - 3y + 2z = 4$ are perpendicular.

11–7 Equations of a line. Let L be a line which passes through a given point $P_1(x_1, y_1, z_1)$ and is parallel to a given nonzero vector

$$\mathbf{V} = A\mathbf{i} + B\mathbf{j} + C\mathbf{k}.$$

If $P(x, y, z)$ is a point on the line, then the vector $\overrightarrow{P_1P}$ is parallel to $\mathbf{V}$ (Fig. 11–15). Conversely, if $\overrightarrow{P_1P}$ is parallel to $\mathbf{V}$, the point P is on the line L. Hence P is on L if, and only if, there is a scalar t such that

$$\overrightarrow{P_1P} = t\mathbf{V},$$

or

$$(x - x_1)\mathbf{i} + (y - y_1)\mathbf{j} + (z - z_1)\mathbf{k} = At\mathbf{i} + Bt\mathbf{j} + Ct\mathbf{k}. \quad (1)$$

Equating corresponding coefficients of $\mathbf{i}$, $\mathbf{j}$, and $\mathbf{k}$, we obtain the equations

$$x - x_1 = At, \quad y - y_1 = Bt, \quad z - z_1 = Ct,$$

or, transposing,

$$x = x_1 + At, \quad y = y_1 + Bt, \quad z = z_1 + Ct. \quad (2)$$

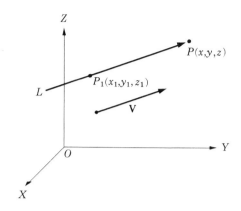

FIGURE 11–15

When t is given any real value, equations (2) determine the coordinates (x, y, z) of a point on the line L. Also there is a value of t corresponding to any point of the line. Equations (2) are called *parametric equations* of the line.

By solving each of the parametric equations for t and equating the equal values, we get

$$\frac{x - x_1}{A} = \frac{y - y_1}{B} = \frac{z - z_1}{C}. \tag{3}$$

These are called the *symmetric equations* of the line.

The planes which contain a line and are perpendicular to the coordinate planes are called *projecting planes*.

Equations (3) represent three projecting planes. This becomes evident when we write the equations as

$$\frac{x - x_1}{A} = \frac{y - y_1}{B}, \qquad \frac{x - x_1}{A} = \frac{z - z_1}{C}, \qquad \frac{y - y_1}{B} = \frac{z - z_1}{C}.$$

These equations, each in two variables, represent planes perpendicular, respectively, to the xy-, xz-, and yz-planes. These equations represent a line, and hence the line is the intersection of the planes. Any two of the equations, of course, determine the line. We note also that any one of the equations can be obtained from the other two.

A line in space may be defined by two planes which pass through the line. Hence there are infinitely many ways of defining a line, since infinitely many planes pass through a line. However, it is usually convenient to deal with the projecting planes.

If a line is parallel to a coordinate plane, one of the quantities A, B, and C in equations (3) is zero, and conversely. In this instance, one mem-

ber of the equation would have zero in the denominator and could not
be used. If, for example, $A = 0$ and B and C are not zero, then the line
passing through $P_1(x_1, y_1, z_1)$ is parallel to the vector $\mathbf{V} = B\mathbf{j} + C\mathbf{k}$.
Hence the line is parallel to the xy-plane and, consequently, the plane
$x = x_1$ contains the line. If two of A, B, and C are zero, say $A = B = 0$, then the line is parallel to the z-axis. Thus the line is the intersection
of the planes $x = x_1$ and $y = y_1$. So we see that when a denominator
of a member of equations (3) is zero, the corresponding numerator equated
to zero represents a plane through the line in question.

EXAMPLE 1. Write the equations of the line through $(2, -1, 3)$ which is
parallel to the vector $\mathbf{V} = -2\mathbf{i} + 4\mathbf{j} + 6\mathbf{k}$.

Solution. The equations of the line in the symmetric form (3) are

$$\frac{x-2}{-2} = \frac{y+1}{4} = \frac{z-3}{6}.$$

We set each member of these equations equal to t and solve for x, y, and z to
find the parametric form (2). This gives

$$x = 2 - 2t, \qquad y = -1 + 4t, \qquad z = 3 + 6t.$$

EXAMPLE 2. A line passes through the points $P_1(2, -4, 5)$ and $P_2(-1, 3, 1)$.
Write its equations.

Solution. The vector from P_2 to P_1,

$$\overrightarrow{P_2P_1} = 3\mathbf{i} - 7\mathbf{j} + 4\mathbf{k},$$

is parallel to the line. Hence we obtain

$$\frac{x-2}{3} = \frac{y+4}{-7} = \frac{z-5}{4}.$$

Had we used the vector $\overrightarrow{P_1P_2}$ instead of $\overrightarrow{P_2P_1}$, the signs would be reversed
in all the denominators.

EXAMPLE 3. Find a symmetric form of the equations

$$x + y - z - 7 = 0, \qquad x + 5y + 5z + 5 = 0.$$

Solution. We multiply the first equation by 5 and add to the second equation
to eliminate z. We subtract the first equation from the second to eliminate x.
This gives the equations

$$6x + 10y - 30 = 0 \qquad \text{and} \qquad 4y + 6z + 12 = 0.$$

By solving each of these for y, we find

$$y = \frac{-3x + 15}{5}, \qquad y = \frac{-3z - 6}{2},$$

and, therefore,

$$\frac{-3x + 15}{5} = y = \frac{-3z - 6}{2}.$$

Then dividing by -3, we obtain the symmetric equations

$$\frac{x - 5}{5} = \frac{y}{-3} = \frac{z + 2}{2}.$$

The symmetric equations can also be written by first finding the coordinates of two points on the line defined by the given equations. When $y = 0$ the equations become $x - z - 7 = 0$, $x + 5z + 5 = 0$. The solution of these equations is $x = 5$, $z = -2$. Hence the point $P_1(5, 0, -2)$ is on the line of intersection of the given planes. Similarly, we find that $P_2(0, 3, -4)$ is on the line. Then the vector

$$\overrightarrow{P_2P_1} = 5\mathbf{i} - 3\mathbf{j} + 2\mathbf{k}$$

is parallel to the line whose equations we seek. Consequently, we obtain, as before, the symmetric equations

$$\frac{x - 5}{5} = \frac{y}{-3} = \frac{z + 2}{2}.$$

EXAMPLE 4. Write the equations of the line passing through the points $P_1(2, 6, 4)$ and $P_2(3, -2, 4)$.

Solution. The vector from P_1 to P_2 is

$$\overrightarrow{P_1P_2} = \mathbf{i} - 8\mathbf{j}.$$

Hence the required line is parallel to the xy-plane. The plane $z = 4$ contains the line. This plane is perpendicular to two of the coordinate planes. We use the first two members of equations (3) to get another plane containing the line. Thus we have the defining equations

$$z = 4, \qquad \frac{x - 3}{1} = \frac{y + 2}{-8},$$

or

$$z = 4, \qquad 8x + y - 22 = 0.$$

Note that we could not use the third member of the symmetric equations because its denominator would be zero. We did, however, set the numerator of that member equal to zero to obtain one of the planes.

11–8 Direction angles and direction cosines. The angles, α, β, and γ which a directed line makes with the positive x-, y-, and z-axes, respectively, are called the *direction angles* of the line. The cosines of the direction angles are called the *direction cosines* of the line. The direction cosines of a line represented by equations of the form (2) or (3), Section 11–7, may be found by the use of vectors. The vector

$$\mathbf{V} = A\mathbf{i} + B\mathbf{j} + C\mathbf{k}$$

is parallel to the line. If one direction along the line is chosen as positive, then $\mathbf{V}$ or its negative points in the positive direction. The direction cosines are easily determined by using the dot product, as in problem 11, Exercise 11–3.

The angles formed by two lines which do not intersect are defined to be equal to the angles formed by two lines which do intersect and are parallel to the given lines. Hence vectors can be employed in finding the angles formed by two lines in space.

EXAMPLE. Assign a positive direction to the line represented by the equations

$$\frac{x-1}{4} = \frac{y+3}{-3} = \frac{z-5}{-2}$$

and find the direction cosines.

Solution. The vectors $4\mathbf{i} - 3\mathbf{j} - 2\mathbf{k}$ and $-4\mathbf{i} + 3\mathbf{j} + 2\mathbf{k}$ are parallel to the line. We select the positive direction of the line upward, so that γ is an acute angle. Then the vector $\mathbf{V} = -4\mathbf{i} + 3\mathbf{j} + 2\mathbf{k}$ points in the positive direction of the line. Using the dot product, we find

$$\mathbf{i} \cdot \mathbf{V} = |\mathbf{i}|\,|\mathbf{V}|\cos\alpha,$$
$$-4 = \sqrt{29}\cos\alpha,$$
$$\cos\alpha = -\frac{4}{\sqrt{29}}.$$

Similarly, $\mathbf{j} \cdot \mathbf{V}$ and $\mathbf{k} \cdot \mathbf{V}$ yield $\cos\beta = \dfrac{3}{\sqrt{29}}$ and $\cos\gamma = \dfrac{2}{\sqrt{29}}.$

EXERCISE 11–5

Write a vector which is parallel to the line represented in each problem 1 through 4. By setting x, y, and z in turn equal to zero, find the points in which the line cuts the coordinate planes.

1. $\dfrac{x-6}{2} = \dfrac{y+2}{1} = \dfrac{z+3}{3}$

2. $\dfrac{x}{-2} = \dfrac{y-2}{1} = \dfrac{z-3}{1}$

3. $\dfrac{x-3}{3} = \dfrac{y}{-1} = \dfrac{z-4}{2}$

4. $\dfrac{x-2}{1} = \dfrac{y+1}{2} = \dfrac{z-4}{3}$

In each problem 5 through 14 write, in two ways, the equations of the line which passes through the given point and is parallel to the given vector.

5. $P(4, -3, 5)$; $-2\mathbf{i} + 3\mathbf{j} + 4\mathbf{k}$ 6. $P(0, 1, -2)$; $\mathbf{i} - \mathbf{j} + 2\mathbf{k}$

7. $P(1, 1, 2)$; $2\mathbf{i} + 3\mathbf{j} - \mathbf{k}$ 8. $P(-2, -2, 3)$; $5\mathbf{i} + 4\mathbf{j} + \mathbf{k}$

9. $P(2, -1, 1)$; $2\mathbf{i} + \mathbf{j}$ 10. $P(3, 3, 3)$; $\mathbf{i} + \mathbf{k}$

11. $P(4, 3, 2)$; $\mathbf{j} + 2\mathbf{k}$ 12. $P(0, 0, 0)$; $\mathbf{i}$

13. $P(0, 0, 0)$; $\mathbf{j}$ 14. $P(0, 0, 0)$; $\mathbf{k}$

Write the equations of the line through the two points in each problem 15 through 22.

15. $(1, 2, 3)$, $(-2, 4, 0)$ 16. $(0, 0, 0)$, $(3, 4, 5)$

17. $(1, 0, 2)$, $(0, 2, 1)$ 18. $(2, 4, 0)$, $(1, 2, 8)$

19. $(2, 5, 4)$, $(2, 4, 3)$,   20. $(0, 4, 3)$, $(0, 4, 4)$

21. $(-1, 3, 4)$, $(3, 3, 4)$ 22. $(0, 0, 2)$, $(0, 0, 4)$

Find a symmetric form for each pair of equations in problems 23 through 26.

23. $x - y - 2z + 1 = 0$,   24. $x + y - 2z + 8 = 0$,
    $x - 3y - 3z + 7 = 0$ $2x - y - 2z + 4 = 0$

25. $x + y + z - 9 = 0$ 26. $x + y - z + 8 = 0$,
    $2x + y - z + 3 = 0$ $2x - y + 2z + 6 = 0$

27. Find the direction cosines of the lines defined in problems 1 through 4 of this exercise. In each case select the positive direction of the line so that γ is an acute angle.

Find the cosine of the acute angle formed by each pair of lines in problems 28 through 31.

28. $\dfrac{x-1}{2} = \dfrac{y+1}{1} = \dfrac{z-3}{2}$, $\dfrac{x-1}{2} = \dfrac{y+1}{-2} = \dfrac{z-3}{1}$

29. $\dfrac{x+2}{3} = \dfrac{y+2}{6} = \dfrac{z}{2}$, $\dfrac{x-1}{1} = \dfrac{y-1}{2} = \dfrac{z-4}{-2}$

30. $x = 3 + t$, $y = 5 - 8t$, $z = 2 + 4t$;
    $x = 3 + 4t$, $y = 5 - 2t$, $z = 2 - 4t$

31. $x = t$, $y = -2t$, $z = 3t$;
    $x = 6t$, $y = 4t$, $z = -2t$

11–9 The vector product. We now introduce another kind of product of two vectors. Let $\mathbf{A}$ and $\mathbf{B}$ be nonparallel, nonzero vectors forming an angle θ, where $0 < \theta < 180°$ (Fig. 11–16). The *vector product*, or *cross product*, denoted by $\mathbf{A} \times \mathbf{B}$, is defined by the following statements:

1. $\mathbf{A} \times \mathbf{B}$ is a vector perpendicular to the plane determined by $\mathbf{A}$ and $\mathbf{B}$.

2. $\mathbf{A} \times \mathbf{B}$ points in the direction a right-threaded screw would advance when its head is turned from $\mathbf{A}$ (the first vector) to $\mathbf{B}$ through the angle θ.

3. $|\mathbf{A} \times \mathbf{B}| = |\mathbf{A}|\,|\mathbf{B}|\sin\theta$.

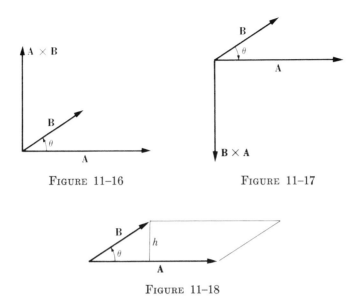

FIGURE 11–16   FIGURE 11–17

FIGURE 11–18

If **A** and **B** are parallel ($\theta = 0°$ or $\theta = 180°$), the vector product is defined by statement 3. This makes the product equal to zero since $\sin \theta = 0$. The vector product is zero if either **A** or **B**, or both, is equal to zero.

From statement 2, we see that the interchange of the factors in vector multiplication reverses the direction of the product (Fig. 11–17). Hence

$$\mathbf{A} \times \mathbf{B} = -\mathbf{B} \times \mathbf{A},$$

and multiplication of this kind is not commutative.

The magnitude of the cross product has a simple geometric interpretation. The area of the parallelogram in Fig. 11–18 is $|\mathbf{A}|h$. But $h = |\mathbf{B}| \sin \theta$ and therefore

$$|\mathbf{A} \times \mathbf{B}| = |\mathbf{A}|\,|\mathbf{B}| \sin \theta = |\mathbf{A}|h.$$

Hence the area of the parallelogram of which two adjacent sides are vectors is equal to the absolute value of the cross product of the vectors. One-half the absolute value of the cross product is, of course, equal to the area of the triangle determined by the vectors.

It can be shown that vector multiplication is distributive. (See problem 34, Exercise 11–6.) The distributive property is expressed by the equation

$$\mathbf{A} \times (\mathbf{B} \times \mathbf{C}) = \mathbf{A} \times \mathbf{B} + \mathbf{A} \times \mathbf{C}.$$

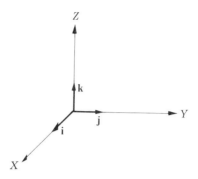

FIGURE 11–19

Suppose we apply the definition of vector multiplication to the unit vectors **i**, **j**, and **k** (Fig. 11–19). Clearly it follows that

$$\mathbf{i} \times \mathbf{j} = \mathbf{k} \qquad \text{and} \qquad \mathbf{j} \times \mathbf{i} = -\mathbf{k},$$
$$\mathbf{j} \times \mathbf{k} = \mathbf{i} \qquad \text{and} \qquad \mathbf{k} \times \mathbf{j} = -\mathbf{i},$$
$$\mathbf{k} \times \mathbf{i} = \mathbf{j} \qquad \text{and} \qquad \mathbf{i} \times \mathbf{k} = -\mathbf{j},$$
$$\mathbf{i} \times \mathbf{i} = \mathbf{j} \times \mathbf{j} = \mathbf{k} \times \mathbf{k} = 0.$$

These equations and the distributive property of vector multiplication permit us to derive a convenient formula for the vector product when the vectors are expressed in terms of **i**, **j**, and **k**. Thus

$$
\begin{aligned}
\mathbf{A} \times \mathbf{B} &= (a_1\mathbf{i} + a_2\mathbf{j} + a_3\mathbf{k}) \times (b_1\mathbf{i} + b_2\mathbf{j} + b_3\mathbf{k}) \\
&= a_1b_1\mathbf{i} \times \mathbf{i} + a_1b_2\mathbf{i} \times \mathbf{j} + a_1b_3\mathbf{i} \times \mathbf{k} \\
&\quad + a_2b_1\mathbf{j} \times \mathbf{i} + a_2b_2\mathbf{j} \times \mathbf{j} + a_2b_3\mathbf{j} \times \mathbf{k} \\
&\quad + a_3b_1\mathbf{k} \times \mathbf{i} + a_3b_2\mathbf{k} \times \mathbf{j} + a_3b_3\mathbf{k} \times \mathbf{k} \\
&= 0 + a_1b_2\mathbf{k} - a_1b_3\mathbf{j} - a_2b_1\mathbf{k} + 0 \\
&\quad + a_2b_3\mathbf{i} + a_3b_1\mathbf{j} - a_3b_2\mathbf{i} + 0.
\end{aligned}
$$

Hence

$$\mathbf{A} \times \mathbf{B} = (a_2b_3 - a_3b_2)\mathbf{i} + (a_3b_1 - a_1b_3)\mathbf{j} + (a_1b_2 - a_2b_1)\mathbf{k}.$$

This equation provides a formula for the cross product; however, a more convenient form results when the right member of the equation is expressed as a determinant. Thus, alternatively, we discover that

$$
\mathbf{A} \times \mathbf{B} = \begin{vmatrix} \mathbf{i} & \mathbf{j} & \mathbf{k} \\ a_1 & a_2 & a_3 \\ b_1 & b_2 & b_3 \end{vmatrix}.
$$

EXAMPLE 1. The vectors **A** and **B** make an angle of 30°. If the length of **A** is 5 and the length of **B** is 8, find the area of the parallelogram of which **A** and **B** are consecutive sides.

Solution. The area of the parallelogram is equal to the absolute value of **A** × **B**. From the definition of a cross product,

$$|\mathbf{A} \times \mathbf{B}| = |\mathbf{A}| \, |\mathbf{B}| \sin \theta = (5)(8) \sin 30° = 20.$$

The area of the parallelogram is 20 square units.

EXAMPLE 2. The points $A(1, 0, -1)$, $B(3, -1, -5)$, and $C(4, 2, 0)$ are vertices of a triangle. Find the area of the triangle.

Solution. The vectors $\overrightarrow{AB}$ and $\overrightarrow{AC}$ form two sides of the triangle. The magnitude of the cross product of the vectors is equal to the area of the parallelogram of which the vectors are adjacent sides. The area of the triangle, however, is one-half the area of the parallelogram. Thus we find

$$\overrightarrow{AB} = 2\mathbf{i} - \mathbf{j} - 4\mathbf{k}, \qquad \overrightarrow{AC} = 3\mathbf{i} + 2\mathbf{j} + \mathbf{k},$$

and

$$\overrightarrow{AB} \times \overrightarrow{AC} = \begin{vmatrix} \mathbf{i} & \mathbf{j} & \mathbf{k} \\ 2 & -1 & -4 \\ 3 & 2 & 1 \end{vmatrix} = 7\mathbf{i} - 14\mathbf{j} + 7\mathbf{k}.$$

The magnitude of this vector is $\sqrt{49 + 196 + 49} = 7\sqrt{6}$. Therefore the area of the triangle is $\frac{7}{2}\sqrt{6}$.

EXAMPLE 3. The points $A(2, -1, 3)$, $B(4, 2, 5)$, and $C(-1, -1, 6)$ determine a plane. Find the distance from the plane to the point $D(5, 4, 8)$.

Solution. The dot product of a unit vector perpendicular to the plane and a vector from a point of the plane to D yields the required distance. Accordingly, we write

$$\overrightarrow{AD} = 3\mathbf{i} + 5\mathbf{j} + 5\mathbf{k}, \qquad \overrightarrow{AB} = 2\mathbf{i} + 3\mathbf{j} + 2\mathbf{k}, \qquad \overrightarrow{AC} = -3\mathbf{i} + 3\mathbf{k},$$

$$\overrightarrow{AB} \times \overrightarrow{AC} = \begin{vmatrix} \mathbf{i} & \mathbf{j} & \mathbf{k} \\ 2 & 3 & 2 \\ -3 & 0 & 3 \end{vmatrix} = 9\mathbf{i} - 12\mathbf{j} + 9\mathbf{k}.$$

The vector $9\mathbf{i} - 12\mathbf{j} + 9\mathbf{k}$ is perpendicular to $\overrightarrow{AB}$ and $\overrightarrow{AC}$ and therefore is perpendicular to the plane of A, B, and C. We divide this vector by its length, $3\sqrt{34}$, to obtain a unit vector. Finally, the distance d from the plane to D is given by

$$d = (3\mathbf{i} + 5\mathbf{j} + 5\mathbf{k}) \cdot \frac{3\mathbf{i} - 4\mathbf{j} + 3\mathbf{k}}{\sqrt{34}} = \frac{2\sqrt{34}}{17}.$$

EXAMPLE 4. Find the equations, in symmetric form, of the line of intersection of the planes $2x - y + 4z = 3$ and $3x + y + z = 7$.

Solution. We may write the desired equations immediately if we know the coordinates of any point of the line and any vector parallel to the line. By setting $z = 0$ in the equations of the planes and solving for x and y, we find that $(2, 1, 0)$ is a point of the line. Normals to the planes are given by the vectors

$$\mathbf{N}_1 = 2\mathbf{i} - \mathbf{j} + 4\mathbf{k}, \qquad \mathbf{N}_2 = 3\mathbf{i} + \mathbf{j} + \mathbf{k}.$$

The cross product of the vectors is parallel to the line of intersection of the planes. We find

$$\mathbf{N}_1 \times \mathbf{N}_2 = \begin{vmatrix} \mathbf{i} & \mathbf{j} & \mathbf{k} \\ 2 & -1 & 4 \\ 3 & 1 & 1 \end{vmatrix} = -5\mathbf{i} + 10\mathbf{j} + 5\mathbf{k}.$$

We divide this vector by 5 and write the equation of the line as

$$\frac{x - 2}{-1} = \frac{y - 1}{2} = \frac{z}{1}.$$

We note that this is the same kind of problem as that of Example 3, Section 11–7.

11–10 The distance from a line to a point. Let L (Fig. 11–20) be a line passing through the point $P_0(x_0, y_0, z_0)$ and parallel to a unit vector $\mathbf{u}$. Then let $P_1(x_1, y_1, z_1)$ be any point not on the line and let $\mathbf{V}$ be the vector $\overrightarrow{P_0P_1}$. To find the perpendicular distance from line L to P_1, we take the vector product of $\mathbf{V}$ and $\mathbf{u}$. Thus

$$d = |\mathbf{V}| \sin \theta = |\mathbf{u}| \, |\mathbf{V}| \sin \theta = |\mathbf{u} \times \mathbf{V}|.$$

EXAMPLE. Find the distance from the line passing through $P_2(3, 0, 6)$ and $P_3(5, -2, 7)$ to the point $P_1(8, 1, -3)$.

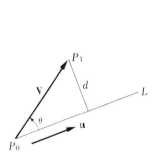

FIGURE 11–20

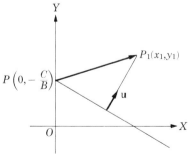

FIGURE 11–21

Solution. The vector $\overrightarrow{P_3P_2} = -2\mathbf{i} + 2\mathbf{j} - \mathbf{k}$, and $\mathbf{u} = \frac{1}{3}(-2\mathbf{i} + 2\mathbf{j} - \mathbf{k})$. The vector $\overrightarrow{P_2P_1} = \mathbf{V} = 5\mathbf{i} + \mathbf{j} - 9\mathbf{k}$. Hence

$$\mathbf{u} \times \mathbf{V} = \frac{1}{3} \begin{vmatrix} \mathbf{i} & \mathbf{j} & \mathbf{k} \\ -2 & 2 & -1 \\ 5 & 1 & -9 \end{vmatrix} = \frac{1}{3}(-17\mathbf{i} - 23\mathbf{j} - 14\mathbf{k}),$$

and

$$d = |\mathbf{u} \times \mathbf{V}| = \frac{13}{3}\sqrt{6}.$$

In Section 2–4 we derived a formula for the distance from a line to a point when both are in the xy-plane. Now we give a much shorter derivation by employing vectors.

The equation $Ax + By + C = 0$, in three space, represents a plane parallel to the z-axis (Section 10–3); the vector $A\mathbf{i} + B\mathbf{j}$ is perpendicular to the plane (Section 11–6). The intersection of the plane and the xy-plane is a line, and the x- and y-coordinates of all points of the intersection satisfy the equation $Ax + By + C = 0$. Restricting ourselves to the xy-plane, we have a line and a vector perpendicular to the line. Now let $P_1(x_1, y_1)$ be any point in the xy-plane (Fig. 11–21). If $B \neq 0$, the line cuts the y-axis at $P(0, -C/B)$. The scalar product of the vector $\overrightarrow{PP_1}$ and a unit vector $\mathbf{u}$, perpendicular to the line, gives the distance d. Since

$$PP_1 = x\mathbf{i} + \left(y_1 + \frac{C}{B}\right)\mathbf{j} \quad \text{and} \quad \mathbf{u} = \frac{A\mathbf{i} + B\mathbf{j}}{\pm\sqrt{A^2 + B^2}},$$

we have

$$d = \left[x_1\mathbf{i} + \left(y_1 + \frac{C}{B}\right)\mathbf{j}\right] \cdot \frac{A\mathbf{i} + B\mathbf{j}}{\pm\sqrt{A^2 + B^2}} = \frac{Ax_1 + By_1 + C}{\pm\sqrt{A^2 + B^2}}.$$

Thus a scalar product yields at once the desired formula. The ambiguity as to sign is discussed in Section 2–4.

EXERCISE 11–6

In each problem 1 through 6 find the cross product, $\mathbf{A} \times \mathbf{B}$, of the vectors and a unit vector perpendicular to the two given vectors.

1. $\mathbf{A} = 3\mathbf{i} - 4\mathbf{j} - 2\mathbf{k}$,
   $\mathbf{B} = \mathbf{i} - 2\mathbf{j} - 2\mathbf{k}$
2. $\mathbf{A} = 6\mathbf{i} - 3\mathbf{j} + 14\mathbf{k}$,
   $\mathbf{B} = 3\mathbf{i} - 2\mathbf{j} + 3\mathbf{k}$
3. $\mathbf{A} = \mathbf{i} + \mathbf{j} + \mathbf{k}$,
   $\mathbf{B} = \mathbf{i} - \mathbf{j} - \mathbf{k}$
4. $\mathbf{A} = 2\mathbf{i} - \mathbf{k}$,
   $\mathbf{B} = \mathbf{j} + 2\mathbf{k}$
5. $\mathbf{A} = 4\mathbf{i} - 3\mathbf{j}$,
   $\mathbf{B} = 3\mathbf{i} + 4\mathbf{j}$
6. $\mathbf{A} = \mathbf{i} - 2\mathbf{j} + 3\mathbf{k}$,
   $\mathbf{B} = 4\mathbf{i} + 5\mathbf{j} - 6\mathbf{k}$

Compute the area of the parallelogram described in problems 7 through 10.

7. $\mathbf{A} = 3\mathbf{i} + 2\mathbf{j}$ and $\mathbf{B} = \mathbf{i} - \mathbf{j}$ are adjacent sides.

8. $\mathbf{A} = 4\mathbf{i} - \mathbf{j} + \mathbf{k}$ and $\mathbf{B} = 3\mathbf{i} + \mathbf{j} + \mathbf{k}$ are adjacent sides.

9. The points $A(4, 1, 0)$, $B(1, 2, 1)$, $C(0, 0, 6)$, and $D(3, -1, 5)$ are vertices of the parallelogram $ABCD$.

10. The points $A(1, -1, 1)$, $B(3, 3, 1)$, $C(4, -1, 4)$, and $D(2, -5, 4)$ are vertices of the parallelogram $ABCD$.

Find the area of the triangle described in problems 11 through 14.

11. The vertices are $A(-1, 3, 4)$, $B(1, 2, 5)$, and $C(2, -3, 1)$.

12. The vertices are $A(1, 0, 4)$, $B(3, -3, 0)$, and $C(0, 1, 2)$.

13. The vectors $\mathbf{A} = 2\mathbf{i} - 3\mathbf{j}$ and $\mathbf{B} = \mathbf{i} - \mathbf{j}$, drawn from the origin, are two sides.

14. The tips of the vectors $\mathbf{A} = 4\mathbf{i} + \mathbf{j}$, $\mathbf{B} = \mathbf{i} + 2\mathbf{j} + \mathbf{k}$, and $\mathbf{C} = 3\mathbf{i} - \mathbf{j} + 5\mathbf{k}$, drawn from the origin, are the vertices.

15. Find the area of the triangle in the xy-plane whose vertices are the points (x_1, y_1), (x_2, y_2) and (x_3, y_3). Use a vector product and compare your result with the formula in problem 34, Exercise 1–2.

16. Write the equation of the plane which passes through the points $(2, -4, 3)$, $(-3, 5, 1)$, and $(4, 0, 6)$.

17. Write the equation of the plane which contains the points $(2, 1, 0)$, $(3, 0, 2)$, and $(0, 4, 3)$.

18. Find the distance from the point $(6, 7, 8)$ to the plane of the points $(-1, 3, 0)$, $(2, 2, 1)$, and $(1, 1, 3)$.

19. Find the distance from the point $(-4, -5, -3)$ to the plane passing through the points $(4, 0, 0)$, $(0, 6, 0)$, and $(0, 0, 7)$.

20. Find the equations of the line passing through the point $(3, 1, -2)$ and parallel to each of the planes $x - y + z = 4$ and $3x + y - z = 5$.

21. Find the equations of the line which passes through the origin and is parallel to the line of intersection of the planes $2x - y - z = 2$ and $4x + 2y - 4z = 1$.

22. Find a parametric representation of the line of intersection of the two planes of problem 20 and also of problem 21.

23. A plane passes through the point $(1, 1, 1)$ and is perpendicular to each of planes $2x + 2y + z = 3$ and $3x - y - 2z = 5$. Find its equation.

24. A plane passes through the point $(0, 0, 0)$ and is perpendicular to the line of intersection of the planes $5x - 4y + 3z = 2$ and $x + 2y - 3z = 4$. Find the equation of the plane.

25. A line passes through the points $(1, 3, 1)$ and $(3, 4, -1)$. Find the distance from the line to the point $(4, 4, 4)$.

26. A line passes through $(3, 2, 1)$ and is parallel to the vector $2\mathbf{i} + \mathbf{j} - 2\mathbf{k}$. Find the distance from the line to $(-3, -1, 3)$.

27. Find the distance from the line $x/2 = y/3 = z/1$ to the point $(3, 4, 1)$.

28. Find the distance from the line $(x - 2)/2 = y/2 = (z - 1)/1$ to the point $(0, 0, 0)$.

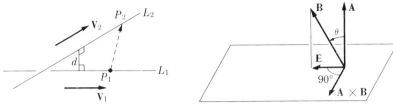

FIGURE 11–22   FIGURE 11–23

29. Let L_1 and L_2 (Fig. 11–22) be lines which are not parallel and do not intersect. Let $\overrightarrow{P_1P_2}$ be a vector extending from any point on L_1 to any point on L_2, V_1 a vector parallel to L_1, and V_2 parallel to L_2. Then $V_1 \times V_2$ is perpendicular to both lines. Show that the perpendicular distance between L_1 and L_2 is

$$d = |\overrightarrow{P_1P_2} \cdot \mathbf{u}|,$$

where $\mathbf{u}$ is a unit vector parallel to $V_1 \times V_2$.

Find the perpendicular distance between the two lines in problems 30 through 33.

30. L_1 passes through $P_1(2, 3, 1)$ in the direction of $V_1 = i + 2j - 3k$, and L_2 passes through $P_2(4, 2, 0)$ in the direction of $V_2 = 3i - j + k$.

31. L_1 passes through $(2, 1, -1)$ and $(-1, 3, 2)$. L_2 passes through $(4, 0, 5)$ and $(3, 4, 0)$.

32. The equations of L_1 are $(x + 2)/3 = (y + 3)/2 = z/2$. The equations of L_2 are $(x - 1)/2 = (y + 4)/3 = (z - 2)/4$.

33. L_1 passes through $(4, 1, 0)$ and $(0, 0, 6)$. L_2 passes through $(1, 2, 1)$ and $(3, -1, 5)$. Do the lines intersect?

34. In Fig. 11–23, the vector E is the projection of B on a plane perpendicular to A. Vector E is rotated through $90°$, as indicated, and then multiplied by $|A|$ to yield $A \times B$. Tell why these operations lead to $A \times B$.

Next, let B, C, and $B + C$ form a triangle. Project this triangle on the plane perpendicular to A, thus forming another vector triangle. Rotate the new triangle through $90°$ and multiply each side by $|A|$. Observe that the sides of the final triangle are $A \times B$, $A \times C$, and $A \times (B + C)$, and that

$$A \times (B + C) = A \times B + A \times C.$$

TABLE I

POWERS AND ROOTS

No.	Sq.	Sq. Root	Cube	Cube Root	No.	Sq.	Sq. Root	Cube	Cube Root
1	1	1.000	1	1.000	51	2,601	7.141	132,651	3.708
2	4	1.414	8	1.260	52	2,704	7.211	140,608	3.733
3	9	1.732	27	1.442	53	2,809	7.280	148,877	3.756
4	16	2.000	64	1.587	54	2,916	7.348	157,464	3.780
5	25	2.236	125	1.710	55	3,025	7.416	166,375	3.803
6	36	2.449	216	1.817	56	3,136	7.483	175,616	3.826
7	49	2.646	343	1.913	57	3,249	7.550	185,193	3.849
8	64	2.828	512	2.000	58	3,364	7.616	195,112	3.871
9	81	3.000	729	2.080	59	3,481	7.681	205,379	3.893
10	100	3.162	1,000	2.154	60	3,600	7.746	216,000	3.915
11	121	3.317	1,331	2.224	61	3,721	7.810	226,981	3.936
12	144	3.464	1,728	2.289	62	3,844	7.874	238,328	3.958
13	169	3.606	2,197	2.351	63	3,969	7.937	250,047	3.979
14	196	3.742	2,744	2.410	64	4,096	8.000	262,144	4.000
15	225	3.873	3,375	2.466	65	4,225	8.062	274,625	4.021
16	256	4.000	4,096	2.520	66	4,356	8.124	287,496	4.041
17	289	4.123	4,913	2.571	67	4,489	8.185	300,763	4.062
18	324	4.243	5,832	2.621	68	4,624	8.246	314,432	4.082
19	361	4.359	6,859	2.668	69	4,761	8.307	328,509	4.102
20	400	4.472	8,000	2.714	70	4,900	8.367	343,000	4.121
21	441	4.583	9,261	2.759	71	5,041	8.426	357,911	4.141
22	484	4.690	10,648	2.802	72	5,184	8.485	373,248	4.160
23	529	4.796	12,167	2.844	73	5,329	8.544	389,017	4.179
24	576	4.899	13,824	2.884	74	5,476	8.602	405,224	4.198
25	625	5.000	15,625	2.924	75	5,625	8.660	421,875	4.217
26	676	5.099	17,576	2.962	76	5,776	8.718	438,976	4.236
27	729	5.196	19,683	3.000	77	5,929	8.775	456,533	4.254
28	784	5.292	21,952	3.037	78	6,084	8.832	474,552	4.273
29	841	5.385	24,389	3.072	79	6,241	8.888	493,039	4.291
30	900	5.477	27,000	3.107	80	6,400	8.944	512,000	4.309
31	961	5.568	29,791	3.141	81	6,561	9.000	531,441	4.327
32	1,024	5.657	32,768	3.175	82	6,724	9.055	551,368	4.344
33	1,089	5.745	35,937	3.208	83	6,889	9.110	571,787	4.362
34	1,156	5.831	39,304	3.240	84	7,056	9.165	592,704	4.380
35	1,225	5.916	42,875	3.271	85	7,225	9.220	614,125	4.397
36	1,296	6.000	46,656	3.302	86	7,396	9.274	636,056	4.414
37	1,369	6.083	50,653	3.332	87	7,569	9.327	658,503	4.431
38	1,444	6.164	54,872	3.362	88	7,744	9.381	681,472	4.448
39	1,521	6.245	59,319	3.391	89	7,921	9.434	704,969	4.465
40	1,600	6.325	64,000	3.420	90	8,100	9.487	729,000	4.481
41	1,681	6.403	68,921	3.448	91	8,281	9.539	753,571	4.498
42	1,764	6.481	74,088	3.476	92	8,464	9.592	778,688	4.514
43	1,849	6.557	79,507	3.503	93	8,649	9.644	804,357	4.531
44	1,936	6.633	85,184	3.530	94	8,836	9.695	830,584	4.547
45	2,025	6.708	91,125	3.557	95	9,025	9.747	857,375	4.563
46	2,116	6.782	97,336	3.583	96	9,216	9.798	884,736	4.579
47	2,209	6.856	103,823	3.609	97	9,409	9.849	912,673	4.595
48	2,304	6.928	110,592	3.634	98	9,604	9.899	941,192	4.610
49	2,401	7.000	117,649	3.659	99	9,801	9.950	970,299	4.626
50	2,500	7.071	125,000	3.684	100	10,000	10.000	1,000,000	4.642

TABLE II

Natural Trigonometric Functions

Angle					Angle				
De-gree	Ra-dian	Sine	Co-sine	Tan-gent	De-gree	Ra-dian	Sine	Co-sine	Tan-gent
0°	0.000	0.000	1.000	0.000					
1°	0.017	0.017	1.000	0.017	46°	0.803	0.719	0.695	1.036
2°	0.035	0.035	0.999	0.035	47°	0.820	0.731	0.682	1.072
3°	0.052	0.052	0.999	0.052	48°	0.838	0.743	0.669	1.111
4°	0.070	0.070	0.998	0.070	49°	0.855	0.755	0.656	1.150
5°	0.087	0.087	0.996	0.087	50°	0.873	0.766	0.643	1.192
6°	0.105	0.105	0.995	0.105	51°	0.890	0.777	0.629	1.235
7°	0.122	0.122	0.993	0.123	52°	0.908	0.788	0.616	1.280
8°	0.140	0.139	0.990	0.141	53°	0.925	0.799	0.602	1.327
9°	0.157	0.156	0.988	0.158	54°	0.942	0.809	0.588	1.376
10°	0.175	0.174	0.985	0.176	55°	0.960	0.819	0.574	1.428
11°	0.192	0.191	0.982	0.194	56°	0.977	0.829	0.559	1.483
12°	0.209	0.208	0.978	0.213	57°	0.995	0.839	0.545	1.540
13°	0.227	0.225	0.974	0.231	58°	1.012	0.848	0.530	1.600
14°	0.244	0.242	0.970	0.249	59°	1.030	0.857	0.515	1.664
15°	0.262	0.259	0.966	0.268	60°	1.047	0.866	0.500	1.732
16°	0.279	0.276	0.961	0.287	61°	1.065	0.875	0.485	1.804
17°	0.297	0.292	0.956	0.306	62°	1.082	0.883	0.469	1.881
18°	0.314	0.309	0.951	0.325	63°	1.100	0.891	0.454	1.963
19°	0.332	0.326	0.946	0.344	64°	1.117	0.899	0.438	2.050
20°	0.349	0.342	0.940	0.364	65°	1.134	0.906	0.423	2.145
21°	0.367	0.358	0.934	0.384	66°	1.152	0.914	0.407	2.246
22°	0.384	0.375	0.927	0.404	67°	1.169	0.921	0.391	2.356
23°	0.401	0.391	0.921	0.424	68°	1.187	0.927	0.375	2.475
24°	0.419	0.407	0.914	0.445	69°	1.204	0.934	0.358	2.605
25°	0.436	0.423	0.906	0.466	70°	1.222	0.940	0.342	2.748
26°	0.454	0.438	0.899	0.488	71°	1.239	0.946	0.326	2.904
27°	0.471	0.454	0.891	0.510	72°	1.257	0.951	0.309	3.078
28°	0.489	0.469	0.883	0.532	73°	1.274	0.956	0.292	3.271
29°	0.506	0.485	0.875	0.554	74°	1.292	0.961	0.276	3.487
30°	0.524	0.500	0.866	0.577	75°	1.309	0.966	0.259	3.732
31°	0.541	0.515	0.857	0.601	76°	1.326	0.970	0.242	4.011
32°	0.559	0.530	0.848	0.625	77°	1.344	0.974	0.225	4.332
33°	0.576	0.545	0.839	0.649	78°	1.361	0.978	0.208	4.705
34°	0.593	0.559	0.829	0.675	79°	1.379	0.982	0.191	5.145
35°	0.611	0.574	0.819	0.700	80°	1.396	0.985	0.174	5.671
36°	0.628	0.588	0.809	0.727	81°	1.414	0.988	0.156	6.314
37°	0.646	0.602	0.799	0.754	82°	1.431	0.990	0.139	7.115
38°	0.663	0.616	0.788	0.781	83°	1.449	0.993	0.122	8.144
39°	0.681	0.629	0.777	0.810	84°	1.466	0.995	0.105	9.514
40°	0.698	0.643	0.766	0.839	85°	1.484	0.996	0.087	11.43
41°	0.716	0.656	0.755	0.869	86°	1.501	0.998	0.070	14.30
42°	0.733	0.669	0.743	0.900	87°	1.518	0.999	0.052	19.08
43°	0.750	0.682	0.731	0.933	88°	1.536	0.999	0.035	28.64
44°	0.768	0.695	0.719	0.966	89°	1.553	1.000	0.017	57.29
45°	0.785	0.707	0.707	1.000	90°	1.571	1.000	0.000	

Table III

Exponential Functions

x	e^x	e^{-x}	x	e^x	e^{-x}
0.00	1.0000	1.0000	2.5	12.182	0.0821
0.05	1.0513	0.9512	2.6	13.464	0.0743
0.10	1.1052	0.9048	2.7	14.880	0.0672
0.15	1.1618	0.8607	2.8	16.445	0.0608
0.20	1.2214	0.8187	2.9	18.174	0.0550
0.25	1.2840	0.7788	3.0	20.086	0.0498
0.30	1.3499	0.7408	3.1	22.198	0.0450
0.35	1.4191	0.7047	3.2	24.533	0.0408
0.40	1.4918	0.6703	3.3	27.113	0.0369
0.45	1.5683	0.6376	3.4	29.964	0.0334
0.50	1.6487	0.6065	3.5	33.115	0.0302
0.55	1.7333	0.5769	3.6	36.598	0.0273
0.60	1.8221	0.5488	3.7	40.447	0.0247
0.65	1.9155	0.5220	3.8	44.701	0.0224
0.70	2.0138	0.4966	3.9	49.402	0.0202
0.75	2.1170	0.4724	4.0	54.598	0.0183
0.80	2.2255	0.4493	4.1	60.340	0.0166
0.85	2.3396	0.4274	4.2	66.686	0.0150
0.90	2.4596	0.4066	4.3	73.700	0.0136
0.95	2.5857	0.3867	4.4	81.451	0.0123
1.0	2.7183	0.3679	4.5	90.017	0.0111
1.1	3.0042	0.3329	4.6	99.484	0.0101
1.2	3.3201	0.3012	4.7	109.95	0.0091
1.3	3.6693	0.2725	4.8	121.51	0.0082
1.4	4.0552	0.2466	4.9	134.29	0.0074
1.5	4.4817	0.2231	5	148.41	0.0067
1.6	4.9530	0.2019	6	403.43	0.0025
1.7	5.4739	0.1827	7	1096.6	0.0009
1.8	6.0496	0.1653	8	2981.0	0.0003
1.9	6.6859	0.1496	9	8103.1	0.0001
2.0	7.3891	0.1353	10	22026	0.00005
2.1	8.1662	0.1225			
2.2	9.0250	0.1108			
2.3	9.9742	0.1003			
2.4	11.023	0.0907			

TABLE IV

COMMON LOGARITHMS OF NUMBERS

N	0	1	2	3	4	5	6	7	8	9
0	. . . .	0000	3010	4771	6021	6990	7782	8451	9031	9542
1	0000	0414	0792	1139	1461	1761	2041	2304	2553	2788
2	3010	3222	3424	3617	3802	3979	4150	4314	4472	4624
3	4771	4914	5051	5185	5315	5441	5563	5682	5798	5911
4	6021	6128	6232	6335	6435	6532	6628	6721	6812	6902
5	6990	7076	7160	7243	7324	7404	7482	7559	7634	7709
6	7782	7853	7924	7993	8062	8129	8195	8261	8325	8388
7	8451	8513	8573	8633	8692	8751	8808	8865	8921	8976
8	9031	9085	9138	9191	9243	9294	9345	9395	9445	9494
9	9542	9590	9638	9685	9731	9777	9823	9868	9912	9956
10	0000	0043	0086	0128	0170	0212	0253	0294	0334	0374
11	0414	0453	0492	0531	0569	0607	0645	0682	0719	0755
12	0792	0828	0864	0899	0934	0969	1004	1038	1072	1106
13	1139	1173	1206	1239	1271	1303	1335	1367	1399	1430
14	1461	1492	1523	1553	1584	1614	1644	1673	1703	1732
15	1761	1790	1818	1847	1875	1903	1931	1959	1987	2014
16	2041	2068	2095	2122	2148	2175	2201	2227	2253	2279
17	2304	2330	2355	2380	2405	2430	2455	2480	2504	2529
18	2553	2577	2601	2625	2648	2672	2695	2718	2742	2765
19	2788	2810	2833	2856	2878	2900	2923	2945	2967	2989
20	3010	3032	3054	3075	3096	3118	3139	3160	3181	3201
21	3222	3243	3263	3284	3304	3324	3345	3365	3385	3404
22	3424	3444	3464	3483	3502	3522	3541	3560	3579	3598
23	3617	3636	3655	3674	3692	3711	3729	3747	3766	3784
24	3802	3820	3838	3856	3874	3892	3909	3927	3945	3962
25	3979	3997	4014	4031	4048	4065	4082	4099	4116	4133
26	4150	4166	4183	4200	4216	4232	4249	4265	4281	4298
27	4314	4330	4346	4362	4378	4393	4409	4425	4440	4456
28	4472	4487	4502	4518	4533	4548	4564	4579	4594	4609
29	4624	4639	4654	4669	4683	4698	4713	4728	4742	4757
30	4771	4786	4800	4814	4829	4843	4857	4871	4886	4900
31	4914	4928	4942	4955	4969	4983	4997	5011	5024	5038
32	5051	5065	5079	5092	5105	5119	5132	5145	5159	5172
33	5185	5198	5211	5224	5237	5250	5263	5276	5289	5302
34	5315	5328	5340	5353	5366	5378	5391	5403	5416	5428
35	5441	5453	5465	5478	5490	5502	5514	5527	5539	5551
36	5563	5575	5587	5599	5611	5623	5635	5647	5658	5670
37	5682	5694	5705	5717	5729	5740	5752	5763	5775	5786
38	5798	5809	5821	5832	5843	5855	5866	5877	5888	5899
39	5911	5922	5933	5944	5955	5966	5977	5988	5999	6010
40	6021	6031	6042	6053	6064	6075	6085	6096	6107	6117
41	6128	6138	6149	6160	6170	6180	6191	6201	6212	6222
42	6232	6243	6253	6263	6274	6284	6294	6304	6314	6325
43	6335	6345	6355	6365	6375	6385	6395	6405	6415	6425
44	6435	6444	6454	6464	6474	6484	6493	6503	6513	6522
45	6532	6542	6551	6561	6571	6580	6590	6599	6609	6618
46	6628	6637	6646	6656	6665	6675	6684	6693	6702	6712
47	6721	6730	6739	6749	6758	6767	6776	6785	6794	6803
48	6812	6821	6830	6839	6848	6857	6866	6875	6884	6893
49	6902	6911	6920	6928	6937	6946	6955	6964	6972	6981
50	6990	6998	7007	7016	7024	7033	7042	7050	7059	7067
N	0	1	2	3	4	5	6	7	8	9

TABLE IV

COMMON LOGARITHMS OF NUMBERS

N	0	1	2	3	4	5	6	7	8	9
50	6990	6998	7007	7016	7024	7033	7042	7050	7059	7067
51	7076	7084	7093	7101	7110	7118	7126	7135	7143	7152
52	7160	7168	7177	7185	7193	7202	7210	7218	7226	7235
53	7243	7251	7259	7267	7275	7284	7292	7300	7308	7316
54	7324	7332	7340	7348	7356	7364	7372	7380	7388	7396
55	7404	7412	7419	7427	7435	7443	7451	7459	7466	7474
56	7482	7490	7497	7505	7513	7520	7528	7536	7543	7551
57	7559	7566	7574	7582	7589	7597	7604	7612	7619	7627
58	7634	7642	7649	7657	7664	7672	7679	7686	7694	7701
59	7709	7716	7723	7731	7738	7745	7752	7760	7767	7774
60	7782	7789	7796	7803	7810	7818	7825	7832	7839	7846
61	7853	7860	7868	7875	7882	7889	7896	7903	7910	7917
62	7924	7931	7938	7945	7952	7959	7966	7973	7980	7987
63	7993	8000	8007	8014	8021	8028	8035	8041	8048	8055
64	8062	8069	8075	8082	8089	8096	8102	8109	8116	8122
65	8129	8136	8142	8149	8156	8162	8169	8176	8182	8189
66	8195	8202	8209	8215	8222	8228	8235	8241	8248	8254
67	8261	8267	8274	8280	8287	8293	8299	8306	8312	8319
68	8325	8331	8338	8344	8351	8357	8363	8370	8376	8382
69	8388	8395	8401	8407	8414	8420	8426	8432	8439	8445
70	8451	8457	8463	8470	8476	8482	8488	8494	8500	8506
71	8513	8519	8525	8531	8537	8543	8549	8555	8561	8567
72	8573	8579	8585	8591	8597	8603	8609	8615	8621	8627
73	8633	8639	8645	8651	8657	8663	8669	8675	8681	8686
74	8692	8698	8704	8710	8716	8722	8727	8733	8739	8745
75	8751	8756	8762	8768	8774	8779	8785	8791	8797	8802
76	8808	8814	8820	8825	8831	8837	8842	8848	8854	8859
77	8865	8871	8876	8882	8887	8893	8899	8904	8910	8915
78	8921	8927	8932	8938	8943	8949	8954	8960	8965	8971
79	8976	8982	8987	8993	8998	9004	9009	9015	9020	9025
80	9031	9036	9042	9047	9053	9058	9063	9069	9074	9079
81	9085	9090	9096	9101	9106	9112	9117	9122	9128	9133
82	9138	9143	9149	9154	9159	9165	9170	9175	9180	9186
83	9191	9196	9201	9206	9212	9217	9222	9227	9232	9238
84	9243	9248	9253	9258	9263	9269	9274	9279	9284	9289
85	9294	9299	9304	9309	9315	9320	9325	9330	9335	9340
86	9345	9350	9355	9360	9365	9370	9375	9380	9385	9390
87	9395	9400	9405	9410	9415	9420	9425	9430	9435	9440
88	9445	9450	9455	9460	9465	9469	9474	9479	9484	9489
89	9494	9499	9504	9509	9513	9518	9523	9528	9533	9538
90	9542	9547	9552	9557	9562	9566	9571	9576	9581	9586
91	9590	9595	9600	9605	9609	9614	9619	9624	9628	9633
92	9638	9643	9647	9652	9657	9661	9666	9671	9675	9680
93	9685	9689	9694	9699	9703	9708	9713	9717	9722	9727
94	9731	9736	9741	9745	9750	9754	9759	9763	9768	9773
95	9777	9782	9786	9791	9795	9800	9805	9809	9814	9818
96	9823	9827	9832	9836	9841	9845	9850	9854	9859	9863
97	9868	9872	9877	9881	9886	9890	9894	9899	9903	9908
98	9912	9917	9921	9926	9930	9934	9939	9943	9948	9952
99	9956	9961	9965	9969	9974	9978	9983	9987	9991	9996
100	0000	0004	0009	0013	0017	0022	0026	0030	0035	0039
N	0	1	2	3	4	5	6	7	8	9

TABLE V

NATURAL LOGARITHMS OF NUMBERS

n	$\log_e n$	n	$\log_e n$	n	$\log_e n$
0.0	*	4.5	1.5041	9.0	2.1972
0.1	7.6974	4.6	1.5261	9.1	2.2083
0.2	8.3906	4.7	1.5476	9.2	2.2192
0.3	8.7960	4.8	1.5686	9.3	2.2300
0.4	9.0837	4.9	1.5892	9.4	2.2407
0.5	9.3069	5.0	1.6094	9.5	2.2513
0.6	9.4892	5.1	1.6292	9.6	2.2618
0.7	9.6433	5.2	1.6487	9.7	2.2721
0.8	9.7769	5.3	1.6677	9.8	2.2824
0.9	9.8946	5.4	1.6864	9.9	2.2925
1.0	0.0000	5.5	1.7047	10	2.3026
1.1	0.0953	5.6	1.7228	11	2.3979
1.2	0.1823	5.7	1.7405	12	2.4849
1.3	0.2624	5.8	1.7579	13	2.5649
1.4	0.3365	5.9	1.7750	14	2.6391
1.5	0.4055	6.0	1.7918	15	2.7081
1.6	0.4700	6.1	1.8083	16	2.7726
1.7	0.5306	6.2	1.8245	17	2.8332
1.8	0.5878	6.3	1.8405	18	2.8904
1.9	0.6419	6.4	1.8563	19	2.9444
2.0	0.6931	6.5	1.8718	20	2.9957
2.1	0.7419	6.6	1.8871	25	3.2189
2.2	0.7885	6.7	1.9021	30	3.4012
2.3	0.8329	6.8	1.9169	35	3.5553
2.4	0.8755	6.9	1.9315	40	3.6889
2.5	0.9163	7.0	1.9459	45	3.8067
2.6	0.9555	7.1	1.9601	50	3.9120
2.7	0.9933	7.2	1.9741	55	4.0073
2.8	1.0296	7.3	1.9879	60	4.0943
2.9	1.0647	7.4	2.0015	65	4.1744
3.0	1.0986	7.5	2.0149	70	4.2485
3.1	1.1314	7.6	2.0281	75	4.3175
3.2	1.1632	7.7	2.0412	80	4.3820
3.3	1.1939	7.8	2.0541	85	4.4427
3.4	1.2238	7.9	2.0669	90	4.4998
3.5	1.2528	8.0	2.0794	95	4.5539
3.6	1.2809	8.1	2.0919	100	4.6052
3.7	1.3083	8.2	2.1041		
3.8	1.3350	8.3	2.1163		
3.9	1.3610	8.4	2.1282		
4.0	1.3863	8.5	2.1401		
4.1	1.4110	8.6	2.1518		
4.2	1.4351	8.7	2.1633		
4.3	1.4586	8.8	2.1748		
4.4	1.4816	8.9	2.1861		

ANSWERS TO ODD-NUMBERED PROBLEMS

Exercise 1–1

5. (a) On the x-axis, (b) on the y-axis.

7. (a) On the line bisecting the first and third quadrants, (b) on the line bisecting the second and fourth quadrants.

9. $(0, 3\sqrt{3})$, $(0, -3\sqrt{3})$, $9\sqrt{3}$ square units.

11. $(5, 5)$.   13. $(-1, -4)$, $(-3, 2)$, $(9, 4)$.

Exercise 1–2

1. $AB = 3$, $AC = 7$, $BC = 4$, $BA = -3$, $CA = -7$, $CB = -4$.

5. 13.   7. 13.

9. $3\sqrt{2}$.   11. $\sqrt{13}$, $\sqrt{10}$, $\sqrt{5}$.

13. $3\sqrt{2}$, 1, 5.

25. Each point is 5 units from $(-2, 3)$.

27. On a line   29. Not on a line.

31. 2.   35. 9.

37. $23\frac{1}{2}$.   39. 19.

Exercise 1–3

5. 1, 0, $\sqrt{3}$, $-\sqrt{3}$, -1.   7. $-\frac{8}{3}$, $111°$.

9. $\frac{4}{3}$, $53°$.   11. $\frac{7}{6}$, $49°$.

15. On a line.   17. Not on a line.

19. $\tan A = \frac{11}{16}$, $A = 35°$; $\tan B = \frac{11}{10}$, $B = 48°$; $\tan C = -\frac{22}{3}$, $C = 98°$.

21. $\tan A = \frac{9}{37}$, $A = 14°$; $\tan B = \frac{9}{13}$, $B = 35°$; $\tan C = -\frac{9}{8}$, $C = 132°$.

23. $85°$, $95°$.   25. $56°$.

27. $\frac{22}{9}$ 29. $9x - 8y + 14 = 0$

31. $6x - 5y = 37$.

Exercise 1–4

1. $(1, 0)$, $(2, 4)$, $(3, 6)$, $(\frac{3}{2}, \frac{3}{2})$.   3. $(3, \frac{3}{2})$, $(3, \frac{3}{2})$.

5. $(2, 3)$, $(4, -1)$.   7. $(2, \frac{2}{3})$, $(4, \frac{7}{3})$.

9. $(1, 4)$.   11. $(\frac{19}{2}, \frac{13}{2})$, $(-\frac{9}{2}, -\frac{15}{2})$.

13. $r = 2$.   15. $r = 3$.

17. $\left(\dfrac{x_1 + x_2 + x_3}{3}, \dfrac{y_1 + y_2 + y_3}{3} \right)$

19. $(3, 4)$, $(1, 2)$, $(-2, -1)$, $(-5, -4)$.

Exercise 1–6

1. $2x - y = 0$.   3. $x - 2y + 8 = 0$.

5. $x = 6$.   7. $y = 3$.

9. $3x + 5y + 2 = 0$.   11. $x^2 + y^2 = 25$.

13. $y^2 = 10x - 25$.   15. $x - 3y + 1 = 0$.

17. $x^2 + y^2 - x - 3y = 10$.

19. $8x^2 + 8y^2 + 56x - 70y + 223 = 0$.

21. $3x^2 - y^2 + 10x - 25 = 0$.   23. $x^2 - 2x - 4y + 13 = 0$.

25. $7x^2 - 9y^2 + 118x + 54y - 98 = 0$.

27. $x^2 + y^2 - x - 4y - 11 = 0$.   29. $100x^2 + 36y^2 = 225$.

Exercise 2–1

1. $m = 4, a = 3, b = -12; y = 4x - 12$.

3. $m = -1, a = -4, b = -4; y = -x - 4$.

5. $m = \frac{3}{4}, a = 4, b = -3; y = \frac{3}{4}x - 3$.

7. $m = -\frac{1}{7}, a = 11, b = \frac{11}{7}; y = -\frac{1}{7}x + \frac{11}{7}$.

9. $m = -\frac{7}{3}, a = -\frac{6}{7}, b = -2; y = -\frac{7}{3}x - 2$.

11. $m = -\frac{8}{3}, a = \frac{1}{2}, b = \frac{4}{3}; y = -\frac{8}{3}x + \frac{4}{3}$.

13. $y = 3x - 4$.   15. $y = -4x + 5$.   17. $y = \frac{2}{3}x - 2$.

19. $y = 7$.   21. $2x - y = 5$.   23. $2x - 3y + 4 = 0$.

25. $x + 2y + 15 = 0$.   27. $y = 3$.   29. $8x + 3y = 0$.

31. $6x + 7y = 11$.   33. $2x + y - 2 = 0$.   35. $x = 3$.

37. $8x - 27y = 58$.   39. $y + 1 = 0$.   41. $2x + 3y = 6$.

43. $3x - 4y = 12$.   45. $x + y + 2 = 0$.   47. $3x + 4y = 2$.

51. $2x - 3y = 5, 3x + 2y = 14$.

53. $7x + 5y = 41, 5x - 7y + 13 = 0$.

55. $8x - y - 19 = 0, x + 8y + 22 = 0$.

57. $y = 1, x = -1$.

59. $9x + y - 63 = 0, x - 9y - 7 = 0$.

61. (a) $y = 0, 2x + y = 12; x - y = 0$.

     (b) $2x - 5y = 0, x + 2y = 6, 4x - y = 12, (\frac{10}{3}, \frac{4}{3})$.

     (c) $x - 2y = 0, x + y = 6; x = 4, (4, 2)$.

     (d) $x = 3; x - 2y = 1; x + y = 4, (3, 1)$.

63. (a) $x - 4y - 1 = 0, 3x - y - 3 = 0, 2x + 3y - 24 = 0$.

     (b) $4x - 5y = 4; x + 7y = 23, 5x + 2y = 27, (\frac{13}{3}, \frac{8}{3})$.

     (c) $3x - 2y = 3; x + 3y = 15, 4x + y = 18, (\frac{39}{11}, \frac{42}{11})$.

     (d) $4x + y = 21; x + 3y = 11, 3x - 2y = 10, (\frac{52}{11}, \frac{23}{11})$.

Exercise 2–2

1. $\frac{99}{13}$.   3. $3\sqrt{2}$.   5. $-\frac{5\sqrt{29}}{29}$.   7. 3.

9. 5.   11. alt $= \frac{25}{\sqrt{73}}$, $BC = \sqrt{73}$, area $= 12.5$.

13. $99x + 27y = 256$.   15. $x - y = 5, 3x + 3y + 1 = 0$.

19. $y - 4 = m(x + 3)$.   21. $5x + 2y = C$.

23. $\frac{x}{a} + \frac{y}{10 - a} = 1, a \neq 10$.   25. $32x + a^2y = 32a, a \neq 0$.

27. All have slope 2. 29. All pass through $(3, -4)$.

31. The y-intercept of each line exceeds the x-intercept by 4.

33. All pass through the intersection of $4x + y + 1 = 0$ and $3x + 7y = 0$.

35. $3x + y + C = 0$, $3x + y \pm 5\sqrt{10} = 0$.

37. $3x - 2y +1 \pm 4\sqrt{13} = 0$. 39. $3x + y = 0$.

41. $4y + 3 = 0$. 43. $x - 3y = 0$.

45. $7x + 7y - 1 = 0$, $x - 2y - 3 = 0$, $15x - 9y - 25 = 0$.

EXERCISE 2-3

1. $(x - 2)^2 + (y + 6)^2 = 25$. 3. $x^2 + (y - 4)^2 = 16$.

5. $(x + 12)^2 + (y - 5)^2 = 169$. 7. $(x - \frac{1}{2})^2 + (y + 3)^2 = 11$.

9. $x^2 + y^2 + 8x - 6y = 0$. 11. $x^2 + y^2 - 8x - 4y = 14$.

13. $x^2 + y^2 + 8x - 2y + 16 = 0$. 15. $x^2 + y^2 - 14y = 95$.

17. $(x - 3)^2 + (y + 2)^2 = 25$. 19. $(x + 4)^2 + (y + 1)^2 = 16$.

21. $(x - 4)^2 + (y - 3)^2 = 25$. 23. $(x - 2)^2 + (y + 6)^2 = 48$.

25. $(x - 3)^2 + (y + \frac{1}{2})^2 = \frac{35}{4}$. 27. Circle.

29. The point $(-1, 0)$. 31. Circle.

33. The point $(-1, -5)$. 35. No locus.

37. $x^2 + y^2 - 4y - 1 = 0$. 39. $(x - 7)^2 + (y - 6)^2 = 26$.

41. $(x - 1)^2 + (y + 3)^2 = 25$. 43. $x^2 + y^2 - 5x - y = 0$.

45. $x^2 + y^2 - 2x + 2y - 23 = 0$.

47. $x^2 + y^2 - 16x - 10y + 24 + k(x^2 + y^2 - 4x + 8y - 6) = 0$,
$5x^2 + 5y^2 - 32x + 22y = 0$.

EXERCISE 2-4

1. $(0, 0)$. 3. $(-9, 5)$. 5. $(-3, 3)$. 7. $(-1, -2)$.

9. $x'^2 + y'^2 = 4$. 11. $x'^2 + y'^2 = 16$.

13. $(2, 4)$, $x'^2 + y'^2 = 17$. 15. $(\frac{5}{2}, -1)$, $x'^2 + y'^2 = \frac{49}{4}$.

EXERCISE 3-1

1. $F(1, 0)$; ends of latus rectum $(1, -2)$, $(1, 2)$; directrix $x = -1$.

3. $F(0, -\frac{5}{2})$; ends of latus rectum $(-5, -\frac{5}{2})$, $(5, -\frac{5}{2})$; directrix $y = \frac{5}{2}$.

5. $F(-\frac{3}{4}, 0)$; ends of latus rectum $(-\frac{3}{4}, -\frac{3}{2})$, $(-\frac{3}{4}, \frac{3}{2})$; directrix $4x = 3$.

7. $y^2 = 12x$. 9. $y^2 = 24x$. 11. $x^2 = -12y$.

13. $3x^2 + 16y = 0$. 15. $y^2 = -x$. 17. $x^2 = 400y$.

EXERCISE 3-2

1. $(y - 3)^2 = 16x$. 3. $(y - 3)^2 = 16(x - 2)$.

5. $(y - 3)^2 = -24(x - 3)$. 7. $(x + 1)^2 = -12(y + 2)$.

9. $(y - 1)^2 = -12(x - 2)$.

11. $y^2 = 8(x - 1)$; $V(1, 0)$, $F(3, 0)$; $(3, -4)$, $(3, 4)$.

13. $y^2 = -12(x - 4)$; $V(4, 0)$, $F(1, 0)$; $(1, -6)$, $(1, 6)$.

15. $(x + 2)^2 = 16y$; $V(-2, 0)$, $F(-2, 4)$; $(-10, 4)$, $(6, 4)$.

17. $(y - 4)^2 = -6x$; $V(0, 4)$, $F(-\frac{3}{2}, 4)$; $(-\frac{3}{2}, 1)$, $(-\frac{3}{2}, 7)$.

19. $(y + 2)^2 = -8(x - 4)$; $V(4, -2)$, $F(2, -2)$; $(2, -6)$, $(2, 2)$.

21. $(x - 4)^2 = -6(y - 4)$; $V(4, 4)$, $F(4, \frac{5}{2})$; $(1, \frac{5}{2})$, $(7, \frac{5}{2})$.

23. $(y + 7)^2 = 24(x + 7)$; $V(-7, -7)$, $F(-1, -7)$; $(-1, -19)$, $(-1, 5)$.

25. $(x + 1)^2 = 2(y + 2)$.   27. $y^2 - x + 2y - 2 = 0$.

29. $y^2 + x - 3y - 4 = 0$.   31. $5x^2 + 3x - 6y - 20 = 0$.

EXERCISE 3–3

1. $F(0, \pm 4)$; $V(0, \pm 5)$; $B(\pm 3, 0)$; $(\pm \frac{9}{5}, -4)$, $(\pm \frac{9}{5}, 4)$.

3. $F(\pm 5, 0)$; $V(\pm 13, 0)$; $B(0, \pm 12)$; $(-5, \pm \frac{144}{13})$, $(5, \pm \frac{144}{13})$.

5. $F(\pm 2\sqrt{6}, 0)$; $V(\pm 7, 0)$; $B(0, \pm 5)$; $(2\sqrt{6}, \pm \frac{25}{7})$, $(-2\sqrt{6}, \pm \frac{25}{7})$.

7. $F(0, \pm \sqrt{21})$; $V(0, \pm 5)$; $B(\pm 2, 0)$; $(\pm \frac{4}{5}, -\sqrt{21})$, $(\pm \frac{4}{5}, \sqrt{21})$.

9. $F(0, \pm \sqrt{3})$; $V(0, \pm 2)$; $B(\pm 1, 0)$; $(\pm \frac{1}{2}, -\sqrt{3})$, $(\pm \frac{1}{2}, \sqrt{3})$.

11. $\dfrac{x^2}{16} + \dfrac{y^2}{9} = 1$.   13. $\dfrac{y^2}{20} + \dfrac{x^2}{4} = 1$.   15. $\dfrac{x^2}{36} + \dfrac{y^2}{27} = 1$.

17. $\dfrac{x^2}{54} + \dfrac{y^2}{30} = 1$.   19. $\dfrac{y^2}{100} + \dfrac{x^2}{75} = 1$.   21. $\dfrac{x^2}{36} + \dfrac{y^2}{9} = 1$.

23. $\dfrac{x^2}{64} + \dfrac{y^2}{16} = 1$.   25. 91.4 and 94.6 million miles.

27. 14.9 ft.

29. $\dfrac{(x - 2)^2}{25} + \dfrac{y^2}{9} = 1$.   Center $(2, 0)$; $V'(-3, 0)$, $V(7, 0)$; $F'(-2, 0)$, $F(6, 0)$; $B'(2, -3)$, $B(2, 3)$.

31. $\dfrac{(x + \frac{1}{2})^2}{8} + \dfrac{(y + \frac{3}{2})^2}{4} = 1$.   Center $(-\frac{1}{2}, -\frac{3}{2})$; $V'(-\frac{1}{2} - 2\sqrt{2}, -\frac{3}{2})$, $V(-\frac{1}{2} + 2\sqrt{2}, -\frac{3}{2})$, $F'(-\frac{5}{2}, -\frac{3}{2})$, $F(\frac{3}{2}, -\frac{3}{2})$; $B'(-\frac{1}{2}, -\frac{7}{2})$, $B(-\frac{1}{2}, \frac{1}{2})$.

33. $\dfrac{(x - 1)^2}{169} + \dfrac{(y + 2)^2}{25} = 1$.   Center $(1, -2)$; $V'(-12, -2)$, $V(14, -2)$, $F'(-11, -2)$, $F(13, -2)$; $B'(1, -7)$, $B(1, 3)$.

35. $\dfrac{(y - 3)^2}{169} + \dfrac{(x - 1)^2}{144} = 1$.   Center $(1, 3)$; $V'(1, -10)$, $V(1, 16)$, $F'(1, -2)$, $F(1, 8)$; $B'(-11, 3)$, $B(13, 3)$.

37. $\dfrac{x^2}{36} + \dfrac{(y - 3)^2}{20} = 1$.   39. $\dfrac{(x - 2)^2}{9} + \dfrac{(y - 3)^2}{4} = 1$.

41. $\dfrac{y^2}{49} + \dfrac{(x + 2)^2}{40} = 1$.   43. $\dfrac{x^2}{36} + \dfrac{y^2}{20} = 1$.

EXERCISE 3–4

1. $V(\pm 4, 0)$; $F(\pm 5, 0)$; $\dfrac{9}{2}$; $\dfrac{x}{4} - \dfrac{y}{3} = 0$, $\dfrac{x}{4} + \dfrac{y}{3} = 0$.

3. $V(0, \pm 3)$; $F(0, \pm \sqrt{13})$; $\dfrac{8}{3}$; $\dfrac{y}{3} - \dfrac{x}{2} = 0$, $\dfrac{y}{3} + \dfrac{x}{2} = 0$.

5. $V(\pm 2, 0)$; $F(\pm 5, 0)$; 21; $\dfrac{x}{2} + \dfrac{y}{\sqrt{21}} = 0$, $\dfrac{x}{2} - \dfrac{y}{\sqrt{21}} = 0$.

7. $V(0, \pm 6)$; $F(0, \pm 6\sqrt{2})$; 12; $x + y = 0$, $x - y = 0$.

9. $\dfrac{x^2}{16} - \dfrac{y^2}{9} = 1$.

11. $\dfrac{y^2}{21} - \dfrac{x^2}{4} = 1$.

13. $\dfrac{x^2}{4} - \dfrac{y^2}{5} = 1$.

15. $\dfrac{x^2}{16} - \dfrac{y^2}{20} = 1$.

23. $\dfrac{(x + 2)^2}{4} - \dfrac{(y + 4)^2}{21} = 1$. Center $(-2, -4)$; $V'(-4, -4)$, $V(0, -4)$, $F'(-7, -4)$, $F(3, -4)$.

25. $\dfrac{(y - 2)^2}{3} - \dfrac{(x - 1)^2}{2} = 1$. Center $(1, 2)$; $V'(1, 2 - \sqrt{3})$, $V(1, 2 + \sqrt{3})$, $F'(1, 2 - \sqrt{5})$, $F(1, 2 + \sqrt{5})$.

27. $\dfrac{(x + 2)^2}{4} - \dfrac{y^2}{5} = 1$.

29. $\dfrac{(x - 2)^2}{9} - \dfrac{(y - 3)^2}{9} = 1$.

31. $\dfrac{x^2}{36} - \dfrac{(y - 2)^2}{64} = 1$.

33. $\dfrac{x^2}{4} - \dfrac{y^2}{12} = 1$.

Exercise 4–1

1. $3x' + 2y' = 0$.

3. $y'^2 = 6x'$.

5. $3x'^2 + 4y'^2 = 8$.

7. $4y'^2 - 5x'^2 = 20$.

9. $x'y' = 11$.

11. $x'^3 - y' = 0$.

13. $(4, 2)$, $x'y' = 12$.

15. $(2, 0)$, $2x'^2 + 2y'^2 = 3$.

17. $(-4, -2)$, $3x'^2 - 2y'^2 = 6$.

19. $(4, -1)$, $x'^2 - x'y' + y'^2 = 48$.

21. $(-2, 2)$, $x'^3 + 2x'y' - x'^2 = 0$.

23. $y'^2 + 4x' = 0$.

25. $y'^2 + 10x' = 0$.

27. $2x'^2 = 7y'$.

Exercise 4–2

1. $y' + 2 = 0$.

3. $x'^2 - y'^2 = 8$.

5. $3x'^2 + y'^2 = 2$.

7. $y'^2 - 4x' = 0$.

9. $45°$.

11. $22\tfrac{1}{2}°$.

Exercise 4–3

1. $\theta = \arctan \tfrac{3}{4}$; $5y' + 6 = 0$.

3. $\theta = 45°$; $y'^2 - 4y' - 4x' - 4 = 0$. Then a translation gives $y''^2 - 4x'' = 0$.

5. $\theta = \arctan \tfrac{4}{3}$; $x'^2 + 4y'^2 + 4x' - 16y' + 16 = 0$. Then a translation gives $x''^2 + 4y''^2 = 4$.

9. $3x'^2 - 10x'y' + 3y'^2 + 8 = 0$, $x''^2 - 4y''^2 = 4$.

11. $104x'^2 + 60x'y' + 41y'^2 - 116 = 0$, $4x''^2 + y''^2 = 4$.

Exercise 4–4

1. Ellipse.   3. Hyperbola.   5. Hyperbola.   7. Ellipse.

17. $x = 2y$, $x = -y - 1$. Two intersecting lines.

19. $y = (1 \pm i)x$. The locus is the single point $(0, 0)$.
21. $y = 1 - 2x$. One line.
23. $y = 4x \pm \sqrt{-x^2 - 4}$. No locus.

EXERCISE 5–3

21. $(3, 2)$.   23. $(0, 0)$, $(2\sqrt[3]{12}, 2\sqrt[3]{18})$.

25. $(-1, 3)$, $\left(\dfrac{1 \pm \sqrt{17}}{2}, \dfrac{9 \pm \sqrt{17}}{2} \right)$.

27. $(\pm 3, 2)$, $(\pm 3, -2)$.

EXERCISE 6–1

1. Period $\frac{2}{3}\pi$, amplitude 1.   3. Period 6π, amplitude 1.
5. Period $\frac{1}{5}\pi$.   7. Period $\frac{1}{3}\pi$.
9. Period $\frac{4}{3}\pi$.   11. Period 4, amplitude 2.

EXERCISE 7–1

1. (a) $(-3, 240°)$, $(-3, -120°)$, $(3, -300°)$.
   (b) $(6, 330°)$, $(-6, 150°)$, $(-6, -210°)$.
   (c) $(-2, 0°)$, $(2, -180°)$, $(-2, 360°)$.
   (d) The point $(0, 10°)$ is the pole and may be represented by $(0, \theta)$, when θ is any angle.
3. (a) $(1, \frac{11}{6}\pi)$, $(1, -\frac{1}{6}\pi)$, $(-1, -\frac{7}{6}\pi)$.
   (b) $(3, -\frac{5}{3}\pi)$, $(3, \frac{1}{3}\pi)$, $(-3, -\frac{2}{3}\pi)$.
   (c) $(-4, -\pi)$, $(4, 0)$, $(4, 2\pi)$.
   (d) $(-4, \frac{3}{2}\pi)$, $(4, \frac{1}{2}\pi)$, $(-4, -\frac{1}{2}\pi)$.
5. (a) and (b) On a circle of radius 4 and center at the pole.
   (c) The pole, (d), (e), (f), and (g) On a line through the origin making the indicated angle with the polar axis.

EXERCISE 7–2

3. $(3, 3)$.   5. $(0, 0)$.
7. $(-\frac{1}{2}, \frac{1}{2}\sqrt{3})$.   9. $(-4, -4)$.
11. $(3, 90°)$.   13. $(0, \theta)$ where $\theta \geq 0°$.
15. $(5, 270°)$.   17. $(12, 330°)$.
19. $(5, 307°)$, nearest degree.   21. $(13, 67°)$.
23. $\rho \cos \theta = 3$.   25. $\rho = \dfrac{3}{2 \cos \theta - \sin \theta}$.
27. $\theta = 45°$.   29. $\rho = 4$.
31. $\rho = 2(\cos \theta - \sin \theta)$.   33. $\rho \sin \theta \tan \theta = 4$.
35. $x^2 + y^2 = 16$.   37. $x - y = 0$.
39. $x^2 + y^2 - 6y + 4x = 0$.   41. $x^2 + y^2 - 8y = 0$.
43. $y = 6$.   45. $2xy = a^2$.
47. $3x^2 + 4y^2 + 6x = 9$.   49. $4x + 3y = 2$.
51. $x - 3y = 1$.

Exercise 7-5

11. $\rho \sin \theta = -2.$

13. $\rho \cos \theta = -3.$

15. $\rho \cos (\theta - 225°) = 4.$

17. $(3, 90°)$, 3.

19. $(-2, 0°)$, 2.

21. $(-\frac{7}{2}, 90°)$, $\frac{7}{2}$.

23. $\rho - 8 \cos \theta = 0.$

25. $\rho + 10 \cos \theta = 0.$

27. $\rho^2 - 8\rho \cos \theta + 12 = 0.$

29. $\rho - 10 \cos (\theta - 45°) = 0$

Exercise 7-6

1. $(1, 60°)$, $(1, 300°)$.

3. $(3\sqrt{2}, 45°)$, $(3\sqrt{2}, 315°)$.

5. $(a, 90°)$, $(a, 270°)$.

7. $(2, 0°)$.

9. $(\frac{4}{3}, 60°)$, $(\frac{4}{3}, 300°)$.

11. $(1, 0°)$, $(-\frac{3}{5}, 233°)$. $\text{Arcsin} (-\frac{4}{5}) = 233°$, to the nearest degree.

13. $(1, 60°)$.

15. $(1, 60°)$, $(1, 300°)$.

17. $(3, 180°)$.

19. $(2, 60°)$, $(2, 300°)$, $(-1, 180°)$.

Exercise 8-1

1. $3x - 2y = 0.$

3. $x + y = 2.$

5. $x - y + 1 = 0.$

7. $y = x^3.$

9. $y^2 = 16x.$

11. $(x - 1)^2 = -4(y - 2).$

13. $y = \dfrac{1}{(x - 3)^3}.$

15. $x^2 + y^2 = 2x.$

17. $9x^2 + 16y^2 = 144.$

19. $y^2 = -2(x - 1).$

21. $x^2 - y^2 = 1.$

23. $x = t^{-1}$, $y = t - t^{-1}.$

25. $x = 5t - t^2$, $y = 4t - t^2.$

27. $x = \dfrac{3t}{1 + t^3}$, $y = \dfrac{3t^2}{1 + t^3}.$

Exercise 8-2

1. $x = 40\sqrt{2}\, t$, $y = 40\sqrt{2}\, t - 16t^2$; $(x - 100)^2 = -200(y - 50).$ The greatest height is 50 ft, and the ball strikes the ground 200 ft away.

3. $x = v_0 t$, $y = -16t^2$; $16x^2 = -v_0^2 y.$ In 2 seconds the projectile falls 64 ft, and travels $2v_0$ ft horizontally.

7. $x = 4\pi t - 2t \sin \pi t$, $y = 4 - 2t \cos \pi t.$

Exercise 9-1

We assume that the data in the problems of Chapter 9 justify the retention of three significant figures in the answers.

1. $y = -0.718x + 8.71.$

3. $y = 0.100x + 10.0.$

5. $N = 1380t + 6300.$

Exercise 9-2

1. $y = 0.121x^{3.13}.$

3. $t = 0.259s^{0.488}.$

5. $p = 103v^{-1.39}.$

Exercise 9–3

1. $y = 2.00 \cdot 10^{0.131x}$.

3. $y = 9.91 \log x + 3.03$.

5. $T = 99.5 \cdot 10^{-0.0989t}$.

7. $V = 3.87 \log P - 0.828$.

Exercise 11–1

1. $-2\mathbf{i} + 8\mathbf{j}$, $6\mathbf{i} - 2\mathbf{j}$.

3. $2\mathbf{i} - 6\mathbf{j}$, $4\mathbf{i} + 2\mathbf{j}$.

5. $\dfrac{3\mathbf{i} + 4\mathbf{j}}{5}$.

7. $\dfrac{12\mathbf{i} - 5\mathbf{j}}{13}$.

9. $\dfrac{\mathbf{i} + 2\mathbf{j}}{\sqrt{5}}$.

11. $\sqrt{2}$, $\dfrac{1}{\sqrt{2}}$.

13. $1, 1$.

15. $\sqrt{13}$, $-\dfrac{3}{\sqrt{13}}$.

17. $4\mathbf{i} - \mathbf{j}$.

Exercise 11–2

1. 11.

3. $\sqrt{102}$.

5. $\overrightarrow{AB} = -6\mathbf{i} - 6\mathbf{j}$, $\overrightarrow{BC} = -6\mathbf{j} - 6\mathbf{k}$, $\overrightarrow{CA} = 6\mathbf{i} + 12\mathbf{j} + 6\mathbf{k}$. The lengths are $6\sqrt{2}$, $6\sqrt{2}$, $6\sqrt{6}$.

7. $\overrightarrow{AB} = \mathbf{i} + 2\mathbf{j} + 2\mathbf{k}$, $\overrightarrow{BC} = -3\mathbf{i} - 3\mathbf{j}$, $\overrightarrow{CA} = 2\mathbf{i} + \mathbf{j} - 2\mathbf{k}$. The lengths are 3, $3\sqrt{2}$, 3.

9. $\dfrac{6\mathbf{i} + 3\mathbf{j} - 6\mathbf{k}}{9}$.

11. $\dfrac{2\mathbf{i} - \mathbf{j} - 3\mathbf{k}}{\sqrt{14}}$.

13. $4\mathbf{i} + \frac{5}{2}\mathbf{j}$, to the mid-point; $3\mathbf{i} - \mathbf{j} + 4\mathbf{k}$ and $5\mathbf{i} + \mathbf{j} + \mathbf{k}$, to the trisection points.

15. Center $(-2, 1, -3)$, radius $\sqrt{14}$.   17. $\mathbf{i} + 2\mathbf{j} + 2\mathbf{k}$.

Exercise 11–3

1. $-2, -\frac{2}{27}$.

3. $13, \frac{13}{105}$.

5. $\frac{19}{3}\sqrt{3}$, $\frac{19}{3}(\mathbf{i} - \mathbf{j} - \mathbf{k})$.

7. $55°$.

9. $64°, 90°, 26°$.

Exercise 11–4

1. $3x - 2y + 5z - 11 = 0$.

3. $2x - 3y - 4z = 8$.

5. $3x + 9y - 4z = 0$.

7. $2x + 3y - 4z - 2 = 0$.

9. $\frac{8}{3}$.

11. $\frac{2}{7}\sqrt{21}$.

15. $\frac{13}{21}$.

17. $\frac{24}{27}$.

19. $C = -10$.

Exercise 11–5

1. $2\mathbf{i} + \mathbf{j} + 3\mathbf{k}$; $(0, -5, -12)$, $(10, 0, 3)$, $(8, -1, 0)$.

3. $3\mathbf{i} - \mathbf{j} + 2\mathbf{k}$; $(0, 1, 2)$, $(3, 0, 4)$, $(-3, 2, 0)$.

5. $\dfrac{x-4}{-2} = \dfrac{y+3}{3} = \dfrac{z-5}{4}$; $x = 4 - 2t$, $y = -3 + 3t$, $z = 5 + 4t$.

7. $\dfrac{x-1}{2} = \dfrac{y-1}{3} = \dfrac{z-2}{-1}$; $x = 1 + 2t$, $y = 1 + 3t$, $z = 2 - t$.

9. $\dfrac{x-2}{2} = \dfrac{y+1}{1}$, $z - 1 = 0$; $x = 2 + 2t$, $y = -1 + t$, $z = 1$.

11. $\dfrac{y-3}{1} = \dfrac{z-2}{2}$, $x - 4 = 0$; $x = 4$, $y = 3 + t$, $z = 2 + 2t$.

13. $x = 0$, $z = 0$; $x = 0$, $y = t$, $z = 0$.

15. $\dfrac{x-1}{3} = \dfrac{y-2}{-2} = \dfrac{z-3}{3}$.   17. $\dfrac{x-1}{1} = \dfrac{y}{-2} = \dfrac{z-2}{1}$.

19. $\dfrac{y-5}{1} = \dfrac{z-4}{1}$, $x = 2$.   21. $y - 3 = 0$, $z - 4 = 0$.

23. $\dfrac{x-2}{3} = \dfrac{y-3}{-1} = \dfrac{z}{2}$.   25. $\dfrac{x}{2} = \dfrac{y-3}{-3} = \dfrac{z-6}{1}$.

27. $\dfrac{2}{\sqrt{14}}, \dfrac{1}{\sqrt{14}}, \dfrac{3}{\sqrt{14}}$; $\dfrac{-2}{\sqrt{6}}, \dfrac{1}{\sqrt{6}}, \dfrac{1}{\sqrt{6}}$; $\dfrac{3}{\sqrt{14}}, \dfrac{-1}{\sqrt{14}}, \dfrac{2}{\sqrt{14}}$; $\dfrac{1}{\sqrt{14}}, \dfrac{2}{\sqrt{14}}, \dfrac{3}{\sqrt{14}}$.

29. $\frac{11}{21}$.   31. $\frac{2}{7}$.

EXERCISE 11–6

1. $4\mathbf{i} + 4\mathbf{j} - 2\mathbf{k}$; $\frac{2}{3}\mathbf{i} + \frac{2}{3}\mathbf{j} - \frac{1}{3}\mathbf{k}$.   3. $2\mathbf{j} - 2\mathbf{k}$; $\dfrac{\sqrt{2}}{2}\mathbf{i} - \dfrac{\sqrt{2}}{2}\mathbf{k}$.

5. $25\mathbf{k}$, $\mathbf{k}$.   7. 5.   9. $7\sqrt{6}$.   11. $\frac{9}{2}\sqrt{3}$.

13. $\frac{1}{2}$.   17. $9x + 7y - z = 25$.

19. $\frac{274}{781}\sqrt{781}$.   21. $\dfrac{x}{3} = \dfrac{y}{2} = \dfrac{z}{4}$.

23. $3x - 7y + 8z = 4$.   25. $\frac{1}{3}\sqrt{170}$.

27. $\dfrac{\sqrt{42}}{14}$.   31. $\dfrac{43\sqrt{227}}{227}$.

33. The lines intersect.

INDEX

228